Underpinning

Underpinning

Edited by
S THORBURN
Thorburn Associates

J F HUTCHISON
Henry Boot Scotland Ltd

SURREY UNIVERSITY PRESS

Glasgow and London

Published by Surrey University Press
A member of the Blackie Group
Bishopbriggs, Glasgow G64 2NZ and
Furnival House, 14–18 High Holborn, London WCIV 6BX

© 1985 Blackie & Son Ltd
First published 1985

British Library Cataloguing in Publication Data

Underpinning.
  1. Scaffolding 2. Shoring and underpinning
  I. Thorburn, S. II. Hutchison, J.F.
  624.1′6   TH5281

ISBN 0-903384-49-3

Photosetting by Thomson Press (India) Limited, New Delhi
Printed in Great Britain by Bell & Bain Ltd., Glasgow

Contributors

A. Perelli Cippo and R. Tornaghi   Rodio S.p.A., Milan

Rodio S.p.A. was founded in Italy in 1921 and is now one of the largest specialist geotechnical engineering contractors in the world.

K.W. Cole   Ove Arup and Partners, London

The Ove Arup Partnership provides consulting engineering services in the fields of civil, industrial, and building engineering. The Geotechnics Group undertakes commissions worldwide in all aspects of ground engineering.

J.S. Harris   Foraky Limited, Colwick, Nottingham

Foraky Limited, an international group of specialized companies, provides a wide range of inground services including prospection drilling for any resource, large diameter drilling for access or extraction, tunnelling and pipejacking, concrete spraying, and artificial ground freezing.

J.F. Hutchison   Henry Boot Scotland Ltd, Glasgow

Henry Boot Scotland Limited, part of the Henry Boot Group, has complete construction capability to carry out building and civil engineering contracts throughout the UK and in selected countries overseas.

G.S. Littlejohn   Bradford University

Professor of Civil Engineering and Head of Department

F. Lizzi   Fondedile S.p.A., Naples

Fondedile SpA is a company formed in Italy in 1941 specializing in piling, underpinning, diaphragm walling, slope stabilization, anchoring, soil consolidation as well as strengthening of buildings.

v

J.F.S. Pryke   Pynford Design Limited, Waltham Abbey

Pynford pioneered the house underpinning market in the UK and
has developed from this base a wide range of expertise in underpinning, shoring, lifting, moving and strengthening buildings of all
sizes. Projects are in hand throughout the UK and overseas.

S. Thorburn   Thorburn Associates, Glasgow and London

Thorburn Associates (formerly Thorburn and Partners) was established in Glasgow in 1966 and now has offices in Edinburgh, Dundee
and London. The practice offers a complete civil and structural
engineering consultancy service with a special interest in the fields of
foundations and ground engineering.

Contents

Preface

The aim of this book is to present a set of chapters concerned with, and exemplifying, different techniques of underpinning structures. Each chapter presents the essential principles of, and basic information on, a particular technique. Case histories illustrate typical problems and describe appropriate solutions which can be used effectively and economically.

The book is intended to provide guidance for practising civil and structural engineers and contractors, and to provide interesting reference material for researchers, students and graduates. The maintenance and repair of building structures have become essential to the well-being of towns and cities because of current economic and social pressures. The natural deterioration in the condition of old buildings, together with the need to integrate old and new foundations in recent refurbishment projects, has focused attention on the art and practice of underpinning. Planning authorities generally wish to maintain the historical character of portions of towns and cities, and the juxtaposition of new and old has highlighted the problems of maintaining the states of balance of old buildings and of avoiding damage due to distortion of often brittle fabrics during and after the periods of construction.

Specialist firms today can draw on techniques which have been developed to provide support to all kinds of civil engineering structures. In this book, however, simple methods of excavation and techniques using traditional methods of piling have not been neglected, since their use can be effective and economical in appropriate circumstances.

A thorough knowledge of underpinning requires an understanding of materials science, combined with an awareness of the hidden distributions of strain and stress unique to a structure and its particular ground support conditions. The paths of load transfer, both primary and secondary, must be fully defined within any structure to be underpinned, as must the probable concentrations of strain and stress in the building while in its passive condition. Similarly it is important to establish the cause of settlement in a building which suddenly displays movement, and, in particular, to know whether the event can be arrested by underpinning alone. Structural strengthening measures may be an essential requirement in conjunction with underpinning to arrest movements. Underpinning may be unnecessary if the event is initiated by a short-term effect and the movements do not disturb significantly the natural state of balance of a building structure. A clear distinction should be made between damage to the primary support elements of a structure and damage to cladding, partitions, and finishes.

In the first chapter, considerable emphasis has been laid on proper and adequate methods of investigation of a structure, its foundations, and the ground support conditions as a prelude to selection of the best method of underpinning. Proper monitoring of structural performance and relative movements are important aspects of investigatory works. The legal aspects of underpinning involving right of support are discussed generally in this chapter. The chapter concludes with an account of an historical work of underpinning, to set a reference against which the modern techniques described in later chapters may be compared. Much of the art and practice evolved successfully in earlier times, and an adequate appreciation of material and structural behaviour was developed then without the benefit of modern knowledge of the physical sciences.

Subsequent chapters describe different methods of underpinning and their advantages and disadvantages. Three chapters discuss techniques of underpinning which have become well established through usage over the past few decades; these include simple methods of excavation, traditional piling, and grouting. A description of underpinning systems devised by Pynford Ltd has been included because of the general acceptance of these techniques within the UK and in recognition of their contribution to the theory and practice of underpinning.

Over the past 25 years, 'pali radice' (root piles) and 'reticolo di pali radice' (reticulated root piles) have been used successfully for the underpinning of ancient and modern structures, and two chapters have been devoted to these specialist methods. The first patents on techniques using pali radice were sought about 1951 by Dr F. Lizzi, and on their expiry in 1968 the techniques were adopted by others, with some variation, and described as 'mini-piling'. It is important to differentiate between underpinning techniques using pali radice as direct loadbearing foundation elements, as with traditional piling, and those using reticulated pali radice to reinforce the soil beneath foundations.

The penultimate chapter discusses ground freezing techniques, which are of particular advantage for temporary load support purposes in difficult situations. One of the earliest reports on the application of ground freezing techniques concerned the sinking of a mine shaft in South Wales in 1892. The circulation of brine, cooled by a Siebe Gorman engine, through tubes installed in the ground, permitted the deep shaft to be sunk successfully through waterbearing strata, and this principle has been used with little change since its inception. F.H. Poetch was granted a patent in Germany in 1883 for the application of this principle, and although the mining industry has made the greatest use of ground freezing techniques, over the past 20 years increasing attention has been given to the particular demands of the construction industry. The benefits provided by modern research into the characteristics of permafrost together with ample availability of liquid nitrogen as a source of cold energy have encouraged the wider application of ground freezing techniques.

It is hoped that this compendium of knowledge and experience will provide the construction industry with a useful work of reference that reflects the progress achieved over the past 25 years.

S.T.
J.H.

1 The philosophy of underpinning

S. THORBURN

L'objet de la construction est d'executer toutes les parties d'un ouvrage projeté avec toute le solidité et la perfection dont elles sont susceptibles, en y employant les matériaux les plus convenables mis en tourne avec art et économie. RONDELET, *L'Art de bâtir*, Vol. 1, p. 8.

1.1 General description

The separate actions of shoring and underpinning generally have been described in the literature, notably in the classic treatise by Cecil Haden Stock in 1882. Stock found that little of the practice of shoring and underpinning had been committed to print in a form suitable for proper study of the subject and he collated and presented the works of various authorities then engaged in that practice. Two discerning comments were made by Stock; firstly, that direct involvement with site works was the only way to gain proper knowledge and adequate practical ability of underpinning, and, secondly, that theoretical knowledge *per se* should not be allowed to interfere with the application of sound techniques derived from long experience. Regardless of the fact that Stock was dealing with ruinous and dangerous building structures constructed before the turn of the century and although considerable technological progress has been made over the past two decades, these statements are still relevant today in the context of underpinning. Much benefit can be obtained from Stock's comprehensive descriptions both of earlier buildings and of the practice of shoring and underpinning at that time. Reference may also be made to Prentis and White (1950), Hunter (1952) and Tomlinson (1978) for useful information on earlier and recent forms of shoring respectively.

Shoring is generally used in conjunction with underpinning, but the temporary nature of the former and the permanent role of the latter must be recognized together with their interactive effects. The temporary relief of load and/or the temporary restraint provided by shoring demands careful assessment and this important subject requires greater treatment than could be afforded by this publication. It is sufficient to state that shoring and propping must be judiciously positioned and stressed to support a structure without damage, while its basal support is strengthened or removed and

1

replaced. Changes to the natural state of balance and pattern of load distribution, however small, are inevitable during the operations of shoring and underpinning. Great care must be taken during the final phase involving removal of all temporary support, since elastic and permanent strain adjustments will be experienced.

This series of individual operations places great demands on the skills of the engineer and the contractor, and a thorough study of the mechanics of a structure is a prerequisite to the successful outcome of the complete sequence of shoring and underpinning operations.

The transfer of load from a structure to its underpinning must be carefully executed and the mechanism of load distribution must be identified and controlled to an extent commensurate either with the simplicity of the operation or with its complexity and the need to restrict movements.

Three main categories of structure and classes of underpinning can be identified.

Categories of structure: (i) Ancient—greater than 150 years since completion
                           (ii) Recent—50 to 150 years since completion
                           (iii) Modern—less than 50 years

Classes of underpinning: (i) Conversion works
                           (ii) Protection works
                           (iii) Remedial works

A knowledge of building construction as previously practised is of great assistance to the engineer preparing designs for each of the three classes of underpinning, and awareness of the effects of age on the materials and fabric of old structures is also of advantage. The determination of the condition of the fabric and foundations of ancient and recent structures can be a major and daunting task for the engineer, particularly where the means of access and working space for investigations are restricted. The underpinning of ancient building structures presents hazards in the form of deterioration of the condition of the materials of loadbearing walls, pillars, piers and buttresses, which are often of composite construction. Historical records reveal that in mediaeval times too great a reliance was placed on the supportive ability of essentially rubble masonry contained by relatively thin ashlar facing stones. Sound ashlar masonry construction should not be expected as a common provision and careful exploratory work should be carried out to ascertain the real nature and condition of all loadbearing components which are important to the safe and successful execution of underpinning works. The loss of the beautiful spire of Chichester Cathedral in 1861 may be attributed to the belief by those responsible for the repair work that the stone filling of the piers, upon which the 83-m spire relied for support, would continue to provide safe support while the ashlar facing stones were being repaired. Tertiary crinoidal limestone quarried at the Isle of Wight had been used for the ashlar facing to the piers, but the internal rubble stone filling had been cemented with chalk–lime mortar. It was alleged by the workmen who carried out the repair work that dry mortar dust poured occasionally from the joints in the ashlar facing to the piers. It is possible that the chalk–lime mortar lost moisture prior to setting due to the hygroscopic nature of the limestone blocks, in addition to the loss of its cementitious properties with age deterioration. The outer shell of ashlar stone, being stronger and stiffer, probably carried a significant proportion of the total load in addition to its containment function. The repairs must have adversely affected the distribution of stress within the piers, and also perhaps caused some loss of fines from the rubble stone filling, to the extent that the highly stressed shell of facing stones failed. Deformation of some or all of the piers must have altered seriously the natural state of balance of the high tower structure and caused the disastrous failure of an historical heritage. That this incident is not singular is attested by the failure of the towers of Winchester Cathedral in the 12th century; of Gloucester Cathedral in 1160; of Worcester Cathedral in 1222; of Ely Cathedral in 1322; and of Norwich Cathedral in 1361. The possibility of the state of balance of an ancient structure being altered during underpinning work should be anticipated and recognized in the design of the shoring. The following incident reflects this possibility and demonstrates that the alterations may result in portions of the structure apparently remote from the loci of the underpinning works being subjected to a new pattern of loading. In 1841, during repairs to the piers of the tower of the Church of St Mary, Stafford, a sudden fracturing of one of the pillars of the chancel occurred with a distinct noise. The chancel provided no direct support to the tower structure. The pillar split from top to bottom due to some change in the natural pattern of load sharing caused by the repairs to the tower.

Buttresses present a similar problem where rough stones were used for the main body of the buttresses and dressed stones for the facing. The dressed stones generally were more compactly laid than the rough interior stones and inequality of stress is a likely result. It is also possible that the outer portions of major buttresses having large projections carry much less load than the portions nearest the walls which they support. A further inequality is experienced from the random combination of soft and hard stones, and it may be safely concluded that the composite loadbearing elements of ancient structures are unevenly stressed and may be highly stressed at critical locations.

It should not be assumed that structural movements are due to foundation settlement alone, since ancient structures founded on bedrock can be subjected to significant differential movements due to poor construction of the loadbearing elements. The practice of allowing parts of the original foundations of ancient building structures to remain during conversion or reconstruction and incorporating them into new foundation systems has always been considered inadvisable but could not always be avoided by earlier builders. The possibility of this circumstance should always be borne in mind.

Arches provide another hazard in the form of lateral components of load derived from thrust at the springers. Loss of restraint in the vicinity of springers must be avoided, and care must be taken in case the spandrel walls of arches contain loose stone filling which could result in failure if the natural restraint is removed. The loose nature of stone infilling between the spandrel walls of a bridge structure is evidenced by the extreme root growth (Figure 1.1) which remained undetected until repairs commenced. It seems obvious that the shoring for an arch should be capable of supporting not only the self-weight of the masonry, but also the loads transmitted to the arch, before any underpinning involving removal of material is attempted. It is advisable to introduce suitable grouts under carefully controlled pressures through the outer shells of the stone facings of all loadbearing elements of ancient structures, and to consolidate any loose stone filling hidden behind the outer facing stones. This injection of grout should be carried out prior to the construction of the major shoring works to ensure that the local concentrations of stress induced by the often high shoring loads do not cause local damage or even result in harmful movements as the shoring accepts its temporary supportive role. In critical situations, or where some uncertainty exists, it is preferable to use only those construction techniques which minimize stress relaxation and loss of restraint; which maintain essentially the natural state of balance and pattern of loading; and which supplement the natural support conditions.

Figure 1.1   Mature growth of tree root in bridge structure.

The hazard provided by inaccurate or poor workmanship in ancient buildings should also be borne in mind, and the following account of the collapse of the Long Room at Custom House, London, in 1825 provides a good illustration of this risk. The site on exposure was found to comprise a confusion of irregular old walls, ancient quays and sewers, and to contain the debris of former building activities. It would appear that extensive site clearance to provide a proper working surface was not carried out, and a new foundation of timber piles was driven through the mass of debris and obstructions. The building had two storeys of vaults formed by a series of stone piers and brick arches. Each pier was supposed to bear upon nine timber piles in a square pattern. Great difficulty was experienced in driving the piles because of the numerous obstructions, and the quantity of debris prevented accuracy both in positioning the piles and verifying their positions later. As a result of the total lack of clarity in respect of the true positions of pile groups, the outer row of piles of one of the foundations was mistaken for the middle row of the nine-pile group and the foundation was constructed with only half of the piles supporting it. The load transmitted eccentrically to this particular pile group by a stone pier eventually caused structural failure, since the debris outside the pile group was very loose and incapable of preventing the rotational, translational, and vertical movements of the pier. This single pier moved sideways off the eccentric pile group and sank about 1.5 metres, causing major movements and imbalance of the vault structure culminating in the total collapse of the building. The assumption should never be made that any structure is accurately located over its foundations.

Stress concentrations should be anticipated in any form of structure, and the following simple incident exemplifies the ease with which this hazard can be created even in an ancient building. The mortar bed for a ceremonial stone was prepared by a mason and took the form of four pats of strong mortar on the foundation stone of the ornamental base of a column. In order to assist the dignitary invited to lay the ceremonial stone, the mason mixed and spread a soft mortar of high workability over the foundation stone between the four stiff pats of strong mortar. The dignitary spread the soft mortar with a great flourish but the stiff pats supported effectively the ornamental base stone and the column itself. About one year after application of the full load on the column, major cracks developed in the base stone which was constrained to span between the hard pats of strong mortar and shoring, and repairs had to be hastily executed. This classic example of stress concentration should be a lesson to designers of modern buildings and a warning to all who design and build masonry structures that a ceremonial stone should not be a critical component of a structure. The ambience of a ceremony is not always conducive to good workmanship because of the danger of distraction.

Recent buildings constructed during the nineteenth century to accommodate the demands of the Industrial Revolution are not without faults despite improvements in building technology in that era. Forms of composite masonry construction used in recent buildings were similar to those used in ancient buildings, where rough stones in the interiors of masonry elements were contained by dressed facing stones. Extensive use of walls was made for recent structures and crosswall construction provided the means of stability against lateral loads. The relatively fast rates of construction sought during the recent period introduced a new hazard, since the walls could be built faster by forming outer leaves of dressed stone, and using irregular wedge-shaped stones, which were the product of the trimming and dressing operations by the mason, for the interiors of the walls. The inequalities caused by the simultaneous use of rough and dressed stones in ancient times were made more acute by the greater use of this poorer material in the heart of walls in recent structures. Portland cement mortar was used as well as lime mortar during the recent period to bind the stone filling, but the nature of the stone fragments and the lack of control over the grouting of the stone filling produced walls of variable quality and strength.

Deterioration has taken place in the condition of walls built during the recent period although some buildings are only a century old. It should not be assumed that the techniques of construction used for recent structures were greatly superior to those of ancient structures, and walls may require to be grouted before the commencement of shoring and underpinning. The wedging action of sharp irregular stones within the heart of a wall due to vertical load must be prevented by the bonding action of the mortar, and its failure as a cementitious agent will be accompanied by an outward thrust on the thin shell of dressed stones. Fortunately, crosswall construction and the smaller rooms required for accommodation during the recent period provided a greater spread of load, and the masonry walls were relatively narrow. The outer stone facings were capable of safely supporting the loads applied at that time, although the stone filling could be of relatively poor quality. The ability of these walls to sustain modern high loads or shoring and underpinning loads without distress should not be assumed, however. The lateral restraint of walls at junctions is dependent on the number of keystones provided over the height of the wall. Experience has shown that the keystones were often few in number, and over the past 100 to 150 years the natural deterioration in the condition of the keystones under tensile stresses has resulted in brittle failure. The interval of time between the complete fracturing of all keystones connecting masonry crosswalls, and facades and failure of the load-bearing walls themselves is relatively short, and the effect can be dramatic. Attempts have been made to repair keystones which have failed, but the task is difficult, and often the situation is irretrievable since the degree of outward movement can be such that progressive movement due to load eccentricity is usually a continuous and gradual process which often culminates with acceleration of movement. Measurements taken of the pattern of outward movement of an ashlar masonry wall of a prestigious building are given in Figure 1.2 and show

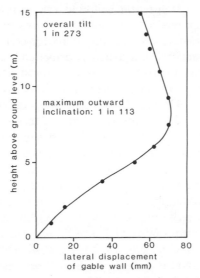

Figure 1.2   Outward movements of masonry wall.

the extent and form of curvature of this external wall subsequent to failure of all internal keystones.

Recent buildings can possess very heavy ornamental stone parapets at roof level, and the removal of this load at such high elevations during structural strengthening and underpinning greatly assists the maintenance of stability of facades, particularly in situations where the keystones to transverse walls have fractured. Deficiencies in the fabrics of recent buildings also result from poor workmanship, building inaccuracies, insufficient bonding to transverse walls, and age deterioration.

The problem of mutual gables or common walls arose during the recent period, and walls built in juxtaposition may require each other to maintain their stability. Often there was no servitude of support and the use of adjacent walls for the purposes of achieving structural stability was clandestine. Situations have arisen where the demolition of recent properties has led to progressive tilt and translational movements to such an extent that demolition became a necessity. The demolition of old property of the recent period within an urban situation should not be carried out without due care. Shoring and propping should be judiciously located to support adjacent buildings before and during the demolition and site clearance works, and certainly before any underpinning commences. The legal situation must be clearly understood by all parties involved with the development of urban sites. Clear definitions of responsibilities should be made at the outset and the criteria for the support works should be carefully and explicitly defined. Basements beneath buildings of the recent period may have been formed or extended after completion of a building and the degree of support afforded to adjacent property by the later construction can be marginal.

Brickwork was extensively used during the recent period, and was bedded with mortars comprising either lime, portland cement or combinations of both cementitious agents. The quality control of brick production has varied, and the changes in the strengths of mortar as well as bricks can present problems during underpinning. In damp conditions, lime mortar can deteriorate to a considerable extent with age. Damp conditions can also result in sulphate attack on mortar, the source of the sulphates being the bricks themselves. Situations have been found where portland cement mortar had deteriorated in strength to such an extent that a scraping action readily removed the mortar between the bricks. The practice, derived from ancient times, of forming a shell of facing stones and infilling with rough stone was also used during the recent period for brick walls and piers having large dimensions. Thick walls and piers of recent structures were shaped by an outer skin of brickwork and loose bricks were hand-placed within the brick shell. The loose bricks were bedded on soft mortar and the surface of each succeeding or alternate layer of bricks was grouted with a liquid mortar. The workmanship is known to have varied widely and loose brick filling with little or no mortar has been found. The need to build quickly on occasions created unfortunate legacies which can present a hazard to underpinning. Grouting of all loose brickwork of this kind is recommended prior to the execution of underpinning works. Fortunately, many brick walls of crosswall construction forming buildings of the recent period were of thicknesses equivalent to only one or one-and-a-half bricks, and such walls may be expected to provide fewer difficulties to underpinning.

Modern structures built within the last 50 years were subject to Building Regulations and Codes of Practice, and their form of construction can often be assessed reasonably easily from a search of plans which are extant and from a thorough structural survey. Modern structures differ from those of ancient and recent times by virtue of the greater use of stronger cementitious materials with the objectives of economy of materials and slenderer structural elements. Higher brick crushing strengths have been achieved through strict control of the composition, kilning and curing procedures. The compressive strengths of bricks have increased by about 50% over the past 50 years, and portland cement mortars have much greater strengths, elastic moduli, and resistance to deterioration. The use of monolithic forms of concrete construction and higher-strength bricks and mortars has changed the response of structures to ground movements. New building materials have also been introduced over the past 20 years which, in conjunction with much stronger bonding agents, have reduced the flexibility of structures and produced brittle behaviour. Ancient and recent masonry and brick structures bonded with relatively weak lime mortars often could accommodate significant ground movements by virtue of small slip strains along the bedding joints and minute tensile strains or microcracks in the vertical joints, in the manner of a discrete material. The total displacements permitted by the extensive development of these small strains produced essentially flexible behaviour of a complete structure. The relative brittleness of modern ceramic or cementitious materials reduces the global flexibility and a few wide cracks can develop rather than numerous microcracks at close intervals. Considerable use has been made in modern structures of composite materials such as brick and blockwork and timber panels with brickwork facades. Cavity wall construction was introduced in modern times and this separation of the inner and outer brick leaves brought a greater dependence upon wall ties for adequate structural behaviour. Internal leaves of concrete blockwork and external leaves of brickwork have introduced inequalities which should be taken into account in underpinning works. The use of precast concrete cladding panels for modern buildings has provided structures which behave in an essentially rigid monolithic manner, and load transfers due to inequalities of ground support are a distinct possibility depending on the strengths of the mechanical connections between the panels. The mechanical levelling devices at the bases of precast concrete panels can cause stress concentrations despite the introduction of low-water-content cement mortar rammed into the gap beneath the panels after completion of the positioning and levelling operations. Figure 1.3 shows the nature and extent of cracking which can develop in a modern structure due to the adverse effects of stress concentrations. Prestressing and post-tensioning of beams in modern structures has introduced considerable strain energies into these structural elements and great care should be taken during conversion or remedial works. The diaphragm action of reinforced concrete floors can be of benefit in respect of providing restraint against lateral movements, provided proper wall-to-floor con-

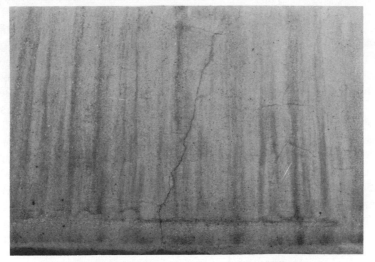

Figure 1.3 Stress cracks in a modern concrete panel structure.

nections were formed. Steel structures of recent and modern times possess considerable ductility and strength, and shoring and underpinning of most types of steel structure are generally simple in concept and construction and present fewer hazards than ancient structures.

The previous descriptive passages of ancient, recent and modern structures are intended to provide a background against which an appreciation of the hazards and problems of underpinning can be developed. Reference should, however, be made to technical literature on the manufacture and properties of engineering materials which are likely to be encountered during underpinning works, since this book cannot cover the subject of materials and their uses in a sufficiently comprehensive manner. The design and construction of shoring and underpinning of all types of structures should err on the conservative side, since uncertainties always exist regardless of the thoroughness of any archive searches and of non-destructive investigations. The objectives of underpinning now require definition before solutions and techniques are presented for the guidance of the reader.

1.1.1 Conversion works

Alteration, improvement, and renewal of old properties may be prompted by the need to preserve national assets of historical importance; to take commerical advantage where existing buildings are essentially suitable for change of use; and often to minimize expenditure on housing provisions.

The architect must ensure that the character of the building after renovation and refurbishment conforms with the present setting or recognizes apparent change in the local environment and avoids incongruity in the modern setting. The planning authorities often insist, therefore, that the existing masonry or brickwork facades of buildings should be preserved although the interior structure of the building may be demolished. These conversion works present a considerable challenge to the engineer who must design his shoring and underpinning works to safeguard the important facades, and construct new support works within working spaces which are very restricted. Figure 1.4 shows the extensive nature of shoring to a masonary facade which had to be provided together with the bored pile foundations which were constructed to support new internal colums.

The engineer must develop a proper understanding of the nature of the building and its relationship to the existing environment, particularly from the aspects of stability and the groundwater regime. Changes in the local environment due to development by conversion can affect adversely both the states of balance of existing buildings and the local groundwater table. Recourse to law can affect redress, but the damage to property will already have happened, with possible serious commercial consequences. A knowledge of building construction as formerly practised is thus of great benefit to the engineer preparing designs for renovation and refurbishment, and an

Figure 1.4 Shoring and underpinning using bored piles.

awareness of the effects of age on the materials and fabric of old buildings is also of advantage.

The proper or adequate determination of the condition of the foundations of old buildings requiring conversion is a major and daunting task for the engineer, particularly where the means of access and working space for investigations are restricted. A judgement must often be made regarding the condition and stability of old building foundations based on a minimal amount of direct information. In these circumstances it is essential to examine archivistic records and study the available history of building performance in the locality, including careful and comprehensive observations of the condition of the building to be refurbished. The condition of the immediately adjacent property must also be examined in case of structural interaction between the buildings, such as reliance upon support from an adjacent wall which may be clandestine. Since investigations of the foundations of old buildings are often restricted and judgements may require to be based on minimal evidence, it is important to be reasonably conservative, and, more important, to employ construction methods which permit adaptation. The ability to contend with unforeseen variations in ground conditions because of a measure of versatility of the chosen construction technique is invaluable during the period of strengthening or of replacing old foundations. Deficiencies of support can also be encountered during conversion works due to age deterioration, errors in the earlier construction, and poor workmanship. Knowledgeable site supervision during the period of the underpinning works is essential.

The relief of stress caused by removal of ground from within a building undergoing conversion in order to provide a basement structure can result in the development of significant elastic and permanent strains, and the effect of these ground displacements on the temporary shoring and permanent underpinning and new construction works should be carefully evaluated. The legal implications of inadequate temporary support provisions during conversion works can be serious and tortuous.

1.1.2 Protection works

Protection works to structures may be necessary in the following situations.

(a) Construction of new buildings in sufficiently close proximity to existing buildings to warrant the provision of underpinning works under the existing properties in order to limit ground movements and protect the existing buildings.

(b) The construction of new basements within existing buildings.

(c) The construction of new buried structures, such as services tunnels and pipelines in close proximity to existing buildings.

(d) The growth of trees in clay soils causing adverse ground displacements due to moisture movements.

(e) The construction of new manufacturing facilities which contain mechanical sources of harmful vibrations to the extent that the ground support beneath existing buildings would be affected.

The construction of new buildings within an urban environment can involve large excavations below the foundations of existing buildings. Shoring and underpinning of existing buildings as a protective measure is often required as shown in Figure 1.5 before the construction of new buildings can commence. Figure 1.6 shows both the magnitudes of vertical ground surface displacements and their distribution as a function of distance from the faces of braced excavations in various types of soil. The displacements and distances are presented in dimensionless form as fractions of the depths of the excavations, and the consolidation settlements which occurred within the construction period are included. This graphical plot was interpreted by Peck (1969) from a relatively small number of observations but it permits a rough evaluation of the vertical ground displacements which may be experienced by existing buildings adjacent to braced excavations for new buildings. Lateral ground displacements will also be experienced adjacent to braced excavations for new buildings and their magnitudes will depend on the design and construction of the retention systems.

The construction of deep trenches for services, sewers and pipelines adjacent to existing buildings presents the possibility of significant movements in ground adjacent to the deep trenches. The Transport and Road Research Laboratory have made observations at a number of sites where trenches were

Figure 1.5   Shoring and underpinning using Franki Mega piles.

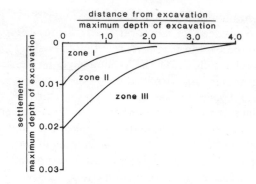

Figure 1.6 Ground movements near braced excavations (Peck, 1969).

excavated to depths of between three and five metres in London Clay (Chard and Symons, 1982). The distribution of lateral surface movements towards the trenches measured at various stages is presented as a dimensionless plot in Figure 1.7.

The installation of traditional piling as part of the foundation works for new buildings can cause harmful vibrations, and it should not be assumed that the cable percussion boring methods used in the construction of small-diameter bored piles will not cause adverse effects on existing structures. These piles are formed using a tripod rig which raises and lowers the cutting tools by means of a cable. The temporary steel casings which are used to support the pile bores are driven into position by a percussive technique, and the vibrations induced by the driving of the casings have been known to cause

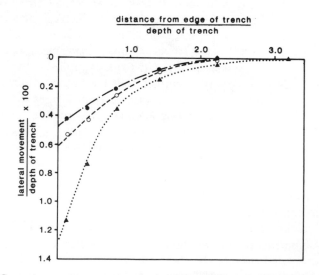

Figure 1.7 Ground movements near trench excavations (Chard and Symons, 1982). ●, 3 days after completion of excavation; ○, 1 day after completion of backfilling; ▲, $7\frac{1}{2}$ weeks after completion of backfilling. No further change after 80 weeks.

damage to adjacent buildings. In medium-dense to dense sands and gravels it is often difficult to advance the temporary steel casings ahead of the bases of the pile bores, and there is always the danger that the boring tools will be used to loosen the granular soils below the leading edges of the steel casings. The loosening of the granular soils permits the temporary casings to be driven with relative ease, but excess volumes of soil have been removed and loosening of the strata takes place. If a sufficient number of piles are installed adjacent to an existing building using this technique then significant ground movements can be experienced by the building and damage can result.

The design of piles should recognize the elastic response of the pile–soil or pile–rock system and no criteria for movement at the head of the pile should be specified which are less than the elastic response of the system to the applied load. Theoretical considerations indicate that linear-elastic analyses of small-diameter piles having length-to-diameter ratios greater than 20 give reasonable predictions of performance provided the service conditions do not impose stresses exceeding 50 % of the limiting stresses from the aspect of soil failure.

Recognition of the necessity for simplicity in routine designs and of the assumptions which must be made concerning soil stiffnesses and structural interaction imposes constraints on the use of more rigorous mathematical approaches. Randolph (1980) has developed methods of analysis of individual piles and pile groups using approximate, but compact solutions for the elastic behaviour of piles. The approximations have been formed from a study of rigorous numerical solutions.

With regard to pile testing procedures, it is important to differentiate between integrity testing and load testing. *Integrity testing* involves the measurement of a property of the body of the pile which can be related to its soundness but does not provide any assurance of the capability of the pile to support safely the service loads. *Load testing* involves the measurement of the response of a pile–soil or a pile–rock system to loads applied to the head of the pile, but does not provide any assurance that the construction of the pile conforms with the requirements of the specification. Proper supervision of piling works by site personnel having adequate and relevant experience is essential to the sound construction of piles.

The installation of steel sheet piling can cause vertical ground displacements due to the effects of vibration. Clough and Chameau (1980) monitored the work of several contractors who were confronted with damage claims from owners of nearby buildings during the construction of new stormwater culverts. The construction works involved the vibratory driving of steel sheet piles, and cracks appeared in both adjacent streets and buildings. The vibratory equipment operated at about 19 Hz and accelerations of as much as $0.4\,g$ were measured close to the sheet piling. The vertical ground displacements resulting from the installation of the steel sheet piles are shown in Figure 1.8 for two sites underlain by granular materials in loose and medium dense states of compaction. The following conclusions were drawn from this

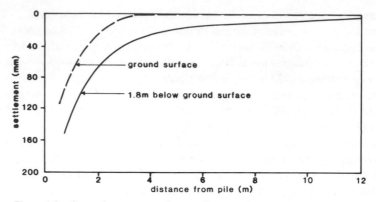

Figure 1.8   Ground movements due to vibratory driving of steel sheet piles.

investigation of the effects of the vibratory driving of steel sheet piles.

  (i) Structures more than 24 metres away from vibratory pile driving should not suffer structural damage.
 (ii) Vibration and noise from pile driving at distances from 24–48 metres were clearly perceptible, and, in some cases, unpleasant to residents.
(iii) Driving into rubble or rock fragments led to ground accelerations and velocities twice as high as those which occurred during normal driving conditions.
(iv) The effects of the vibratory pile driving attenuated rapidly with distance from the piles for all soils.
 (v) Softer soils reduced accelerations more rapidly than denser soils, apparently due to their greater damping capacity.

   The underpinning used for protection works must be founded on suitable bearing strata which will not be affected by the construction operations to be carried out adjacent to the structures to be protected. The protective underpinning must be capable of resisting the vertical and lateral displacements which can result from stress relief, ground vibrations, and stresses imposed by the new construction. Reasonable predictions of the magnitudes of ground displacements caused by stress relief or stress increases can be made by means of finite element analyses using appropriate moduli obtained either from in-situ tests or from reliable data derived from the retrospective analyses of suitable case histories. The quality and quantity of data must be adequate to permit reasonable predictions to be made.

1.1.3 Remedial works

Recent modern buildings which should have continued to perform satisfactorily for some years have often suddenly undergone movements and displayed structural defects which required immediate attention. The determination of the reasons for the change of behaviour, an assessment of the residual strength and stiffness of the building structure and the selection of suitable economical remedial measures can involve much time and expenditure, regardless of the relative importance of the building. The timing and extent of the remedial underpinning works to foundations are important aspects of the process of assessment and care must be taken that the problem has been clearly defined and appropriate remedial measures taken.

The legal implications of over-expenditure on over-conservative solutions confront all engineers preparing designs for remedial works, and care must be taken that improvement of a structure is not achieved at the expense of a party being sued for damages. The expense incurred in addition to that necessary to remedy the situation may be contested successfully by the defender. Remedial works may involve structural strengthening as well as underpinning, particularly if the structural displacements take the form of significant tilt or lateral movements. Masonry structures are particularly prone to separation of facades from internal walls due to fracturing of the keystones, and structural ties are often required in addition to underpinning. The underpinning must bear on suitable ground which is capable of accepting the loads with the minimum of movement. Sound rock, heavily over-consolidated clays, such as glacial soils, and compact sands and gravels are suitable bearing materials for underpinning and the best means of transferring the loads to these materials without causing harmful ground disturbance should be employed. Loose sands and silts should not be used as bearing materials for underpinning, since experience has shown them to be most unsuitable. Recognition must be given in the design of underpinning to the non-linear stress–strain behaviour of soils and the fundamental response of soils which requires displacement of the underpinning in order to mobilize soil resistance. Those techniques which involve minimal displacements to achieve maximum resistance should be employed; particular care must be taken with techniques involving methods of excavation since the underpinning is relatively free of stress after construction, and building movements take place as the loads are transferred from the temporary shoring to the underpinning and the ground beneath the underpinning accepts the direct transfer of load. Figure 1.5 shows a situation where it was necessary to severely restrict building movements and where Franki Mega piles were used. This type of pile is thrust into the ground by means of a hydraulic jack placed between the heads of the segmental piles and the undersides of the footings of the building being underpinned. The vertical displacement required to mobilize the necessary pile resistance is automatically mobilized by this method of underpinning, provided the strata within which the piles are thrust will behave in an essentially elastic manner.

Simple methods of constructing remedial underpinning can be appropriate even in difficult circumstances and Figure 1.9 shows the physical land features which existed at a particular site in 1846 and in 1982. In the nineteenth century

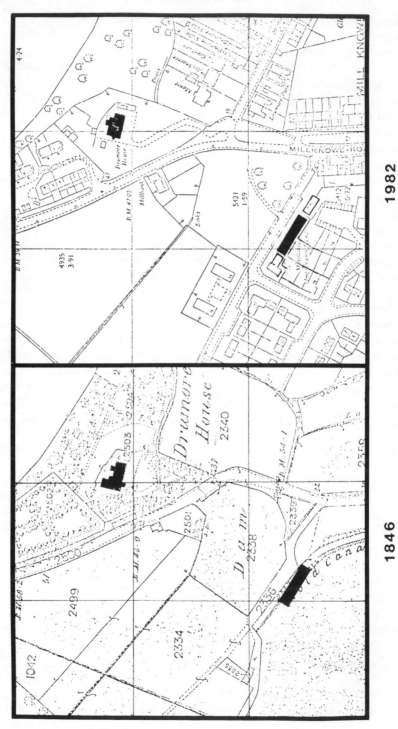

1982

1846

Figure 1.9   Ordance Survey sheets, 1846 and 1982.

the site was traversed by an old canal adjacent to a dam. The modern development of the site in the twentieth century covered the earlier features, and a modern three-storey building was constructed in the position shown on the site plans. The building was subjected to significant differential movements due to the consolidation settlement of the poor-quality fill materials filling and concealing the existence of the old canal cutting. The degree of damage and continuance of building movements necessitated underpinning, which was successfully accomplished by simple methods of excavation at minimal cost.

Grouting of relatively permeable granular soils can be an effective means of consolidating and underpinning the foundations of structures where these rest directly on granular deposits. Care should be taken, however, that the grouts comprise materials which have an adequate life in service. Even using long-life chemical grouts does not necessarily ensure permanent stability in situations where the ground disturbance due to construction operations within an adjacent site is excessive. Demec strain gauge measurements across a major structural crack, favourably orientated with respect to any major and critical building movements, revealed sudden and serious outward movements of the corner and gable of a high and heavy masonry building. A long period of equilibrium had been experienced after grouting of loose medium to fine sands disturbed by bored piling operations within an adjacent site. The cement and chemical-based grouts maintained a period of equilibrium of 220 days (Figure 1.10) but this temporary state of balance suddenly changed and the heavy shoring shown on Figure 1.11 had to be erected in a very short period of time—only two days—to arrest the movements. It would appear that the grouting works effectively consolidated the loose sands beneath the old masonry foundations, but that the state of balance was marginal and depended on the lateral restraint afforded by a few keystones and the diaphragm action of heavy timber floors supported by the masonry facade of the building.

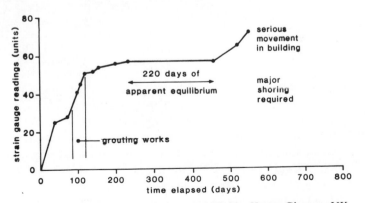

Figure 1.10 Structural movements at Lanarkshire House, Glasgow, UK.

Figure 1.11   Shoring at Lanarkshire House.

1.2 Investigation works

It is important to distinguish between site investigation works and ground
investigation works, since each are separate but equally important phases of
the investigations required to provide proper and adequate information for
the design and construction of underpinning works. The former embraces the
comprehensive investigation of a site, including past use and environmental
constraint, and much of this information can be obtained from a desk study
and a search of local archives. The latter is an exploratory and geotechnical
investigation of the ground conditions to determine the geological structure
and the characteristics of the superficial and solid deposits. Both investigatory
phases should be carried out in accordance with BS 5930:1981, and a useful

guide to investigation procedures and equipment is provided in CIRIA *Special Publication 25 (PSA Civil Engineering Technical Guide 35)*, 1983.

All conversions of building structures and protective and remedial works must be preceded by adequate investigations of the ground conditions and a realistic assessment of the state of the foundations, materials and fabrics of the buildings. Underpinning works present more than just technical risk for the engineer, and uncertainty as to the real character of ground and old foundations occasionally results in unfortunate events involving damage to adjacent property, as well as to the building structure being renovated and refurbished. Also, excessive expenditure on remedial works due to the adoption of over-conservative solutions may be contested by parties involved with construction on adjoining sites or even by the owners of the properties being remedied.

A site investigation generally involves the acquisition of information on the following.

  (i) Historical use of the site
 (ii) Ground conditions
(iii) Groundwater regime
 (iv) Mineral support conditions
  (v) Adjacent buildings.

It is important to identify any buried features associated with the historical use of sites, and proper and extensive search of old records, plans, and memoirs should be made. Bitter experience has established the need for thoroughness of search, particularly in districts known to have experienced historical development.

Made ground is the natural consequence of human activity. In large industrial cities, extensive areas of land surface are artificial, and have resulted from the deposition of a wide variety of materials to elevate low-lying ground and to backfill old stone quarries and clay pits. Fill materials often comprise boiler ash, steelworks slag, coarse discard from former mineral workings, chemical waste, demolition debris and excavation spoil consisting of mixtures of sand, silt and clay. Household refuse can also be found within landfill sites. Ancient watercourses have been culverted throughout the past few centuries and now exist as buried features. All such historical hidden features can remain unknown until exposed by the unwary.

It is important to realize that even the sinking of site investigation boreholes can cause significant ground disturbance. The interception and release of artesian and sub-artesian groundwater can create problems due to the formation of artificial vertical free-flow channels, unless the boreholes are sealed. Overbreak or draw-off can also occur during the sinking of site investigation boreholes through water-bearing non-cohesive strata. Figure 1.12 shows the dramatic effect of the removal of excess volumes of sand on the relative densities of sand deposits caused by the sinking of two 150-mm

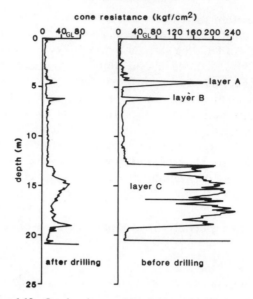

Figure 1.12   Overbreak caused by sinking a borehole in sand.

diameter boreholes to depths of about 20 metres by cable percussion drilling methods. The variations in the cone penetration resistances are a clear indication of the removal of excess volumes of sand, causing loosening of the thick sand layer *C*. It is of interest that loosening of the relatively thin sand layers *A* and *B* also occurred.

It is generally appreciated that lack of definition of variations in ground conditions can result in completely misleading predictions of the performances of underpinning works. Concomitantly, proper methods of sampling and field testing are essential if the characteristics of superficial and solid deposits are to be determined with acceptable accuracy for rigorous analyses of foundation behaviour.

In cohesive soils having soft to firm consistencies, continuous piston sampling is now recognized as the best method of recovering samples in a reasonably undisturbed condition for testing. The U100 open-drive sampler causes serious disturbance to the fabric of clay soils, although its use for recovery of samples of stiff to hard clays will probably continue because of the ability of the sampling equipment to withstand the hard driving stresses in such heavily over-consolidated soils. Figure 1.13 shows the wide scatter of undrained strengths derived from routine triaxial compression tests on U100 samples of a soft to firm late-glacial marine deposit.

In situations where there is a wide variation of results from routine testing which is suspected to result mainly from sampling disturbance, it is recommended that the probable undrained strength of the clay soil be assessed from the stress history of the soil. Overconsolidation related to general stress

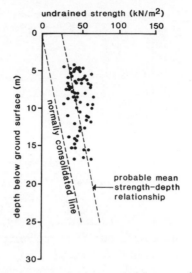

Figure 1.13 Variations in shear strength due to sample disturbance.

history can result from groundwater table movements, soil erosion, glaciation, chemical weathering, cementation, and secondary compression. Overconsolidation related to local stress history is the result of events either natural, and involving desiccation of near-surface layers, or artificial, and related to past loading caused by historical use of the site.

Cone penetration tests (CPT) and self-boring or push-in pressuremeter tests are currently used to determine the undrained strengths of clay soils, and greater use may be expected to be made of in-situ testing to obviate the effects of sampling disturbance on laboratory tests.

With regard to fine-grained non-cohesive soils, information on the in-situ condition of sand deposits can be obtained from the Standard Penetration Test (SPT) as well as the CPT.

However, good drilling and cleaning techniques and careful execution of the SPT are essential in order to ensure that typical values of penetration resistance are obtained from this form of testing. Figure 1.14 compares the penetration resistances obtained from good-quality ground investigation work (Curve 2) with poor-quality work (Curve 1) at the same site. The latter curve reflects the serious disturbance caused by boring operations and completely misrepresents the state of compaction of the sand deposits. These tests were carried out below the water-table in the same uniformly graded fine sand deposit at the same site and within distances of about 15 metres from each other.

A qualitative assessment of the strength of rock strata can be made from visual examination of rock cores and from the rock quality designation (RQD). Compressive strengths obtained from uniaxial compression should be

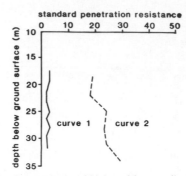

Figure 1.14 Comparisons of high-and low-quality SPT results.

compared with the subjective assessment of strengths as defined by the Geological Society Engineering Group Working Party Report (The Logging of Rock Cores for Engineering Purposes, *Q.J. Eng. Geol.* **3**, 1970, 14) and subsequently referred to in BS 5930, Code of Practice for Site Investigations.

In order to assess intact rock strengths point load tests may be carried out on pieces of rock core. Point load tests permit strength measurements to be carried out on small portions of rock cores. The test gives a Point Load Index which takes account of each individual sample size and is generally normalized to a standard 50-mm sample size. A number of authors have given values for the correlation between Point Load Index (I_s) and the uniaxial compressive strength (UCS). Broch and Franklin (1972) derived a conversion factor of 24, i.e. UCS = 24 I_s, while noting that lower values had been recorded elsewhere. Bieniawski (1975) reported a progressive increase in the conversion factor from 18 to 24 with increasing sample size. Carter and Sneddon (1977) in a series of tests on carboniferous strata recorded results which indicated a value of 20 for the conversion factor. Point Load tests should be carried out axially in order to avoid simply measuring bedding plane separation failures, and also because axial testing involves a loading direction which is more representative of the essentially vertical stresses imposed by foundations.

Considerable use has also been made of the standard penetration test as a means of assessing the strength and stiffness of rocks. An extensive study has been made by Stroud (1974) concerning the standard penetration test (SPT) in insensitive clays and soft rocks. Stroud demonstrated that the SPT can be used to estimate the properties of clays in situ, and extended the correlations for stiff fissured London Clay to a wide variety of clays and weak rocks.

Stroud emphasized that for engineering design purposes the mass shear strength must be determined which takes into account the weakening effect of the system of discontinuities in stiff clays, and indicated that the mass shear strength of fissured London Clay may be only one-quarter to one-half of the shear strength of the intact material. To measure the mass shear strength of a

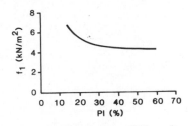

Figure 1.15 Stroud relationship between SPT results and weak rocks.

fissured clay, a large enough volume of material must be tested to properly reflect the weakening effect of the system of discontinuities. The empirical relationship in Figure 1.15 was suggested by Stroud and gives the mass shear strength as a function of the standard penetration resistance (N value), i.e. $C = f_1 \times N$. The factor f_1 was considered to be a constant, essentially independent of depth and the spacing discontinuities, although it could apparently vary from site to site according to the characteristics of the materials.

It is important that in the very large number of tests carried out by Stroud the standard splitspoon sampler was used. In hard materials where the full penetration of 450 mm was not achieved, the tests were stopped at 100 blows and the actual penetrations noted. The number of blows for 300 mm penetration was then obtained by extrapolation. Cole and Stroud (1976) provided the scale of strengths and N values for weak rocks shown in Figure 1.16.

The existence of a groundwater regime and the seasonal behaviour of the groundwater table must be defined during the ground investigation stage of the work. It is particularly important that a proper definition should be made of the groundwater regime in the locality of a building requiring underpinning. Information on the behaviour of the groundwater table is required both to aid the selection of the most suitable form of underpinning and to ensure that no adverse change is made to the groundwater regime during and after construction of the underpinning which would cause damage to adjacent property. Diversion of normal paths of groundwater flow caused by any artificial barriers created by underpinning could result in flooding of basement property formerly enjoying relatively dry conditions. Artificial lowering of the groundwater table to facilitate underpinning operations, or reductions in the water table derived from environmental changes due to the construction of underpinning, can cause significant increases in effective vertical soil stresses which may result in the settlement of adjoining buildings. It should be a requirement of the investigation works to establish the real groundwater conditions within a site in relation to sources, piezometric heads, hydraulic gradients, and the influence of climatic change. The real situation can rarely be determined during the relatively short period of time afforded by boring operations, and open-type piezometers should be installed in boreholes

Shear strength: kN/m²	Approx. N value	Strength/ consistency *	Grade	Breakability	Penetration	Scratch
40000		Strong	A	Difficult to break against solid object with hammer		Cannot be scratched with knife
20000						
10000	600	Moderately strong	B	Broken against solid object with hammer		Can just be scratched with knife
8000						
6000	400					Scratched with knife. Can just be scratched with thumb-nail
4000		Moderately weak	C	Broken in hand by hitting with hammer		
2000	200		D	Broken by leaning on sample with hammer	No penetration with knife	Scratched with thumb-nail
		Weak				
1000			E	Broken by hand	Penetration to about 2mm with knife	
800	100					
600	80	Hard or very weak	F	Easily broken by hand	Penetration to about 5mm with knife	
400	60	Very stiff			Penetrated by thumb-nail and to about 15mm with knife	
200	40	Stiff			Indented by thumb	
100	20					
80		Firm			Penetrated by thumb with effort	
40	10					
	8	Soft			Easily penetrated by thumb	
20	6					
	4					
10	2	Very soft				

* Geol. Soc. Working Party Report (1970) and CP2004 (1972) except that the designation 'hard' for soil materials has been given a separate identity, which is analogous to very weak for materials classifiable as rock.

N.B. Grades and shear strengths for rock refer to intact specimens. The N value, however, is an in situ test and includes some effect of discontinuities. For cohesive soils the correlation between N values and in situ strength assumed is that given by Stroud (1974) for clays of low plasticity.

Figure 1.16 Cole and Stroud relationship for strength of weak rocks.

selected because of their advantageous location within a site in respect of lateral and vertical variations in the ground conditions. The long periods of time (as much as three months) to attain equilibrium of water levels in piezometers installed in low permeability soils emphasize the impossibility of measuring the elevations of a groundwater table during the relatively short times involved in sinking boreholes.

Before selecting and designing underpinning for conversion, protective or remedial works, it is important to carefully assess the mineral support conditions under a site by reference to such bodies as the National Coal Board and the British Geological Survey. The current state of the art is defined in CIRIA Special Publication 32 and the ICE publication, *Ground Subsidence* (ICE, London 1977). The ground displacements caused by mining subsidence are unrelated to the stresses imposed by foundations unless the bases are unknowingly founded immediately above voids caused by mineral extraction. Mining subsidence can adversely affect underpinning which by its very nature is securely integrated with the ground being subjected to large movements.

It is important to realize that ground displacements due to modern active mining may be predicted with reasonable accuracy, but that the local and severe ground movements which are caused by the collapse of old pillar and stall workings can only be estimated roughly by empirical relationships such as that given in Figure 1.17. An over-emphasis on the definition of the ground conditions to the detriment of acquisition of knowledge on the nature and condition of all building structures affected by underpinning works should be avoided. In order to properly assess each particular situation, careful

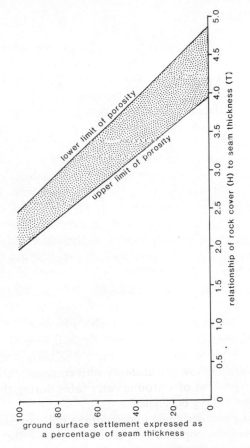

Figure 1.17 Relationship between ground subsidence and rock cover over stoop and room workings.

investigations must be made of the building to be underpinned and the environment as well as the ground. The necessity for dilapidation surveys involving photographic records and subsequent monitoring of building performance are paramount.

The legal situation must be clearly understood by all parties to the underpinning contract. Clear definitions of responsibilities should be made at the outset and the criteria for the support works carefully and explicitly defined.

Nuisance caused by ground and airborne vibrations to the residents of existing buildings must also be assessed to avoid expensive litigation and contractual delays. The selection of the most suitable type of underpinning may be determined by the need to minimize disturbance to adjacent buildings caused by construction operations. Cost need not dictate selection.

1.3 Serviceability limits

As stated in the Preface, it is important to differentiate between damage to the primary support elements of a structure and damage to cladding, partitions, and finishes. Ground movements affect visual appearance as well as function and serviceability, but it is essential to recognize the relative unimportance of purely aesthetic considerations. If the investigatory works establish that the ground movements have ceased and that the state of balance of the structure is adequate, then underpinning is generally unnecessary. Classifications of visible damage to building structures in relation to widths of structural cracks vary considerably and there is the danger that the indiscriminate use of these partly subjective criteria will result in decisions to underpin when it is unnecessary. The decision to underpin a structure should only be taken when there is clear evidence either that movements will continue for an unacceptable period of time, or that the apparent structural equilibrium is only temporary and harmful movements may be experienced in future times. The relationship between serviceability and amount of visible damage is not simple and the structural engineer must make a decision based on an assessment of the particular circumstances. It should be appreciated that slight damage may be unacceptable for a hospital structure in contrast to an industrial building where moderate damage is acceptable since it probably would not affect serviceability or function. Table 1.1 was presented by Jennings and Kerrich (1962) and was intended to act as a guide to ease of repair of brickwork and masonry rather than as a direct measure of the degree of damage and of the necessity for underpinning.

In contrast, Table 1.2 presents a classification of damage to walls of buildings in relation to their use in service. This table was developed by Pynford and was based upon thirty years of experience of the amount of damage which prompted property owners to express concern and their legal

Table 1.1

Degree of damage	Description of typical damage* (ease of repair is italicized)	Approximate crack width (mm)
	Hairline cracks of less than about 0.1 mm width are classed as negligible.	≯ 0.1**
1. Very slight	*Fine cracks which can easily be treated during normal decoration.* Perhaps isolated slight fracturing in building. Cracks in external brickwork visible on close inspection.	≯ 1.0**
2. Slight	*Cracks easily filled. Redecoration probably required.* Several slight fractures showing inside of building. Cracks are visible externally and *some re-pointing may be required externally to ensure weathertightness.* Doors and windows may stick slightly.	≯ 5.0**
3. Moderate	*The cracks require some opening up and can be patched by a mason. Recurrent cracks can be masked by suitable linings. Repointing of external brickwork and possibly a small amount of brickwork to be replaced.* Doors and windows sticking. Service pipes may fracture. Weathertightness often impaired.	5 to 15** or a number of cracks ≥ 3.0
4. Severe	*Extensive repair work involving breaking-out and replacing sections of walls, especially over doors and windows.* Window and door frames distorted, floor sloping noticeably. Walls leaning or bulging noticeably, some loss of bearing in beams. Service pipes disrupted.	15 to 25** but also depends on number of cracks
5. Very severe	*This requires a major repair job involving partial or complete rebuilding.* Beams lose bearing, walls lean badly and require shoring. Windows broken with distortion. Danger of instability.	usually > 25** but depends on number of cracks

*It must be emphasized that in assessing the degree of damage account must be taken of the location in the building or structure that it occurs.
**Crack width is one factor in assessing degree of damage and should not be used on its own as a direct measure of it.

advisers to seek assistance from engineering specialists. Damage should not be related only to the widths of cracks, and any proper assessment of damage should take into account the means by which a structure is supported (i.e. frame or shear wall); its state of balance; the nature of the cracking (i.e. tensile or shear or a combination of both); and whether ground movements may be expected to continue. Differential movements can cause cracking and separation of walls into units which are then capable of articulation without experiencing failure provided the structure is capable of maintaining its state

Table 1.2

Crack width (mm)	Degree of damage			Effect on structure and building use
	Dwelling	Commercial or public	Industrial	
≯ 0.1	Insignificant	Insignificant	Insignificant	None
0.1 to 0.3	Very slight	Very slight	Insignificant	None
0.3 to 1	Slight	Slight	Very slight	Aesthetic only. Accelerated weathering to external features.
1 to 2	Slight to moderate	Slight to moderate	Very slight	
2 to 5	Moderate	Moderate	Slight	The serviceability of the building will be affected, and towards the upper bound, stability may also be at risk.
5 to 15	Moderate to severe	Moderate to severe	Moderate	
15 to 25	Severe to very severe	Moderate to severe	Moderate to severe	
> 25	Very severe to dangerous	Severe to dangerous	Severe to dangerous	Increasing risk of structure becoming dangerous.

of balance. Unfortunately, experience has shown that once cracking develops, from whatever source, it is probable that movements due to other sources will be concentrated at these lines of weakness. Cracking that is initiated by one cause and is initially negligible may become excessive and unacceptable when other movements are superimposed. In such circumstances, underpinning in conjunction with structural strengthening and the introduction of movement joints may be necessary measures.

1.4 Litigation

The legal aspects of underpinning involving right of support are a complex subject, of which the proper treatment is the prerogative of the legal profession. It may be helpful, however, to present the fundamental principles of the laws of Scotland and England as they may be applied by the Courts and Arbiters of these countries, in the hope that some general pointers may emerge.

Scots law has its foundations in Roman or Civil Law, in contrast to English law, which arose as a consequence of the Norman Conquest and has its roots in Common Law and Equity. In general, the rules observed in both Scots and English law are similar but, as we shall see, not identical.

The legal systems comprising International Law may be placed in three basic categories. Some are derived from the Civil or Roman Law, and others are based on the Common Law, which evolved from the actions of English courts and was conveyed by communication and emigration from England.

Civil Law is the basis of the law of Europe and of many former European colonies; Common Law is the basis of the law of most of the United States. Islamic Law is the basis of the law for most of the Middle East and those non-Middle Eastern countries which base their legal systems upon Shiriah law.

In both Scots and English law, every owner of land has a natural right, as an incident of ownership, the right to prevent such use of the neighbouring land as will withdraw support which the neighbouring land naturally affords to his land. In the natural state of land, one part of it receives support from the other, upper from lower strata, and soil from adjacent soil, and, therefore, if one piece of land is conveyed so as to be divided in point of title from another contiguous to it, or (as in the case of mines) below it, the right to support passes with the land as an essential incident to the land itself.

When the natural condition of the surface is changed and pressure upon it has been artificially increased by the erection of buildings, this is a different matter. The right of support to buildings from adjacent land or the right to have buildings supported by other buildings are questions of an acquired right and no longer of a natural right of property. Such a servitude (in Scotland) or easement (in England) may be created by express or implied grant. In England, it may also be acquired by prescription (*Dalton* v. *Angus*) 1881 (6 Appeal Cases at page 740) but this question has not been settled in Scotland. It is, therefore, the position in England that the owner of a new building has no common law right of lateral support for it until the prescriptive period of twenty years elapses and then on the day when the period does elapse the owner acquires an almost absolute right of support. Thus the English doctrine of prescription logically implies acquiescence on the part of the adjoining owner and the power to interrupt prescription running. This means, as Lord Penzance observed, that the owner of the adjoining soil may for twenty years 'with perfect legality dig that soil away and allow his neighbour's house, if supported by it, to fall in ruins to the ground'. It was also held in *Ray* v. *Fairway Motors (Barnstaple) Ltd* (1968) 20 Property and Compensation Reports at page 261, that the owner of the supporting land did not even owe a duty of care in negligence to the owner of the new building and that in the light of *Dalton* v. *Angus* only the House of Lords could introduce such a duty. This, however, would not appear to be the law of Scotland as a common law right of Action in Nuisance may be available. The modern law of Scotland relating to nuisance is directly derived from the Civil Law maxim 'use your own property so as not to injure that of your neighbour'. The judicial approach to nuisance has been expressed thus:

> ... the proper angle of approach to a case of alleged nuisance is rather from the standpoint of the victim of the loss or inconvenience than from the standpoint of the alleged offender; and that if any person so uses his property as to occasion serious disturbance or substantial inconvenience to his neighbour or material damage to his neighbour's property, it is in the general case irrelevant as a defence

for the defender to plead merely that he was making a normal and familiar use of his own property. The balance in all such cases has to be held between the freedom of a proprietor to use his property as he pleases, and the duty of a proprietor not to inflict material loss or inconvenience on adjoining proprietors or adjoining property; and in every case the answer depends on considerations of fact and of degree .... the critical question is whether what he was exposed to was *plus quam tolerabile* when due weight has been given to all the surrounding circumstances of the offensive conduct and its effects... any type of use which in the sense indicated above subjects adjoining proprietors to substantial annoyance, or causes material damage to their property, is *prima facie* not a 'reasonable use'. (Per Lord President Cooper in *Watt* v. *Jamieson* 1954 SLT at page 57.)

In the leading Scottish Case of *Lord Advocate* v. *Reo Stakis Organisation Limited* 1982 SLT page 144, we are provided with important authority on the Law of the Right of Support especially with regard to the lateral support of land to buildings. As a result of this case, it appears the Law of Scotland is that the owner of a building may recover damages for loss of support on the following three grounds:

(1) infringement of the right of support
(2) nuisance
(3) negligence.

It was held in that case that the owner of adjacent land within which excavation work is taking place was under a duty under the Law of Nuisance not to deprive an adjoining building, belonging to his neighbour, of lateral support. This duty and the right of action exist as soon as the new building is constructed and do not accrue after twenty years' prescriptive enjoyment of lateral support as is the case in England.

The boundaries of nuisance as expounded in English law are uncertain but historically breach of support (including a prescriptive right of support of buildings) was a breach of the tort of nuisance and is still treated as such by the standard English texts on tort. This appears to conflict with the opinion of the Court in *Stakis* in which it was observed

... it is no doubt the case that in some instances an occupier whose property suffers such damage (subsidence caused by building operations) may find himself with a remedy *both* under the Law of Nuisance and upon the basis of infringement of an acquired right of support but it is by no means unusual to find that more than one right of action is available upon the same set of facts... the law of support in relation to buildings is part of the law of heritable right. The Law of Nuisance, on the other hand, is part of the Law of Neighbourhood.

It would, therefore, appear that the decision in *Stakis* cannot be reconciled with English decisions in *Dalton* v. *Angus* and *Ray* v. *Fairway Motors (Barnstaple) Ltd.*

In *Stakis*, structural damage had been caused to the pursuer's building in the centre of Glasgow, allegedly as a result of piling operations carried on in connection with the building of a hotel situated across a lane from the damaged building. The old buildings on the site had been demolished and the construction of a new hotel commenced. Structural cracking then appeared at the portion of the pursuer's building nearest to the building site of the new hotel. The representatives of the developer took steps to prevent further subsidence and damage but without success. Thereafter, the pursuer raised a court action in which he sought to recover the cost of his own remedial works. Claims based on nuisance and negligence were made against the developer and their piling contractors, and claims based on negligence against the consulting engineers. At first instance, the judge declined to reject the pursuer's plea of a right of action based on nuisance (1980 SLT 237) and the decision was upheld on appeal (1982 SLT 140). The pursuer had pleaded that 'piling involving boring by cable percussion method is hazardous in that it gives rise to a high risk of subsidence in nearby ground because of the draw-off of the soil . . . resulting in lack of support to the buildings on the ground so affected'. Neither the Court of first instance nor the Appeal Court considered whether the conduct complained of was deliberate, negligent or otherwise. The Court observed that 'the Law of Nuisance applies without exception to provide a remedy for any relevant damage suffered by a neighbouring occupier as a result of any type of use of adjoining subjects by the occupiers thereof' and applied the above-quoted passage from WATT which was described at page 143 as 'the best of the most recent descriptions of our Law of Nuisance'. Subsequent to this decision the view has been expressed that the Court has overstated the rights in nuisance available to a neighbour affected by building operations and a further case is awaited with keen interest.

In brief, the effect of *Stakis* appears to be that although the Judge at first instance appeared to think that the Law of Scotland and England do not diverge, it seems clear that *Stakis* impliedly rejects *Dalton* v. *Angus* and the doctrine of prescriptive acquisition of rights of lateral support of land to buildings.

What is clear, however, in both the Scots law of delict and the English law of tort is that if an engineer or contractor negligently carries out piling, blasting or other excavating operations which cause damage, an action in delict or tort based on the ordinary principles of the reasonable man, duty of care and negligence will arise independent of any right of action which may be available due to loss of support or nuisance.

In Scotland, questions involving the support afforded by one building in favour of another, adjoining or discontiguous, are less frequent and such questions are sometimes dealt with by other branches of the law of property. For example, the law relating to flatted houses known as the Law of the Tenement gives rise to a species of right differing from common property which arises among the owners of subjects possessed in separate portions but still united by their 'common interest'. In the absence of any specific provisions in the Title Deeds to the properties, this common interest is the source of common law rules in connection with the roof, walls, etc. For example, the gables are common to the owner of each flat so far as they bound his property, but he and the other owners in the tenement have cross-rights of common interest to prevent injury to the stability of the building. As adjoining houses, the law of mutual gables is that most usually involved.

In both Scotland and England it appears that a servitude or easement giving right of support by one building to the other may be constituted by express or implied grant and in England by prescription: The absence of such an easement means that in English law if a man pulls down his house and thereby deprives his neighbour's house of the support it has been enjoying, and his neighbour's house is thereby damaged, his neighbour has no cause of action although he must take care to interfere as little as possible with the adjoining house. He is not called upon to take active steps for its protection. Again, in the light of *Stakis* it is likely that a pursuer will sue upon the ground of nuisance which is so favourable as compared with breach of a supposed right of support. Whether the action of a neighbour is founded upon nuisance, negligence or breach of a right of support, his remedy can be interdict, including interim interdict (which if granted would halt the building or excavating operations) and damages for loss sustained or simply damages.

In conclusion, it is perhaps worthy of note that every new subsidence event causing damage grounds a new action for reparation although damages have been awarded for earlier events. It is difficult, in many instances, to state categorically that a building requires the support of adjacent land and the matter is further complicated when the subsidence of a building follows at a significant interval of time after the construction operation which caused the ground movements particularly when doubts may be expressed of the state of repair of the building which is damaged.

The preceding commentary has attempted to explain the possible interpretations of the law in connection with the damage to buildings caused by unsuccessful underpinning operations, but it is important that legal advice should be sought before arriving at a conclusion in any particular set of circumstances.

1.5 Historical background

As a generalization it may be stated that the underpinning of structures in the days of growth of ancient empires depended on the practical skills passed from master to apprentice. Knowledge of soil behaviour would depend on experience within particular localities, with reliance on knowledge of foundation behaviour rather than on an understanding of the reasons for the behaviour. There was no science of foundations.

The application of scientific thought to foundation engineering began in the seventeenth and eighteenth centuries with the gradual development of theoretical concepts from that time. The use of the physical sciences to attain an understanding of why soils behaved in a certain manner under applied loads opened the pathway to enlightenment and gave foundation engineering the opportunity of becoming a science.

The development of the theories of elasticity and plasticity during these exploratory years provided the mathematical tools for engineers to analyse a wide variety of foundation problems. Recognition must always be given to the strains which occur in soils as stress fields are modified by excavation and underpinning.

The year 1925 was a milestone in the development of the science of foundation engineering with the publication of the book *Erdbaumechanik* by Karl Terzaghi. Terzaghi demonstrated that the mechanical behaviour of soils depended on the fluid pressure in the pore spaces between the discrete mineral particles. His theoretical concept of effective stress controlling changes in volume or strength of soils provided a major advance in the science of soil mechanics and greatly advanced the science of foundation engineering. Subsequent research has established that the effective stress concept for fully saturated soils provides solutions with a sufficiently high degree of accuracy for foundation engineering purposes.

Terzaghi also introduced the philosophical thought that indiscriminate application of theory based on poor physical models was inappropriate for practical solutions, and was of the conviction that the development of the science of foundation engineering required careful field observations of real behaviour. In the opinion of Terzaghi the difference between theoretical and real behaviour could only be ascertained by field experience. In every branch of applied mechanics the researcher or theoretician considers the behaviour of an ideal material, and Terzaghi emphasized that it was necessary to be aware that theory must be combined with a thorough knowledge of the physical characteristics of real soils with the additional awareness of the difference between the behaviour of soils in the laboratory and in the field.

It is important to recognize that soils are quite different from structural materials, such as concrete, being discrete particles with the void spaces between the particles containing a liquid. Volume change during shear is an important characteristic of soils and the dependence of mechanical behaviour on effective stress acting between the discrete particles is unique in the sciences of material behaviour. The economical design and safe execution of underpinning requires a sound theoretical knowledge of foundation engineering and a wide experience of real behaviour.

The contributions made by the construction industry from the aspects of the development of plant, techniques, and materials have been significant over the past thirty years and many major underpinning problems have been solved by practical innovation rather than application of theory.

Ingenuity of method and skill of execution is not the prerogative of engineers of the present century and the following account by G.L. Taylor, RIBA, of the methods used in underpinning the Long Storehouse at H.M. Dockyard, Chatham, demonstrates earlier skills and innovative ability.

The Storehouse was a five-storey masonry structure about 165 m long and 16 m wide. The structure displayed serious defects in its walls and floors and the arches of the exterior walls had been damaged by settlement of the piers supporting the arches. The walls leant outwards about 250 mm and settlement of the piers of the order of 225 mm had taken place. Shoring was erected to support the masonry walls and the timber floors were propped to enable them to carry the weight of the fittings and equipment for ships. The propping successfully prevented settlement of the floors but the heavy masonry external walls continued to settle. The differential movements caused severe upward bending (hogging) of the timber floors and the floor girders lost contact at their ends with the walls. It was considered that the masonry walls of the Storehouse were supported by timber piles or on timber sleepers, but the exact nature of the foundations was unknown.

The damage to the building became so serious that the decision was taken to underpin the heavy masonry walls. Investigatory works effected by simple excavation techniques revealed that the walls had been built upon oak timbers founded at depths of about 4.5 metres, as shown in Figure 1.18. The timbers were in poor condition due to natural decay and the several tiers of longitudinal and transverse timbers were being compressed differentially under the weight of the heavy masonry walls.

The initial proposal for the underpinning comprised removal of the timbers and the construction of a thick mass concrete foundation on solid ground of

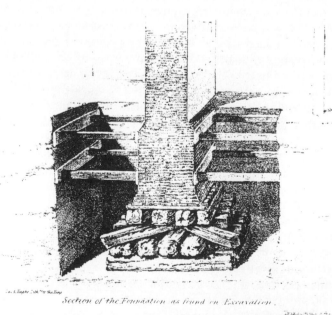

Section of the Foundation as found on Excavation.

Figure 1.18   Underpinning in 1848. Existing foundation.

A. The Concrete partly poured in between the side frames B B

B.B The movable side frames which are withdrawn and the Concrete poured in and compressed between them by the screws.

C.C. The Troughs down which the Concrete is poured into A. after being mixed above.

D. when a length is done the sides D are unscrewed and the whole comes apart and ready for another length.

Sections shewing the Method of underpinning with Concrete, the Store Houses, Chatham Dock Yard.

Figure 1.19   Underpinning in 1848. Underpinning operations.

adequate bearing capacity, leaving a gap of about one metre between the underside of the old masonry wall and the top of the new concrete foundation. The initial proposal was that the gap of one metre was to be carefully filled by a bricklayer making sure that the new brickwork was tightly built into the intervening space.

The innovatory solution which was adopted made use of a strong iron frame as shown in Figure 1.19. The ground was excavated in short 1.8 metre lengths beneath the heavy masonry walls to a depth of 600 mm below the wall to facilitate the extraction of the oak timbers. The excavations were planked and strutted and the bases of the excavations were found to be sound hard chalk. Shuttering was erected within the trench excavation and concrete poured by means of troughs. This mass concrete was poured to within 300 mm of the bottom of the wall which was found to be relatively smooth and planar. Large slates were bedded on the upper surface of the mass concrete before it set and hardened. An iron frame was placed on these slates and positioned as shown in Figure 1.19. The frame was 300 mm high, and measured 1.2 × 2.1 metres, the latter dimension being the width of the base of the masonry wall. Finely ground lime and sharp river gravel in the proportions of one of lime to six of gravel were mixed with hot water, poured into the iron frame, and the cementitious mix squeezed by turning screws until it was in intimate contact with the underside of the old wall. The movable rams within the iron frame were slackened when the first batch of lime concrete had set and succeeding batches of concrete squeezed into position until the entire width of a wall had been underpinned. The heavy masonry walls were shored before the excavation and underpinning works commenced and the entire operation was most successful.

Towards the river the ground conditions worsened and the excavations had to be sunk to depths of about 6 metres and these exposed 3 metres of oak timber laid in a crosswise fashion. Timber piles were found under the walls of a portion of the storehouse and the same form of underpinning was used with equal success.

The philosophy of underpinning is concisely and appropriately contained in the words of Rondelet: 'The aim of construction work is to carry it out with all of the strength and quality required and using reliable materials handled with skill and economy'.

References and further reading

1. Attewell, P.B. and Taylor, R.K. (eds.) (1984) *Ground Movements and their Effects on Structures*. Surrey University Press, Glasgow and London.
2. Bieniawski, Z.T. (1975) The Point Load Test in geotechnical practice. *Eng. Geol. J.* 9, 1–11.
3. Broch, E. and Franklin, J.A. (1972) The Point Load Strength Test. *Int. J. Rock Mech. Ming. Sci. Geomech. Abstr.* 669–696.
4. BS 5930: 1981. Code of Practice for Site Investigation. British Standards Institution, London.
5. Carter, P.G. and Sneddon, M. (1977) Comparison of Schmidt Hammer, Point Load and Unconfined Compression Test in Carboniferous strata. *Proc. Conf. on Rock Engineering*, University of Newcastle on Tyne.
6. Chard, B.M. and Symons, I.F. (1982) Trial trench excavation in London Clay: a ground movement study at Bracknell. *TRRL Report LR 1051*.
7. Clough, G.W. and Chameau, J-L. (1980) Measured effects of vibratory sheet pile driving. *J. Geotech. Eng. Div. ASCE*, October.
8. Cole, K.W. and Stroud, M.A. (1977) Rock socket piles at Coventry Point, Market Way, Coventry. *Piles in Weak Rock, Proc. ICE Symp., ICE*, London.
9. Fleming, W.G.K., Weltman, A.J., Randolph, M.F., and Elson, W.K. (1985) *Piling Engineering*. Surrey University Press, Glasgow and London.
10. Geological Society Engineering Group Working Party (1970) Report on the logging of rock cores for engineering purposes. *Q. J. Eng. Geol.* 3, 14.
11. Healy, P.R. and Head, J.M. (1984) Construction over abandoned mine workings. *CIRIA Special Publication 32*, CIRIA, London.
12. Hunter, L.E. (1952) Underpinning and strengthening of structures. *Contractors Record and Municipal Engineering*.
13. Institution of Civil Engineers (1977) *Ground Subsidence*. ICE, London.
14. Jennings, J.E. and Kerrich, J.E. (1962) The heaving of buildings and the associated economic consequences. *Civil Engineering in South Africa*, 5(5)112.
15. Peck, R.B. (1969) Deep excavations and tunnelling in soft ground. State-of-the-Art Report. *Proc. 7th Int. Conf. on Soil Mechanics and Foundation Engineering*, Mexico City. 225–290.
16. Prentis, E.A. and White, L. (1950) *Underpinning—Its Practice and Applications*. Columbia University Press, New York.
17. Randolph, M.F. (1980) PIGLET: A computer program for the analysis and design of pile groups under general loading conditions. *Cambridge University Engineering Department Research Report*, Soils TR91.
18. Reasonable neighbourhood; the province and analysis of private nuisance in Scots Law. Parts I and II. *J. Law Soc. Scotland*, Dec. 1982, Jan. 1983.
19. Royal Institute of British Architects, (1836–1867) extracts, *Proc. R. Inst. Br. Architects*, London.

20. Stock, C.H. (1902) *A Treatise on Shoring and Underpinning*. Batsford, London.
21. Stroud, M.A. (1974) The Standard Penetration Test in insensitive clays and soft rocks. *Proc. Eur. Symp. on Penetration Testing*, Stockholm.
22. Tomlinson, M.J. (1978) *Foundation Design and Construction*. Pitman, London.
23. Walker, D.M. (1969) *The Scottish Legal System*. 3rd edn. (revised), W. Green, Edinburgh, p. 67.
24. Weltman, A.J. and Head, J.M. (1983) Site Investigation Manual. *CIRIA Special Publication 25*.

2 Simple methods of excavation

J.F. HUTCHISON

2.1 Introduction

'Simple methods of excavation' is a broad title for this chapter and it describes the more commonly used techniques of excavation, shoring and underpinning. These methods have been successful for many years and can today still be effective and economical in certain circumstances. Since underpinning is usually a combination of temporary and permanent works, and the former are generally the responsibility of the contractor and the latter that of the engineer, close co-operation between these two parties is essential at every stage of construction. The simple methods which will be described in the chapter make it easier for this co-operation to take place and, since underpinning is by its nature a complex subject where methods can differ from job to job, the techniques will be couched in general terms.

Due to the modern trend towards refurbishment of existing buildings and other structures, and the development of 'gap' sites in cities, access is almost always very cramped and limited. While the development of the mini-excavator has enabled mechanical plant to be used in many restricted sites, there are many more where hand digging is the only solution to the access problem—as in the situation where the existing structure requires extensive internal propping and shoring. The use of the hand dig technique can also have other benefits; for example, it will enable the engineer to monitor the work step by step where the ground investigation has not, of necessity, been as detailed as he would have wished. It is of paramount importance during excavation for underpinning that the trenches and pits are adequately supported to prevent ground movement. A careful technique such as hand excavation will enable the contractor to control his temporary works and will permit time for modification should this prove necessary.

Where a building is sensitive to minor movements, whether it is the structure being underpinned or an adjacent structure or structures, vibrations will be kept to a minimum by the use of the 'shovel and barrow'. This technique was successfully used in the construction of the Museum of Modern Art in Brussels. Due to environmental and other pressures, the decision was taken to build the Museum underground in a pedestrian square, bounded by elegant 18th century buildings which house the Museum of Classical Art. The construction called for an excavation below existing ground level of up to 8 m, and the first thoughts of supporting this excavation involved a contiguous piled wall. However, space was very limited and the required drilling rig would have had great difficulty in operating successfully. It was also thought that vibrations from the rig would set up unacceptable movements in the adjacent structures.

The solution was to construct a non-contiguous retaining wall of 2 m-diameter shafts. The shafts were hand dug to a depth of 25 m and built up from hand-placed precast segments reinforced with steel hoops. This enabled the bulk excavation to be carried out, and with movements in the existing structures being closely monitored and the excavation carefully phased, maximum recorded displacement was of the order of 15 mm—considered to be acceptable for the magnitude of the excavation.

The previous paragraphs have described situations where hand digging was considered to be advantageous. However, the method has disadvantages too, perhaps the main one being the slow rate of progress which could expose the structure being underpinned to a longer period of risk than more expeditious techniques. Where, too, the excavation is required to be taken to a stratum which requires a depth of excavation of more than say 6 m, the costs of hand digging could prove to be unacceptable. It therefore requires careful consideration before deciding to use these techniques. The following pages will describe underpinning methods which employ hand excavations.

Shoring (Chapter 1) is a vast and varied subject, and requires detailed treatment on its own. However, since shoring and underpinning are frequently complementary to each other, the opportunity will be taken to describe, in general terms, the more commonly used methods of shoring.

2.2 Shoring

Where a building or structure is in poor condition due to settlement, and underpinning has to be carried out to limit or to arrest resulting movements, external shoring will probably be required. If, however, the building has soundly constructed loadbearing walls in good condition, internal ties may be used which would not restrict the access round the building. These ties would normally be supplemented by internal bracing.

The main shoring members can be of timber, steel or scaffolding. Where timber is used, swelling and shrinking will take place and provision should be made, in the shape of hardwood wedges, to allow for any adjustment which will be required. In external shores, changes in the ground will have an effect; for example, freezing and thawing, softening of soils due to heavy rain, and nearby excavation during the underpinning operation causing ground movement. Much of the effect of the first two can be obviated by careful attention to drainage and weather protection, and ground movements can be limited by a good support system to the excavation. Where the structure is

Figure 2.1   Example of raking shore using scaffold tube and fittings.

situated close to a heavily trafficked road, or if it houses heavy machinery, allowance for the effects of vibration should be made in the design of the shoring system. Some thought should also be given to the consequences of accidental impact and steps should be taken to protect the system from these as far as is practicable. Where space permits and loading is not too severe, scaffolding can be most effective in forming shores, flying shores or ties (Figures 2.1–2.3). This method also has the advantage of being less sensitive to weather effects and it is easily adjusted.

No matter which shoring system is used, it is essential that regular checking is done during the underpinning operation so that adjustments and modifications can be carried out without delay, where these are necessary.

The most common forms of shores are

(1) raking shores,
(2) flying shores, and
(3) needles and dead shores.

2.2.1 Raking shores

These are used where a building or structure requires external support, and each raking shore consists of one or more members set at an angle to the

Figure 2.2 Example of raking shore showing treatment at base of shore.

Figure 2.3   Example of flying shore used in 'gap' site.

building. The angle should be no more than 75° to the horizontal and the top of each shore should terminate at a short needle set into the fabric of the building just below each floor level. The tendency of the shore to move upwards is resisted by a cleat fixed to a wall plate set immediately above the needle.

The load from the shores is transferred to the ground by means of grillages on sole plates and, as in all forms of temporary supports, the safe bearing capacity of the soil should be determined and a suitable soleplate designed so that this is not exceeded. Where possible the soleplate should be kept clear of the edge of the underpinning excavation. This distance will depend on the nature of the soil, but should be equal to at least half the depth of the excavation. If, due to lack of room, this is not possible, the excavation supports should be designed to resist any additional surcharge load imposed by the shoring system (Figure 2.4).

2.2.2 Flying shores

Where raking shores are likely to cause an obstruction to underpinning operations and where a 'gap' site is being developed, flying shores can be used. Generally these are used where the distance between the opposing buildings is no more than about 10 m. This limitation is for practical reasons.

Flying shores should be needled as already described in section 2.2.1 and should be taken from the floor level of one building to that of the other if these are on the same horizontal plane. Where this is not so, a stiff vertical member

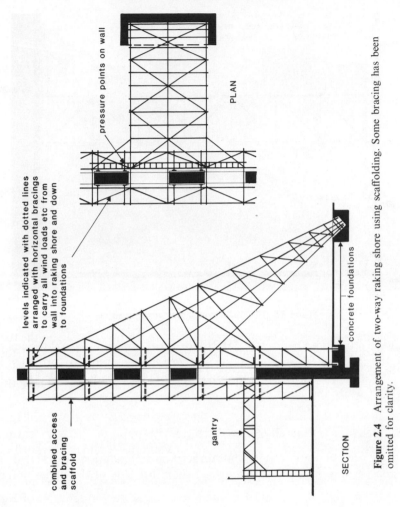

pressure points on wall

PLAN

levels indicated with dotted lines
arranged with horizontal bracings
to carry all wind loads etc from
wall into raking shore and down
to foundations

concrete foundations

combined access
and bracing
scaffold

gantry

SECTION

Figure 2.4 Arrangement of two-way raking shore using scaffolding. Some bracing has been omitted for clarity.

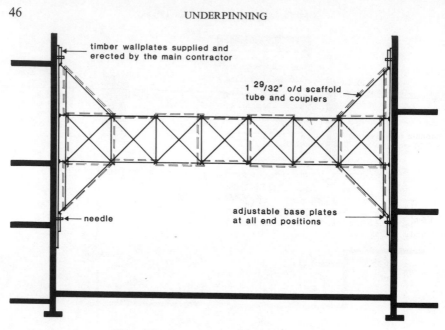

timber wallplates supplied and
erected by the main contractor

1 $^{29}/_{32}$" o/d scaffold
tube and couplers

needle

adjustable base plates
at all end positions

Figure 2.5   Typical arrangement of flying shore.

should be introduced to distribute the load. An example of flying shores using
scaffold tube is shown in Figures 2.5 and 2.6. Flying shores are provided to
prevent bulging or tilting of walls and will not carry loads imposed by self-
weight of walls and floors.

2.2.3 Needles and dead shores

These are used to support walls while underpinning operations are carried out
and consist of vertical members spaced on either side of the underpinning

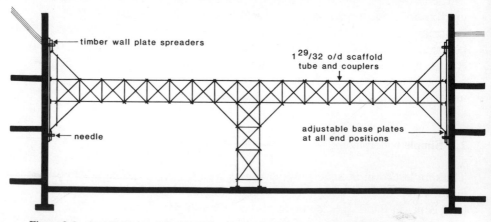

timber wall plate spreaders

1 $^{29}/_{32}$ o/d scaffold
tube and couplers

needle

adjustable base plates
at all end positions

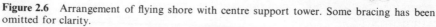

Figure 2.6   Arrangement of flying shore with centre support tower. Some bracing has been
omitted for clarity.

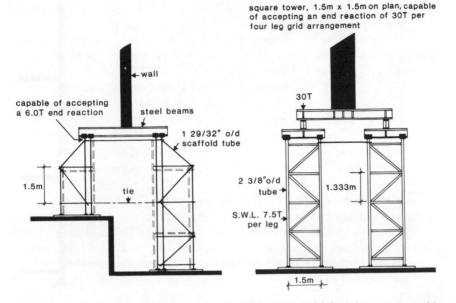

Figure 2.7 (*Left*) dead shore constructed in tube and fittings. (*Right*) dead shore constructed in Triframe 30 components.

excavation. The vertical members in turn support needles spanning between them. These needles should, as far as possible, be placed near to the points of maximum load. Before carrying out this operation, all openings and recesses in the wall should be adequately braced and the holes for the needles should be the minimum size necessary. Horizontal beams may also be used at right angles to the needles on top of the dead shores if it is desirable to limit the number of shores used (Figure 2.7).

The above brief descriptions are of shoring systems which are commonly used and, as mentioned before, careful monitoring is essential. It is also important that a thorough survey of the structure or building is carried out before shoring and underpinning operations are commenced. A record of all cracks, movements and defects, should be compiled. This should be agreed among all interested parties and the record should be continuously updated until all are satisfied that movements have ceased.

2.3 Simple underpinning

The simplest form of underpinning can be used where ground conditions are good, and consists of excavating for and constructing a series of columns, or legs, beneath the wall to be underpinned. The length of these legs is usually determined by the condition of the existing structure, its composition, and the nature of the ground supporting the underpinning. CP 2004 recommends that this length should be between 1 m and 1.4 m for brick and/or stone walls in good condition.

It is good practice to construct the legs on a 'hit or miss' basis up to a maximum of six in a group. This will, of course, depend on the length of the wall or elevation to be underpinned, and Tomlinson (1978) suggests that the sum of the legs being constructed should not exceed one-quarter of the total length of the wall. Where the structure shows some signs of distress this should be reduced to one-fifth or one-sixth of the total length. Careful attention should be paid to the position of openings and piers above the underpinning so that due allowance is made for increased loads in local parts of the structure. Each group of legs should be completed before the next group is commenced (Figure 2.8).

When the legs are constructed of concrete, this should be started immediately after the excavation is completed. If this is not possible, the last few millimetres of the excavation should be left and should be removed immediately before concreting commences. One other method is to protect the solum of the excavation with a 50 mm layer of blinding concrete.

Each leg should be constructed to within 75 mm of the underside of the old foundation or wall and the top should be carefully levelled off to receive the final pinning. The leading edge of each leg should incorporate a vertical groove or chase so that the adjacent leg, when constructed, can be keyed into it and the total length of underpinning can act as a unit. The final pinning should be carried out using a fairly dry concrete mixture with a maximum aggregate size of 10 mm. 'Fairly dry' means that the mixture has the minimum amount of water added so that it will form a ball when squeezed in the hand. This concrete should be well rammed into the gap between the new leg and the old foundation. This final gap can also be filled with a dry mortar mix or brickwork in cement mortar. Where a wide foundation is being underpinned, this should be constructed in steps from back to front. At all times during the construction of this type of underpinning, the sides and ends of the excavations should be supported by temporary timbering or sheeting. Some common methods of doing this will be described later in the chapter.

Where the underpinning is being carried out because of settlement of the existing foundation, or where the safe ground bearing capacity is likely to be exceeded during the construction of the legs, the sections of the wall on either side of the leg being constructed should be supported at of near ground level

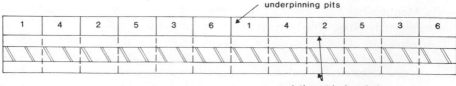

Figure 2.8   Strip foundation. Simple underpinning construction. Sequence of legs.

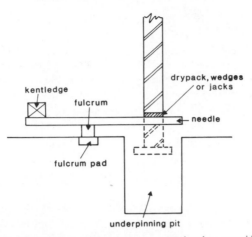

Figure 2.9 Cantilevered needles for access restricted to one side of wall.

by needles as already described. Bedding of the wall on the needles should be done with dry pack and in such a way that overstressing of the wall is avoided. It is good practice to use wedges or jacks to support the wall on the needles.

There will be circumstances where it is not possible to gain access to the inside of a building or structure; for example, where the building is still occupied or its contents cannot be disturbed. On these occasions, a system of cantilevered needles can be constructed with the needles being supported on fulcrum and the counterbalance being supplied by kentledge. This system is shown in Figure 2.9.

It will sometimes be necessary to construct king posts to support one end of the needle; for example, where the ground conditions make it imperative to carry the load to a deeper layer of soil. A typical sequence of operations for this exercise in illustrated in Figure 2.10.

If ground conditions are particularly difficult, or where the water table is higher than the excavation level, also where the legs have to be taken much lower than the existing foundation, a system of pier foundations, with beams spanning between them to carry the wall loads, can be used. This system is only practical where there is a layer of ground of sufficient bearing capacity to carry the heavy loads applied by the piers. The beams spanning between the piers can be constructed in a number of ways, and some of these are described in *Foundation Design and Construction* (Tomlinson, 1978).

Mention has been made of the importance of support to the excavation where underpinning operations are being carried out and since this forms an integral part of the construction, some of the more commonly used methods are described hereafter. As already noted, a careful examination and assessment of the structural soundness of the building to be underpinned should be carried out, and this will have considerable influence on the type of excavation support to be used.

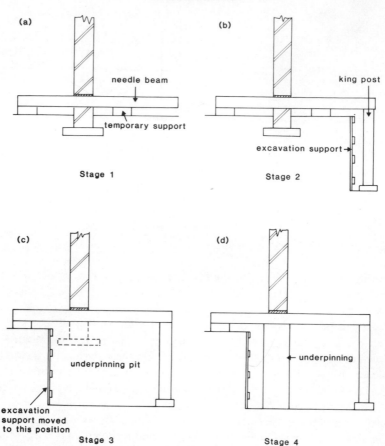

Figure 2.10   Simple needle and kingpost support system.

Traditional timbering methods are applicable in shallower excavations where slight vibrations only can be tolerated. The amount and type of timbering used will also, of course, depend on the type of ground and on the following considerations:

(1) Size and depth of excavation
(2) Variations in soil conditions, e.g. pockets of sand, fissures, or results of previous soil disturbances
(3) Amount of ground water, if any
(4) Surface drainage conditions
(5) Weather and moisture conditions—soil strength can break down through heavy rain or frost, clay can shrink in drying out
(6) Routes and depths of existing underground services, e.g. gas, electricity, telephone cables etc.
(7) Possible draw down of material through prolonged pumping

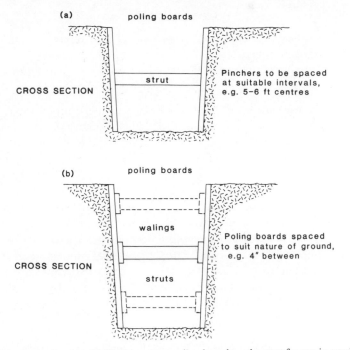

Figure 2.11 Open sheeting. (*a*) Pincher—two poling boards and a strut for use in good ground. (*b*) Frame—any pair of walings on opposite sides together with strut. Alternative arrangements shown dotted. 'Frame' may also include poling boards.

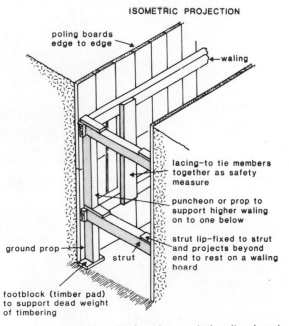

Figure 2.12 Close sheeting. Typical example using vertical poling boards; alternatively, horizontal sheeting could be used.

C

(8) The need to remove supports progressively and replace, as the underpinning operation proceeds
(9) Whether the excavation can be treated as a double-sided or single-sided
support.

If the soil is good firm clay and it is possible to have double-sided support,
then pinchers can be used. These consist of pairs of vertical boards spaced at $\frac{1}{2}$
to 2 metres apart along the length of the excavation and strutted apart across
the width of the excavation. This method is termed open sheeting, and
alternative ways of doing this are illustrated in Figure 2.11. If the ground to be
excavated is of poor quality, e.g. soft clay, sand and gravel, etc., then close
sheeting (Figure 2.12) can be used. This can be done either with close poling
boards (Figure 2.13) or, if the ground is so bad that it will not stand long
enough to permit the placing of the poling boards, then the use of runners will
have to be considered. These consist of long vertical timbers at least 50 mm
thick and with their lower end chisel-shaped. These are driven downwards in
advance of the excavation. Sketches of both methods are shown in

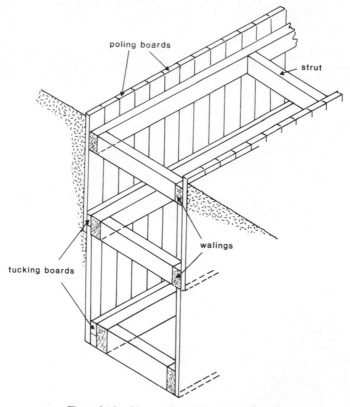

Figure 2.13   Close poling with tucking frames.

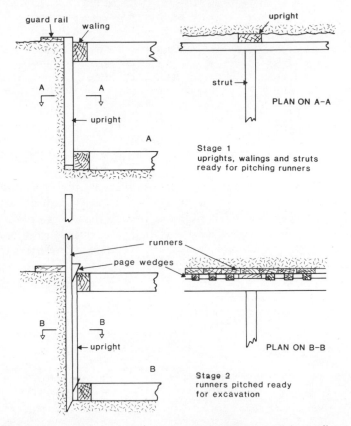

Figure 2.14 Typical methods of sheeting with runners. Stage 1: uprights, walings and struts ready for pitching runners. Stage 2: runners pitched ready for excavation.

Figures 2.14 and 2.15. The above methods may also be used in a single-sided support application where the struts are replaced by raking shores taken down to a thrust-block at the foot of the excavation. Where the excavation is deeper than say 6 m, and vibration is still a consideration, then one method of support would be to use soldier piles of 'H' section located in pre-bored holes with horizontal boards placed and wedged between them as the excavation proceeds. This is illustrated in Figure 2.16.

The control of groundwater during excavation and underpinning operations requires expert soil advice so that the correct method can be adopted and the draw down of fine material from adjacent structures, or indeed, the structure to be underpinned, is avoided. Of equal importance to excavation support is the backfilling operation after the underpinning has been completed. This should be done carefully and with the proper compaction to minimize any future settlement of the replaced material.

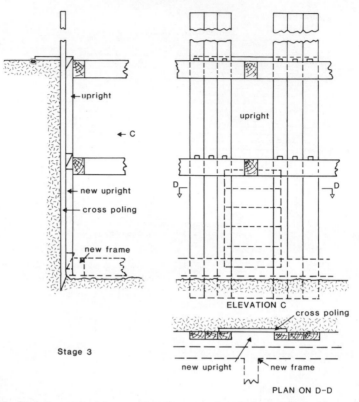

Figure 2.15 Stage 3: runners driven and trench excavated ready for next frame (shown dotted).

2.4 Case study

To illustrate the use of simple excavation methods, the following is a description of a contract which—due to restricted access and the need for careful monitoring during the construction of the foundation—required the use of hand digging techniques.

'Browns of the Mound' is a local name for an eighteenth-century eight-storey block of flats situated at the top of the Mound in the city of Edinburgh. The Mound itself has an interesting history, being originally known as the 'earthen mound', and is even referred to as such in old maps. It was man-made, and was built of the excavated material arising from the construction of the New Town to the North of Princes Street, Edinburgh's main thoroughfare. Its purpose was to form a link from the New Town to the Old Town across what was then the ill-drained Nor'Loch. The situation of 'Browns' is therefore a prime one: the building, together with its neighbouring property, stands high above Princes Street and forms an important part of the Edinburgh skyline.

The contract consisted of the conversion of the existing flats to modern

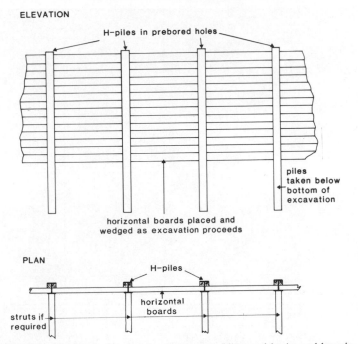

Figure 2.16 Support of excavation by H-pile soldiers and horizontal boards.

executive suites, together with office accommodation and a restaurant, all with upgraded services. Due to the building's prominent position, the need to preserve and restore, where necessary, the north and east elevations was obvious, and the decision was taken to build within the existing facades.

The block stands on the slope of the rock outcrop at the top of the Mound and has two halves divided by a thick masonry cross-wall. The rear half of the building is in fact built over Lady Stair's Museum which was to remain undisturbed. The decision was taken by the architects and consulting engineers (J & W Johnston & Partners and Cundall Johnston & Partners respectively) to upgrade the floors, replacing joists and flooring as necessary.

The front or north half, however, presented a different problem. When the developer took over the structure the north and east elevations were showing signs of movement outwards from the rest of the building and emergency shoring measures were immediately put in hand. These consisted of steel channel sections placed horizontally on the outer face of the masonry at each floor level. These were tied back through window openings to timber trusses again placed horizontally against the inner face of the walls. The timber trusses gained their end support from heavy steel angle sections bolted to the masonry cross-walls and were carried on vertical timber legs on the existing floors.

The new reinforced concrete structure was designed to be built within the

Figure 2.17   View of timber truss support to east elevation.

north and east elevations, the masonry being tied into the new floors at each level. It was therefore important to maintain the temporary shoring system ahead of the construction of the new frame, and each set of trusses was left in place together with the timber floor supporting them until the new floor had been constructed at the level below. This involved substantial temporary propping of the existing floors from ground floor level and imposed further restrictions on an already difficult access. The truss arrangement is shown in Figure 2.17.

The rock level below the existing building, established by exploratory pits and boreholes, dipped quite steeply from back to front and from south-west to north-east corners. The rock was overlain by a stiff clay of varying thickness. During the excavation for ground floor beams and column footings, it was discovered that the heavy masonry cross-wall dividing the north and south halves of the building was not (as had been expected) built on the rock, but on

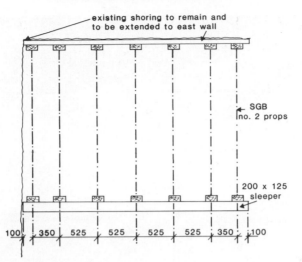

Figure 2.18 Plan of shoring arrangement.

Notes: (1) Existing props to remain until S.G.B. props are in position
(2) All uprights to be 150×75 and to be driven to rock
(3) Sleepers to be staggered and make-up pieces to be inserted as shown on elevation
(4) Excavation for sleeper wall to be kept neat and all voids behind sleepers to be packed with soil well compacted.

the overlying clay layer. Since the level of the underside of the new ground beams was some 1 m to 1.5 m below the underside of the cross-wall, immediate steps had to be taken to prevent loss of ground from under the wall.

To allow time for the engineer to redesign the foundations to incorporate underpinning of the cross-wall, a temporary timber support to the exposed clay face to the excavation was erected; see Figures 2.18, 2.19 and 2.21. Construction then proceeded on the remaining beams and column footings, and some of the columns were also built. This enabled a more positive support system to be implemented using the foot of one of the permanent columns as a thrust-block; Figure 2.20 illustrates the actual method used.

The permanent underpinning of the cross-wall was achieved by using a vertical reinforced concrete wall cantilevered from the ground floor slab in the manner of a basement wall. This was constructed on a 'hit and miss' basis, the temporary propping system being removed section by section as the permanent structure was completed.

Although not a large underpinning job, the contract described serves to illustrate some of the points made at the beginning of the chapter, viz.:

(1) Because of restricted access and the need for careful excavation, hand digging was decided upon.
(2) Close co-operation between the contractor and the engineer enabled measures to be put in hand immediately the unexpected situation arose.

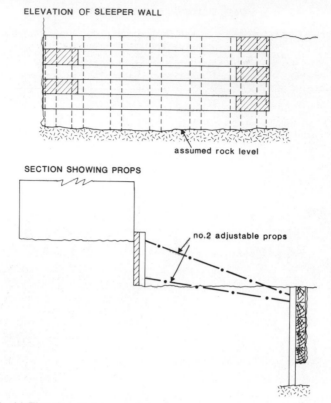

ELEVATION OF SLEEPER WALL

assumed rock level

SECTION SHOWING PROPS

no.2 adjustable props

Figure 2.19 (*a*) Elevation of sleeper wall.

Note: (1)   Make-up pieces shown hatched.
           (*b*)   Section showing props.
Note: (1)   Props to be wedged securely to prevent movement in any direction.

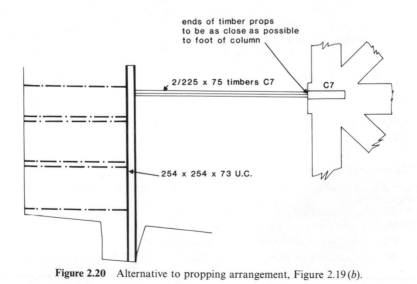

ends of timber props
to be as close as possible
to foot of column

2/225 x 75 timbers C7

C7

254 x 254 x 73 U.C.

Figure 2.20   Alternative to propping arrangement, Figure 2.19 (*b*).

Figure 2.21 Temporary support of clay face under main cross-wall.

(3) The existing structure was closely observed during the whole construction and propping was frequently checked.

The outcome was a successful structure in which no movement took place during construction nor has any taken place since construction was completed.

Acknowledgement

Figures 2.1, 2.2 and 2.3 were provided by Mr A.S. White, SGB Building Equipment Division, Mitcham, Surrey.

References

1. CP 2004: 1972. Foundations British Standards Institution, London.
2. Tomlison, M.J. (1978) *Foundation Design and Construction*. Pitman, London.

3 Conventional piles in underpinning

K.W. COLE

This chapter concerns itself with the use of conventional piles as underpinning. As already described (Chapter 1) the objective of underpinning is to create new foundations on to which the existing load may be wholly or partially transferred without harmful movements. The need to use piles comes about when

(a) the normal procedure of underpinning by excavating and forming mass concrete foundations (see Chapter 2) is not possible, or is uneconomical either because of the depths to which the excavations would to be taken, or because of problems caused by groundwater; or
(b) the loads on the ground from the existing structure are so great that the large dimensions of the excavations necessary for normal underpinning would cause the structure (or other nearby structures) to settle or move sideways by unacceptable amounts.

There are many ways in which piles can present problems during and subsequent to installation. The problems mainly arise through two causes.

(i) The pile type is not easily constructed in the prevailing ground conditions. In extreme cases the pile type selected may be entirely inappropriate; for example a bored pile where the underlying strata are waterlogged fine sands and gravels.
(ii) The pile is not constructed properly.

The Construction Industry Research and Information Association (CIRIA), in association with the Department of the Environment, commissioned and published in the period 1977 to 1980 a series of guidebooks on various subjects concerned with piling, of which reports PG2, PG3, PG4, PG8 and PG9 deal especially with 'problems' during the installation of piles and with methods of detecting problems. Other guidebooks in the series are mentioned in the appropriate parts of this chapter.

3.1 Connecting piles to the structure

The cardinal rule in underpinning is that whatever method is used, the structure being underpinned should not be irreparably damaged by the

60

underpinning process, as otherwise the whole point of underpinning is lost. In practical terms this means that if installing the underpinning will be damaging, a prior stage of underpinning will be necessary.

This is illustrated in Figure 3.1 (*a*) which shows a temporary 'needle' beam inserted to support the load while the existing footing is undermined to insert the new spreader beam which distributes the load to the new pile foundations. As illustrated in Figures 3.1 (*a*) and (*d*), pockets can be made to allow the insertion of jacks, or the entire structural arrangement can be made suitable for lifting the existing structure to a higher elevation. Figures 3.1 (*b*) and (*c*) illustrate how the new underpinning piles can be connected to the existing foundations either by being constructed in holes drilled through them or pockets cut out of them, or by transferring the load through a 'corset' structure.

In all cases a large measure of symmetry of the new pile positions about the existing loads is desirable to prevent large bending moments and consequent high stresses being imposed on the existing structure.

Where possible the piles should be placed close to the lines of action of the loads so as to minimize the amount of connection structure. In many cases the headroom required by conventional drilling and driving equipment will be greater than is available immediately adjacent to the loads to be supported, and structural arrangements of varying degrees of complexity, such as those illustrated in Figures 3.1 (*e*), (*f*) and (*g*), may be necessary.

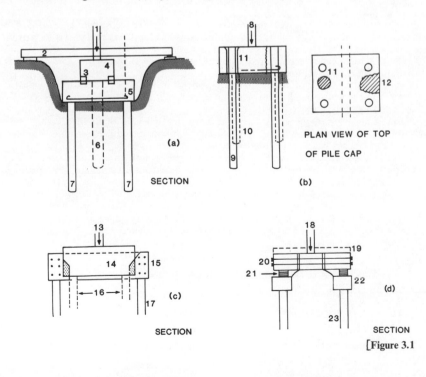

[Figure 3.1

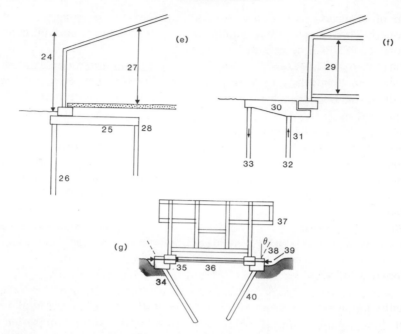

Figure 3.1 (*a*) Spreader beams as temporary and permanent underpinning. 1, structure load; 2, spreader beam to support structure load while new pile cap is built under existing; 3, pockets for jacks if required; 4, existing footing or pile cap; 5, new pile cap also acts as spreader beam; 6, existing piles; 7, new piles.

(*b*) Underpinning piles installed through existing foundation. 8, structure load; 9, piles; 10, existing piles; 11, pile cap drilled through for new pile; 12, pile cap broken out for new pile.

(*c*) Corset structure to take load from existing foundation. 13, structure load; 14, existing footing or pile cap; 15, foundation reinforced to act as corset and to transmit load to new piles; 16, existing piles; 17, new piles.

(*d*) Structure arranged for lifting to higher elevation. 18, structure load; 19, existing foundations 20, new corset structure using prestressing to 'clamp' existing foundation lifted by jacks; 21, jacks and packing; 22, new pile cap; 23, new piles.

(*e*) Using extended bearing beam to overcome headroom difficulty. 24, no headroom problems when outside; 25, new bearing beam; 26, new piles; 27, headroom required for piling equipment; 28, piles and bearing beams installed at intervals.

(*f*) Using 'balancing' beam when headroom is inadequate for piling equipment. 29, headroom inadequate; 30, new 'balancing' beam; 31, new piles installed outside structure; 32, compression pile; 33, tension pile.

(*g*) Using a combination of steeply raked piles and prestressing when access to structure is obstructed. 34, new piles to provide reaction installed at same rake (θ); 35, flat jacks if required; 36, reaction beams at intervals along structure; 37, working clearance for piling equipment; 38, longitudinal pile cap; 39, prestressing cables; 40, piles installed at a rake (θ) at allow working clearance on existing structure.

The alternatives if headroom is less than that required by conventional equipment, are as follows.

(i) Adopt a method which installs the piles in short sections. For driven piles this can be done using short pile lengths of either precast concrete or steel H-section or tubular piles, and a low head driving frame requiring about

5 m of headroom. Joints are expensive, vulnerable to damage if not properly aligned, and time-consuming to complete, so the cost of using short sections will be greater than for unrestricted conventional piling. One pile type, the Franki Mega pile, is designed specifically to be installed in short lengths using a hydraulic jack to thrust the pile into the ground against the reaction of the existing structure. Details are given in Tomlinson (1977).

(ii) Construct bored piles using very low headroom tripod rigs and percussion boring equipment. The rate of construction is likely to be slow, and the process may produce large amounts of mud slurry of which it is difficult to dispose. The minipiling processes described in Chapter 5 may offer less disruptive and more economical methods, particularly in circumstances where the piles have to be installed from basements or such places where access is confined.

3.2 Conventional piles

Conventional piles are those which in usual circumstances are constructed to support new structures but can be adapted to the role of underpinning; non-conventional piles are described in Chapters 4 and 5, and many are especially suitable for underpinning, particularly in circumstances where the space available to construct piles is restricted.

The conventional piles considered in this chapter have the following principal characteristics.

(a) Types of piles. Conventional piles are available from a wide range of types, all falling within the categories of displacement types or non-displacement types as shown in Figure 3.2. Displacement piles are forced or driven into the ground by vibratory or thrust techniques, whereas for non-displacement piles the ground is (to a large extent) excavated and the pile placed or formed within the excavation. Detailed descriptions of the principal bearing pile types are given in 'A review of pile bearing types', (DoE/CIRIA, 1977), and in Tomlinson (1977).

(b) Material. Piles used for underpinning consist generally of steel and concrete or grout (sand–cement mix) reinforced with steel. The steel reinforcement may be of rods, structural sections, wires or tendons.

(c) Shapes. Piles installed by vibratory devices or by hydraulic jacking techniques have sections that combine the greatest possible stiffness with lightness, so that they do not deform unduly while being handled and installed, and yet are light in weight for economy in handling and use of materials. Bored piles are cylindrical in shape, being formed either by percussion boring

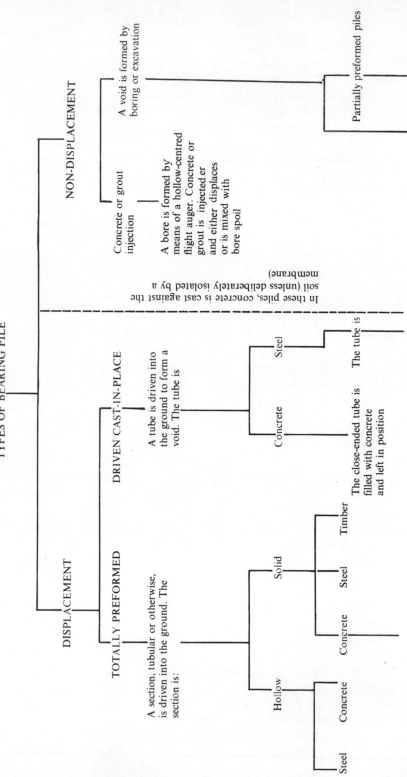

TYPES OF BEARING PILE

DISPLACEMENT

NON-DISPLACEMENT

TOTALLY PREFORMED

A section, tubular or otherwise, is driven into the ground. The section is:

Hollow
 Steel
 Concrete

Solid
 Concrete
 Steel
 Timber

DRIVEN CAST-IN-PLACE

A tube is driven into the ground to form a void. The tube is

Concrete

Steel

The close-ended tube is filled with concrete and left in position

The tube is

(In these piles, concrete is cast against the soil (unless deliberately isolated by a membrane)

Concrete or grout injection

A void is formed by boring or excavation

A bore is formed by means of a hollow-centred flight auger. Concrete or grout is injected er and either displaces or is mixed with bore spoil

Partially preformed piles

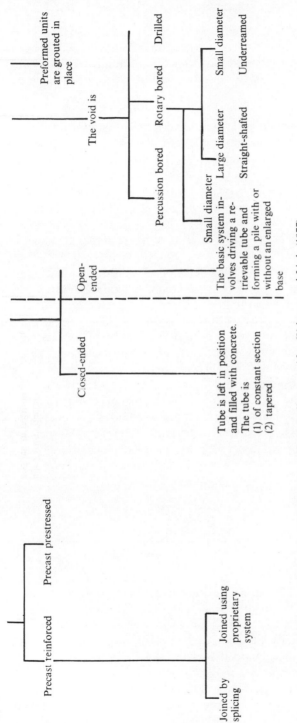

Figure 3.2 Classification of bearing pile types. After Weltman and Little (1977)

or by rotating machinery, and often have concentric enlargements of the excavations called 'bells' or 'bulbs'. A cylindrical excavation, with or without cylindrical steel 'lining' tube to support the ground, is inherently the most stable shape likely to remain open, and in good condition to receive the plastic concrete.

(d) Sizes. The two dimensions which characterize the size of a pile are its diameter (or side dimension, if square) and length. The diameter often quoted is nominal, meaning that a cylindrical pile should nowhere be less than the diameter stated, or for an octagonal pile it is the diameter of the equivalent circular pile. Piling contractors often offer a range of sizes, and care should be taken to establish the actual size as constructed, rather than to rely on the nominal size described.

A pile is considered to be of 'large' size if it has a nominal diameter (a) greater than 750 mm for a bored pile; and (b) greater than 600 mm nominal diameter (or width) for a driven pile. A pile is considered to be 'small' if it has a nominal diameter or width of (a) less than 300 mm for a bored pile; or (b) less than 150 mm for a driven pile. There is no special term for piles with intermediate dimensions. Piles with lengths greater than 20 times their nominal diameter or longer than 20 m are considered to be 'long'; piles of such length exposed above the ground surface usually require support against buckling. For piles largely beneath the ground buckling is unlikely to be a problem unless the ground is very weak.

The above characteristics are used to describe the piles illustrated in Figure 3.3: (*a*) shows small-diameter, driven, precast reinforced concrete or tubular steel piles; (*b*) driven universal bearing piles; and (*c*) small-diameter, bored, cast-in-place, reinforced concrete piles. Large-diameter bored reinforced concrete piles may be used in certain situations to form pier foundations.

3.3 Designing piles

The process of designing piles for underpinning consists of

   (i) gathering together and understanding information about the site, the existing structures and the ground conditions;

  (ii) conducting ground investigations to determine the soil, rock and groundwater properties;

 (iii) conducting investigations into the shape, strength and stability of the structure to be underpinned, and also of any nearby structures that may be affected by the underpinning;

 (iv) selecting a type of pile (or types of piles) suitable for the ground conditions, and able to withstand the groundwater conditions; driven piles must not be used if their installation would adversely affect the environment or the condition of surrounding buildings.

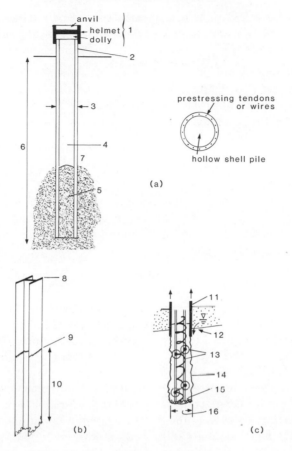

(a)

(b)   (c)

Figure 3.3 Piles of differing types.
(*a*) Driven, precast, reinforced concrete or steel tubular pile. 1, fabricated steel driving head—designed to distribute impact stresses evenly; 2, cutting pile head to required level must be done carefully or damage and weakness will result; 3, typical diameter 300–450 mm; 4, void (may be filled with concrete); 5, plug of soil forced up inside cylinder; 6, typical length 10–25 m; 7, pile wall thickness must be sufficient to preclude overstressing during driving and handling.
(*b*) Driven steel H-section pile. 8, after driving pile head can be 'flame cut' to level; 9, butt welding is most common method of joining lengths; 10, pile sections are generally approx. 300 × 300 or 350 × 350 mm with weights in the range 75 to 150 kg/m. Lengths up to 26 m are available but 10–15 m lengths are generally easier to handle.
(*c*) Bored, cast-in-place reinforced concrete pile. 11, temporary lining tube lifted upwards and removed after concrete is poured and while it is still wet; 12, water in sandy layers may cause problems as lining tube is removed; 13, reinforcement 'cage' with 'spacer' wheels to ensure correct cover to reinforcement; 14, surface of hole may be roughened to increase load capacity of pile; 15, some excavation debris may not be removed from base of pile; 16, pile diameter typically 350–550 mm.

(v) performing calculations (or, if calculations are not relevant, making judgements) to establish the likely levels at which the bases of the piles should be founded.

The outcome of the design should be drawings showing in plan the positions of the piles, and if they are to be inclined from the vertical ('raked'), the deviation and amount of rake. Sections should be drawn to show how the piles are related to the assumed ground and groundwater conditions, and how they are to be finished at the heads of the piles and then connected to the existing structure.

The design normally also includes a specification, which stipulates the qualities of, and tests on, the materials to be used in making the piles, and lays down constraints on construction methods, and procedures for testing the load–settlement behaviour of trial piles (special piles made to be tested well above the expected load, to confirm the margin of safety) and procedures for testing piles installed as underpinning.

3.3.1 Assessment of ground and groundwater conditions

It is preferable that the ground and groundwater conditions across the whole length and breadth of the structure to be underpinned should be known and understood, as only then can it be possible to ascertain the limitations of underpinning by normal methods, and make rational decisions on the types and size of pile that should be installed.

Very often the amount of investigation it is possible to undertake is restricted, either for the practical reasons of lack of spaces to make boreholes and trial pits because parts of the structure are in occupation and cannot be entered, or because making multiple boreholes or trial pits would be too expensive in proportion to the cost of the works. In such cases judgement is necessary in deciding when enough information has been obtained to make a reasonable design and estimate of likely costs. Such judgement is best entrusted to a person or persons of experience in the field of geotechnics who is especially experienced in piling.

In the most complicated ground conditions it would be true to claim that the ground and groundwater investigations continue until all the under-pinning foundations are completed, and that, at best, only a partial knowledge can result from investigation prior to undertaking the works. Nevertheless, embarking upon a potentially difficult, hazardous and expensive undertaking such as underpinning without some understanding of the likely outcome of the methods proposed should be regarded as foolhardy.

3.3.2 Quality and costs of investigations

Ground investigations before anything is built in 'open' sites are usually expected to represent between 0.5% and 5% of the cost of the structural works, although the upper end of this range is not common and is only likely where deep piled foundations are found to be necessary. For the conditions under which investigations are made for underpinning, costs are likely to be within the range of 2% to 15%. A major part of an investigation with piling in mind is likely to be into the shape, reinforcement and condition of the existing structure, as the connections of piles to existing structures may pose difficult problems.

The quality of investigation profoundly influences the reliability of the information obtained. Good guidance on investigation and testing methods and procedures are given in BS 5930 (Site Investigations) and BS 1377 (Methods of Testing Soils) and a comprehensive review of site investigation is given in Clayton *et al.* (1982).

With good guidance on method and procedures, there remains the need to ensure these are correctly and economically applied to the project in hand. A good specification of requirements is essential and an engineer or engineering firm specializing in geotechnics (the all-embracing name for soils and rock engineering) is best able to provide this; the geotechnics specialist should also supervise the investigation fieldwork and report on the result. If it is not appropriate to involve a specialist geotechnics engineer, guidance on specifications can be obtained from *Piling, Model Procedures and Specifications* (ICE, 1978), which includes a model ground investigation specification. (Note that 'site investigation' is taken to refer to the complete investigation of a site, including the desk study of geology and site history, whereas 'ground investigation' refers specifically to physical investigation of ground materials by borehole, sampling, laboratory test, etc.)

3.3.3 Interpretation of ground and groundwater conditions

Of the conditions which are likely to give rise to foundation failures, unexpectedly weak ground and abundant groundwater released on penetrating into strata of high permeability are the most common.

The 'buildability' of foundations is of as great an importance as bearing capacity. It is therefore essential that each ground investigation should concentrate not only on finding and recording the properties of the strata likely to take a significant part in supporting the possible types of foundations to be used as underpinning, but that the intimate details of the factors which may have greatest influence on the choice of foundation should also be obtained. There is likely to be little scope in most underpinning work for a major redesign of the foundations, without incurring a massive increase in costs.

Weak ground can be easily missed during boring and drilling for samples; particularly in core samples taken by drilling, the weak ground is likely to have been washed away and be part of the 'lost' core. Repeated drillholes with cored samples taken one after the other to produce 'continuous' samples may be necessary to obtained recovery of sufficient samples of weak ground for identification and tests.

In weak (soft) soils the 'continuous' samples may be obtained by taking piston samples taken one after the other, or by the Delft continuous sampler, Details of coring and sampling equipment are given in BS 5930, and the procedures for classifying the soils and rocks, and obtaining their 'index' (basic) properties and strength and compression characteristics are explained by Clayton *et al.* (1982).

Groundwater conditions are identified by observations made during the processes of drilling and boring, and by means of specially constructed standpipes and piezometers in those holes. As the depth to groundwater at each instrument usually takes some time (several hours to several weeks, depending upon the permeability of the ground and of the standpipe or piezometer installation) to reach a constant value, readings of depth to water in all instruments should continue for as long as necessary to be satisfied either that a constant value has been reached, or that the depth to water fluctuates. If the depth to water fluctuates, it is essential to discover why this is, because the highest water level (least depth to water) may be critical either to the underpinning foundation during construction, or affect the foundation performance.

3.3.4 *Examples of adverse ground and groundwater conditions*

When all that is known of the ground and groundwater conditions at a particular site are placed upon a plan and cross-sections of the site and its surrounding ground, then the process of interpretation can begin. The factual data from two imaginary sites are depicted in Figures 3.4 and 3.5. In both cases piling is the most obvious method of providing underpinning to the existing building.

The problems with the piles underpinning the brick building (Figure 3.4) are likely to occur where they penetrate the silty sand with gravelly layers. Non-displacement piles will be especially difficult to construct, as there is a possibility both that an excess of silty sand will be excavated (causing further subsidence) and that water in gravelly layers could displace the wet concrete in the piles (making the piles undersized or 'necked'). Difficulties would also be possible if closely placed displacement piles were adopted, as the weaker mudstone layer would probably cause adjacent piles to uplift or move laterally.

For the case of the proposed factory extension the problems are likely to be that displacement piles cannot easily be driven through the glacial till (unless a separate pre-boring operation is undertaken to provide a 'pilot' hole), and all types of non-displacement piles are likely to run into considerable construction difficulties once they penetrate the water-bearing sand with some

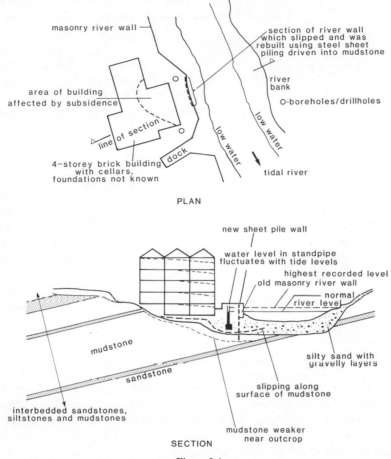

PLAN

SECTION

Figure 3.4

gravel. Large-diameter bored piles founding near (but not too near) the base of the glacial till could be the correct solution, but access difficulties with the large plant required and the high cost would probably make this uneconomical.

3.3.5 Estimation of pile bearing capacity

3.3.5.1 Pile behaviour. For practically the whole range of possible combinations of pile material and ground material, the pile material is the stronger and stiffer. Therefore, for most practical purposes, it is the ground which fails first, and it is generally only the ground which fails when a pile reaches its maximum load capacity.

Only for timber piles founded in weak rocks and concrete piles founded in

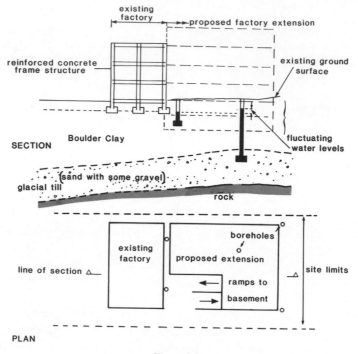

Figure 3.5

strong rocks is the pile likely to be the weaker element, unless there is a defect in the pile or the pile is caused to deform and break in a manner for which it has not been designed (as when a precast pile is lifted with the slings in the wrong places, for example).

Because ground behaviour dominates the process of piles carrying load, pile movements are also dominated by ground movements. Most ground materials are weak compared with structural materials such as concrete and steel, unless they are cemented or the particles are otherwise tightly interlocked. The ground is therefore likely to have low stiffness with the stress–strain behaviour such that pile movements under 'working' loads are likely to be between 5 and 50 mm.

When a pile is loaded above the allowable load, the movement (also called 'deflection' or 'settlement') increases more and more rapidly with increasing load, until the pile reaches a condition where it will accept no further load. This load is called the pile failure load, (although correctly it should be called the ground failure load) or the pile 'ultimate' load. The methods of carrying out pile loading tests are described in detail in 'Pile Load Testing Procedures' (CIRIA, 1980).

A typical load–deflection curve for a medium-sized pile (450 mm diameter, 15 m long, in stiff clay) is shown in Figure 3.6. It is quite usual to plot pile

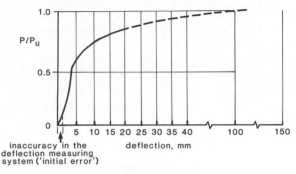

Figure 3.6

deflection (measured at the head of the pile) in an upward direction even though the pile in reality moves downward. P is the load applied to the pile and P_u is the failure ('ultimate') load. As shown, it is not unusual for the curve to reveal inaccuracies in the measuring system at low values of P/P_u, and such 'initial error' should be deducted from the measured deflections.

It is apparent that the pile has two modes of behaviour (or rather, the ground supporting the pile is exhibiting two modes of behaviour). Up to a value of P/P_u of about 0.6, the deflection increases more or less linearly with the increasing load. The ground is said to be 'behaving elastically' as if Hooke's Law applied, but in fact this is a 'one-way' elasticity, as unloading the pile from any load reached does not usually result in full recovery, there being some residual or 'non-recoverable' deflection as shown in Figure 3.7. The curves of offloading are usually closely parallel to one another as shown, so that the amount of residual settlement increases with increased load. Usually, when further loading is applied after unloading, the load–deflection curve resumes the same path as if it had not been unloaded. If it does not do this, either the ground or the pile must be suspected of having a defect.

When the load is increased above a value of P/P_u of about 0.6, the amount of deflection increases more and more with increasing load, and the ground supporting the pile is said to be behaving 'plastically'. This is particularly

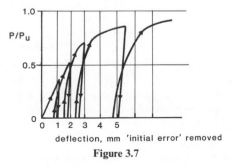

Figure 3.7

marked by large increases in residual (non-recoverable) settlements when the pile is offloaded, as Figure 3.7.

3.3.5.2 Selection of factor of safety. The actual shape of the P/P_u v. deflection curve varies for piles of the same size in different ground conditions, and a selection of curves is shown in Figure 3.8 (deflection being plotted to the same linear scale). These curves are taken from Butler and Morton (1971) in which are considered

(i) a rational approach to the selection of the appropriate load factor (commonly called Factor of Safety, *F*) relating the ultimate load P_u to the design load P_d, in the equation

$$P_d = \frac{P_u}{F}$$

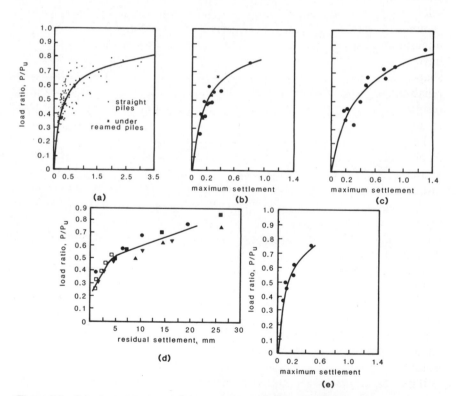

Figure 3.8   Selection of P/P_u curves for various ground conditions.
(a) Load ratio v. maximum settlement/base diameter curve; all London clay sites.
(b) Load ratio v. maximum settlement curve; Hull, silty clays over glacial till.
(c) Load ratio v. maximum settlement curve; Gorbals, Glasgow, silty fine sand.
(d) Load ratio v. residual settlement curve; driven precast concrete piles in chalk.
(e) Load ratio v. maximum settlement curve; Belfast, soft silty clay over Boulder Clay.
(a), (b), (c) and (e) from Butler and Morton (1970); (d) from Lord (1977).

(ii) criteria for the acceptance of contract piles (piles installed to support a structure) using non-destructive pile loading test procedures.

The relationship of design load P_d to allowable load P_a varies with the circumstances of each structure. If the piles are widely spaced, so that they do not interact upon loading, and there are no down drag or other forces affecting the piles, then $P_a = P_d$. In most cases, however, P_a is somewhat less than P_d, so that the sum of P_a plus interactive forces plus downdrag, etc., equals P_d. The working load P_w applied by the structure must not exceed P_a.

Although Butler and Morton (1971) considered piles in clay, their criteria are equally applicable to piles in all particulate or granular soils. They are not applicable to piles in cemented soils and rocks, although similar criteria may be developed.

Ideally, selection of the appropriate P/P_u v. deflection curve load factor should be made after considering the results of a series of pile tests in which piles of various sizes have been taken to ultimate load in the appropriate ground conditions. The possibility of doing such a series of tests for underpinning at a particular site is remote, and in the majority of cases P_u will have to be obtained by calculation or assessment from case histories. The shape of the P/P_u v. deflection curve can usually be selected with reasonable reliability from the 'library' of curves given in Figure 3.8, or obtained from the results of tests on piles in the soil under consideration, if the soil is not similar to any of those given.

There are two 'factors of safety' relevant to the estimation of the design load P_d of a pile. The first is a factor against failure (against the ultimate load being attained), and this has been found to have a value of about 1.3 to 1.4 when the ultimate load P_u has been obtained; this means in effect that no similar pile is likely to have an ultimate load lower than $1/1.3$ or $1/1.4$ (0.77 or 0.71) of the expected ultimate load. This factor of safety has little practical value, as pile settlements are likely to be unacceptably large at such high values of P/P_u, as illustrated in Figure 3.8.

The second factor of safety is against a pile suffering excessive deflection (settlement) under the design load P_d. As can be from the P/P_u v. deflection curves in Figure 3.8, the 'point' (or more appropriately 'zone') at which the ground supporting the pile ceases to behave in an 'elastic' manner varies from soil to soil, and lies between about 0.55 and 0.75. At loads above the 'point' value the settlement curves for individual piles tend to vary widely as shown dotted in Figure 3.8, and individual piles may undergo quite large settlements.

If it could be guaranteed that every pile made in the given ground conditions would have the same ultimate load P_u, then the design load P_d could be between 0.55 and 0.75 of ultimate, that is the factor of safety could be $1/0.55$ ($= 1.82$) to $1/0.73$ ($= 1.33$). However, as discussed above, the actual values of P_u may be as little as $1/1.4$ ($= 0.71$) of the value of P_u from tests, so it is appropriate to 'scale down' the 'point' values of P/P_u to $0.55 \times 0.71 = 0.39$ and $0.75 \times 0.71 = 0.53$, giving factors of safety in the range $1/0.39 = 2.56$ to

$1/0.53 = 1.88$, which have a magnitude more familar to those experienced in designing piles. In practical terms this means that if the ultimate load of a given type and size of pile in given ground conditions is known, then the factor of safety (load factor) should be between 2.0 for a pile in 'stiff' ground to 2.5 for a pile in 'soft' ground. Clay strata at the depths (15 to 30 m) to which piles commonly penetrate are generally 'stiff' if they are overconsolidated, and 'soft' if they are normally consolidated.

In many cases the value of P_u for a given type and size of pile at a given underpinning site will not be known, and an additional factor of safety to allow for the possibility of error in assessing P_u should be made. The magnitude of this additional factor is discussed in the following sections dealing with soils and weak rocks.

3.3.5.3. Estimation of load capacity. Because of the shape of piles they have a 'base' which bears down upon the underlying ground, and a 'shaft' which follows the base down, at the same time shearing the adjacent soil at the interface. In some piles the base is very small; for instance the typical steel-H pile has a 'base' area of only $0.02\,\text{m}^2$, whereas its shaft surface may be 25 to $100\,\text{m}^2$. In large bored piles the base may be enlarged by underreaming to give a base area of $20\,\text{m}^2$, and the shaft area may be also 25 to $100\,\text{m}^2$.

The mechanisms of the resistance offered by the ground are different between shaft and base, and this is recognized in the analysis of pile behaviour and the methods of design. As there is very little interaction between the two mechanisms, the ultimate loads that can be supported by the shaft and the base are assessed separately using the formula

$$P_u = Q_{su} + Q_{bu}$$

where Q_{su} and Q_{bu} are respectively the ultimate resistances of the shaft moving through the ground and the base moving through the ground.

For most piles the factor of safety of 2.0 to 2.5 (or such higher values as are discussed in the following sections) is applied directly to the combined ultimate resistances to give the design load:

$$P_d = \frac{P_u}{F} = \frac{Q_{su} + Q_{bu}}{F}$$

The value of P_a, the allowable load, is then derived from P_d, by taking into account pile interaction and downdrag.

When the pile base area exceeds about one-tenth of the pile shaft area, the movement of the pile base under load dominates the pile behaviour, and a factor of safety of 3.0 (or larger value, as discussed in the following sections) is applied to the base component only, with the magnitude of shaft resistance selected to be appropriate to large movement through the ground:

$$P_d = Q_{su} \text{ (large movement)} + \frac{Q_{bu}}{3}$$

3.3.6 Piles in particular soil and rock types

In the following sections descriptions are given of the problems associated with broad categories of rock and soils.

Rocks are generally intersected by joints and bedding surfaces, the more weathered rocks near to the interface with overlying soil or to the exposed surface of the rock itself, commonly being more frequently intersected than is the case for rocks at depth. The individual pieces of rock between the joints or bedding surfaces may be strong, but the behaviour of the rock mass is dominated by the strength available along the joint and bedding surfaces.

Soils are derived from rocks, and may be the result of weathering of the underlying rock (residual soils) or the result of deposition after having been moved by air, water, glaciers or gravity (transported soils). Some soils are cemented and others contain or are derived from organic materials. From the many ways in which soils are derived and laid down it is to be expected that their properties will be very variable.

Soils may be separated into mainly granular or (non-cohesive) materials such as boulders, cobbles, gravels and sands, and the cohesive materials silt and clay. The engineering distinctions relate mainly to (i) the far faster rate at which water can pass through granular materials than through cohesive materials—hence any excesses in water pressure within the soil dissipate far more rapidly in granular soils; and (ii) the manner in which cohesive materials stick together and to the surfaces of structural materials. Cohesive clay soils are further distinguished into normally consolidated (NC) clays, which have not in the past been subjected to pressures greater than the present overburden pressure, and overconsolidated (OC) clays which have been subjected to pressures greater (sometimes much greater) than the present overburden pressure. The important effect from the point of view of pile design is that OC clays are generally stronger than NC clays of the same composition, but the OC clays may weaken (soften) rapidly after having been strained to generate their peak resistance, as illustrated in Figure 3.9.

3.3.7 Piles in cohesive soils

Cohesive soils include not only the 'fatty' clays such as London, Gault and Oxford clays, but also the silty clays such as the Kimmeridge and Lias, the widely graded stony Boulder Clays of glacial origin, and the silty sandy alluvial clays found in river valleys and estuaries. In temperate climates the clays are nearly always found in a saturated or near saturated condition, except in the upper 2 to 3 metres affected by seasonal weathering and vegetation.

When a pile is loaded, the load *v.* settlement behaviour is different between the base and the shaft, as illustrated in Figure 3.9. Around the cylinder or 'shaft' of a pile only the soil nearest to the pile is dragged downwards, until, as the pile load increases, a shear surface (or shear surfaces) develops within the cohesive soil and close to the surface of the pile, leaving a skin of cohesive soil

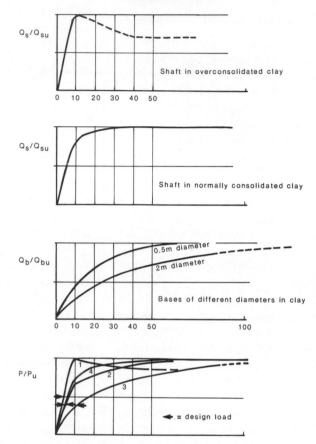

Figure 3.9 Load ratio curves for shafts and bases separately and combined. Clay types, sizes of piles and proportions of loads.
 (i) OC clay 1. 0.5 m diameter base, $Q_{su} = 3Q_{bu}$
            2. 0.5 m diameter base, $Q_{su} = Q_{bu}/3$
            3. 2.0 m diameter base, $Q_{su} = Q_{bu}/9$
(ii) NC clay 4. 0.5 m diameter base, $Q_{su} = 3Q_{bu}$

adhering to the pile, as illustrated in Figure 3.10. The peak adhesion of the shear surface depends upon the pile type, the pile material and the method of pile construction, and guidance is given in CIRIA publication PG5 (DoE/CIRIA, 1978). Pile movement of between 2 and 10 mm from its initial unloaded position is normally sufficient to reach peak adhesion. For over-consolidated soils, the adhesion falls to about 35% of the undrained shear strength if the pile is moved five to ten times the movement for peak adhesion.

Below the base of a pile the soil compresses at first loading; then as the load on the base is increased, it deforms and shear surfaces develop in the soil surrounding the base. With increasing load the pile begins to settle more and more, and either large volume changes have to take place to compress the soil

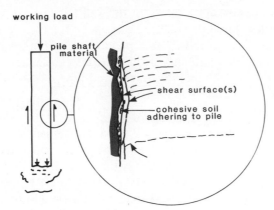

Figure 3.10 Piles in cohesive soil.

surrounding the base, or the ground surface has to heave upwards, as shown in Figure 3.11 *a* and *b*.

The procedure for the design of piles in cohesive soils is as follows:

(i) Select a cross-section shape and length of pile.
(ii) Select the values of soil strength that will be relevant to the calculation of shaft load capacity and base capacity.
(iii) Calculate separately shaft and base ultimate loads and hence estimate the load *v*. settlement curves for each component.
(iv) Combine shaft and base loads at various pile settlements to see what design loads (P_d) can be achieved for various pile lengths.
(v) Check that the selected design loads (P_d) have the appropriate factor of

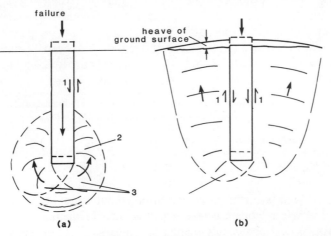

Figure 3.11 (*a*) Compression takes place entirely within ground, to accommodate pile penetration. (*b*) Ground heaves in response to pile penetration. 1, shaft adhesion or friction at or beyond peak value; 2, soil compress; 3, soil heavily sheared.

safety against exceeding the critical 'point' on the appropriate P/P_u against settlement curve.

(iv) Select the allowable load P_a as a proportion of the design load P_d, if downdrag and pile interaction are likely to affect behaviour. Guidance on the method of calculating downdrag and interaction can be found in Tomlinson (1977) and Whitaker (1976).

It is recommended that the factor of safety used in the calculation in (v) above should not be less than 2.0 for piles in stiff to hard cohesive soils and 2.5 for piles in soft to firm soils, if trial piles are to be made and tested to determine P_u. If no trial piles are to be made and only the calculated values of P_u are to be relied upon, then it is recommended that the factor of safety should be at least 2.5 and 3.0 respectively, with higher values still if the soil information is poor, or the ground conditions are known to vary widely.

Two methods of calculation of pile shaft ultimate load Q_{su} are available. In one the value of adhesion is assumed to be a proportion (α) of the undrained shear strength of the cohesive soil through which the pile passes; in the other method the cohesive soil is assessed as having a friction value β typical for the soil in which it is installed. The α method is explained in Burland et al. (1966), and the β method in Burland (1973). Piles in non-fatty clay such as boulder clay require special consideration, and this is given in CIRIA publication PG5 (1978).

3.3.8 Piles in granular soils

In essence the method of designing piles in granular soils differs only in the way in which the base and shaft components of ultimate load are derived.

Granular soils depend upon the precise details of particle size, orientation, packing and confining stresses for the shear strength they develop. The smallest change in one of the factors caused by disturbance during attempts to take samples can effect a large change in strength. And even if perfect samples could be taken and tested, Terzaghi (1953), in a lecture looking back over the previous 50 years of ground investigation, pointed out:

> The relative density of natural sand deposits commonly varies in an erratic manner in both horizontal and vertical directions. Hence even in the event that one sample has been secured and tested for every foot (0.3 m) of depth along vertical lines spaced 50 feet (15 m) both ways, the density profile constructed on the basis of the laboratory test results may be entirely fictitious. Therefore it is commonly preferable to judge the average density of a natural sand deposit and the variations of density within that deposit on the basis of cone penetration tests in situ.

Very little development has occurred to invalidate that view; the open-shoe sampler and driven cone, together with the jacked cone (cone penetrometer) remain the most effective and economical means of obtaining design information on sands and other granular strata to this day.

Methods of using information from the standard penetration test (SPT) and the cone penetration test (CPT) in the design of piles are described in detail by Tomlinson (1977), Whitaker (1976), and Fleming and Thorburn (1983).

As piles in granular soil are usually long compared to their cross-section dimension, an overall factor of safety to limit settlement to an acceptable amount is normally applied to the combined ultimate base and shaft resistances:

$$P_d = \frac{P_u}{F} = \frac{Q_{su} + Q_{bu}}{F}$$

These values should take into account the manner of construction of the pile, particularly if it is constructed by boring through the granular deposit, in which case the density can be markedly reduced and the strength likewise.

Because of the inherent variability in the behaviour of driven piles a generous factor of safety is appropriate, ranging from 2.5 if several piles are subjected to ultimate load tests, to 4.0 in the absence of tests and good soils information including cone test results.

3.3.9 Piles in weak rocks

In respect of piling, weak rocks are separately identified from strong rocks by the need to consider the interaction of the pile shaft with the surrounding rock, in addition to bearing support derived at the pile base. The rock material is mainly weaker and less stiff than the structural material of the pile. The principal weak rocks are the Chalk, the Keuper Marl, and the weathered or otherwise weakened superficial few metres of such rocks as the Devonian and the Carboniferous, generally shaly mudstones and siltstones. Drilling equipment of sufficient power to drill holes into the rock for bored piles, and hammers big enough to drive tubular and H-piles into the rock, have been available for some 20 years.

As with piles in soil, there needs to be a margin of safety against loading the pile as its ultimate load. Large differences in ultimate load may exist between apparently similar piles, as is evident from a study of the pile tests reported in the ICE symposium, 'Piles in Weak Rock' (ICE, 1977). This indicates that a conservative value of the factor of safety is desirable against the ultimate load, either obtained by testing, or calculated. Values of 2.5 and 4.0 respectively are appropriate.

The wide variations in ultimate capacity are a direct result of the behaviour of the rock being dictated by the strength developed along joint and bedding surfaces; as no two piles will encounter identical arrays of such surfaces, wide variations in bearing capacity at large displacements can be expected.

In one of the contributions to the ICE symposium 'Piles in Weak Rock' (ICE, 1977), Cole and Stroud sought methods of analysing the stiffness of a pile in weathered Coal Measure Series mudstones, siltstones and sandstones.

In essence the method for the medium to large bored piles assumes that they are formed in 'sockets' in the surface of the weak rock, and that for each pile the applied load is transferred to the rock through the surface of the shaft and base of the socket, there being negligible contribution from the overlying strata. The method proposed recognized that the stiffness of the ground beneath base is commonly some 20 times the stiffness of the rock surrounding the shaft acting in shear. By deducing ground stiffness from ground investigation and pile test results, the load v. settlement performance of each pile was predicted having regard to the details of the strata.

In another paper in the same symposium, Lord examined the behaviour of a selection of common medium-sized proprietary driven piles founded in chalk, and found good agreement with the stiffness moduli of various grades (qualities) of chalk. Other papers give test results on a variety of pile types in various weak rocks, but some of the results have to be carefully considered as they indicate faults in piles and bring into question the appropriateness of certain pile types as weak rock foundations.

The special problems of piles in chalk are described in the publication 'Piling in Chalk' (CIRIA, 1979).

3.3.10 Piles founded on strong rocks

When piles are founded on strong rocks, it must be ensured that the piles cannot move or be moved from the initial area of contact. The surface shape of rock buried beneath soil cannot be known with certainty and thus measures have to be taken to ensure that the piles are well 'keyed' into the rock surface.

If the rock is stronger than the pile material the keying-in needs to be no more than to ensure that the rock materials can sustain the load from the pile, even though they may be locally fractured. Bored piles are for this reason usually given a shallow 'socket' of depth about half the pile diameter.

With steel H-piles it is usual to drive the piles until the number of blows for a given penetration using a rated hammer is more than a specified number, viz. 15 blows for 25 mm. If the rock surface is likely to be irregular, a 'rock point' should be fitted to the base of the pile and this in theory enables the pile to 'wedge' itself into the rock surface, rather than being deflected down dip.

References

1. BS 5930: 1981 Code of Practice for Site Investigations. British Standards Institution, London.
2. BS 1377: 1975 Methods of Testing Soils for Engineering Purposes. BSI, London.
3. Burland J.B., Butler, F.G. and Duncan, P. (1966) The behaviour and design of large diameter bored piles in stiff clay. *Proc. Conf. on Large Bored Piles.* ICE, London.
4. Burland J.B. (1973) Shaft friction of piles in clay. *Ground Eng.* 6 (3).
5. Butler F.G. and Morton K. (1971) Specification and performance of test piles in clay. *Proc. Symp. on Behaviour of Piles*, ICE, London.

6. Clayton, C.R.I., Simons, N.E. and Matthews, M.C. (1982) *Guidance to site and ground investigations. A handbook for engineers.* Granada, St. Albans.
7. Department of the Environment (DoE) and Construction Industry Research and Information Association (CIRIA), Piling Development Group.
    ———(1977) A review of bearing pile types. *Report PG1.*
    ———(1977)Review of problems associated with the construction of cast-in-place piles. *Report PG2.*
    ———(1977)The use and influence of bentonite in bored pile construction. *Report PG3..*
    ———(1977) Integrity testing of piles; a review. *Report PG4.*
    ———(1978) Piling in Boulder Clay and other Glacial Tills. *Report PG5.*
    ———(1979) Piling in Chalk. *Report PG6.*
    ———(1980) Pile load testing procedures. *Report PG7.*
    ———(1980) Survey of problems associated with the installation of displacement piles *Report PG8.*
    ———(1980) Noise and vibration from piling operations. *Report PG9. CIRIA, London.*
8. Fleming, W.G.K. and Thorburn, S. State of the art report on recent piling advances. *Proc. Conf. on Piling and Ground Treatment,* Thomas Telford, London.
9. Institution of Civil Engineers (1977) *Piles in Weak Rock, Proc. ICE Symp.,* ICE, London.
10. Institution of Civil Engineers (1978) *Piling, Model Procedures and Specifications.* ICE, London.
11. Terzaghi, K. (1953) Fifty years of subsoil exploration. *3rd Int. Conf. on Soil Mechanics and Foundation Engineering,* Zurich.
12. Tomlinson, M.J. (1977) *Pile Design and Construction Practice.* Viewpoint Publications, Leatherhead.
13. Whitaker, T. (1976) *The Design of Piled Foundations.* (2nd edn.) Pergamon, Oxford.

4 'Pali radice' (root piles) and 'reticulated pali radice'

F. LIZZI

4.1 Man and his construction problems

The engineer is continually presented with new problems in construction. Whenever possible, he solves these problems with the help of his previous experience, collected as consolidated theory and science.

Theory provides the basis for calculation and design and in the majority of cases, when correctly applied, gives a reasonable degree of safety. However, this is not always so; for any science is a knowledge in progress and has, therefore, its temporal limits. When science falls short, man has to revert to his intuition and imagination, as he has done since the beginning, to push it further. New, tentative systems are suggested and elaborated, and must be proved in the field before they become part of reliable science.

That was the case with 'pali radice' (root piles) and 'reticolo di pali radice' (reticulated root piles). The invention of both systems which were of the same elementary structure (the 'palo radice') was prompted by important and urgent problems for which conventional systems had proved inadequate, leading sometimes to complete failure. One of these problems was connected with the reconstruction or restoration of old buildings, particularly ancient monuments, in areas such as Italy that had been severely affected by the Second World War. Another, which appeared at the same time, was the ground reinforcement and retention systems necessary for excavations to be executed close to existing buildings (as is the case, for instance, with underground railways) and, more generally, to guard against landslides, which became more and more frequent as space was made for new construction (highways, enlargement of urban areas, etc.).

4.2 The problem of underpinning old buildings subject to settlement

The major factor of instability affecting an old building is ground settlement, owing to various causes, such as water-table movements, natural soil consolidation, seismic events, and traffic vibration and other human activity. Any action on a building subject to settlement has to take into account the

84

essential fact that the construction already 'exists', and during the repair work there is, therefore, the risk of worsening, rather than improving its critical condition. *Primum non nocere* (first do not harm) warns an old Latin saying. This is the rule with underpinning; but, of course, other points must be considered: a modern foundation reinforcement demands that several conditions be satisfied, i.e.

— The reinforcement must be reliable and based on confirmed loadbearing elements.
— The strengthening work has to proceed as quickly as possible, giving a progressive relief to the structure.
— The reinforcement once installed must give an immediate response to any, even the most minimal, further movement of the building.

4.3 The state of the art in underpinning before the introduction of pali radice (1950)

The problem of protecting and salvaging old buildings has worried man throughout his history, and all the techniques available at the time have always been summoned to help solve it.

4.3.1 Underpinning with additional foundation masonry

A settlement of a foundation is always a consequence of the lack of balance between the load of the structure and the bearing capacity of the soil at foundation level. The bearing capacity can, at a particular moment, approach the limit of failure, owing to events endured by the building and the subsoil. The idea of lowering the level of the base of the walls to take advantage of deeper soils, which are usually more compact, is therefore quite logical. It is not necessary to spend much time describing this method, which, although it did in the past save many buildings on the point of collapse, had numerous failures.

There are many reasons for this.

(i) First, it requires great skill—not always available, especially today.
(ii) Underpinning, which is necessarily carried out 'by sections' gives rise at the end to a general relaxation of the structure as a whole.
(iii) It is difficult to obtain an adequate compaction of the new foundation soil: the simple weight of the additional masonry is certainly not sufficient to achieve this. As a consequence, the soil is loaded only when the total weight of the building rests upon it; which sometimes happens at the cost of appreciable settlement.
(iv) Attempts at preloading the soil by more modern means introduce serious complications and can prove to be harmful rather than useful.
(v) In any case, underpinning generally cannot be extended deeper than the

level of the water table: it would be very dangerous to dewater in order to reach deeper levels.

4.3.2 Consolidation of soil by means of grouting

This method (see Chapter 8) can sometimes prove effective due to very recent developments in chemical grouts, some of which have a viscosity very near to that of water. Nevertheless it is advisable not to generalize too much, for this method of soil consolidation has some limitations that must be taken into consideration.

(i) The soil must have a minimal amount of permeability; today it is possible to inject soils having a permeability of $K = 10^{-4}$ cm/sec. More impermeable soils, through which even water will not pass, are not injectable. These are clay and silty soils, which are the soils most frequently found below damaged buildings.
(ii) The lower the viscosity of chemical grout used, the lower its strength.
(iii) To be effective this method demands uniform spreading of the grout below the foundation; but the heterogeneity of many soils makes such a uniform spread difficult. The permeation has so decisive an influence on the success or otherwise of the operation, that little or no advantage, economically, is gained by this method used in unsuitable ground conditions.
(iv) Grouting does not produce a sound connection between the structure and the subsoil. So while the structure rests upon the subsoil, it is not anchored to it, whereas this connection, especially in the case of slender structures like towers, is highly desirable.

4.3.3 Underpinning by means of conventional (drilled or driven) piles

The introduction of piling in the foundation technique for new buildings was one of the greatest advances in modern construction methods since the early Thirties. It marked the beginning of geotechnics as a science. Steel piles, precast concrete piles and cast-in-situ piles replaced the old shallow foundation systems. The most important feature of this piling technique was the opportunity to design the foundation on the basis of the loadbearing capacity of a single pile which could be checked, when necessary, by direct load test. While driven piles could be installed vertically as well as at a rake, cast-in-situ piles could originally be installed only vertically. Their diameter, according to the European Rules then in force, could not be less than 40 cm.

Considering the success of piling in foundations it was logical to investigate the possibility of using the same system for underpinning. Driven piles have to be discounted immediately on account of the vibration they introduce in nearby structures. Some attempts were made with cast-in-place piles of the type then in use (vertical piles, minimum diameter: 40 cm). The piles were constructed as close as possible to the walls, to which they were then connected by reinforced concrete beams. This involved major cutting in the walls, a dangerous state of crisis during the construction period, before the final connection of the piles to the walls, and a marked hampering of the functionability of the buildings. This method had a short and difficult life; some moderately acceptable results were outweighed by several failures.

4.3.4 Underpinning by means of jacked-down piles

This method, described in another section of this book, has been used widely and is still in use. Nevertheless, it is not applicable where the presence of boulders, old foundations or other obstructions makes penetration of the soil with segmented piles difficult or impossible.

4.4 The 'palo radice' (root pile)

The problems and, in some cases, complete failure of the current systems of foundation strengthening urged the introduction of new, more reliable and safer systems. Such was the situation in 1950–52 when the first patents for what would afterwards be called 'palo radice' were applied for by the author of these notes, on behalf of the Italian firm Fondedile of Naples.

A typical scheme of an underpinning by means of pali radice (root piles) is shown in Figure 4.1. The foundation reinforcement is formed by a double series of small-diameter piles, rotary drilled through the existing masonry and taken to an adequate depth in the subsoil below. When concreted, the pile is automatically bonded with the upper structure: there is no need of complementary connecting structures, no risky cuts in the walls, and no disturbance to the building's activities.

The construction of the piles, spaced out along the foot of the walls, does not present any risk to the stability of the existing structures. No vibration is involved. The construction of the piles does not introduce any particular stress in the wall or the soil: this is of vital importance in buildings, especially ancient monuments, in which the conservation of the existing, however precarious, equilibrium is of paramount importance. Pali radice can be drilled in any soil, no matter what boulders, old foundations or other obstructions it may contain.

4.4.1 The technology of a palo radice

Figure 4.2 shows the construction sequence of a palo radice.

(i) The drilling is performed by a rotating casing progressively introduced

a) VERTICAL CROSS-SECTION

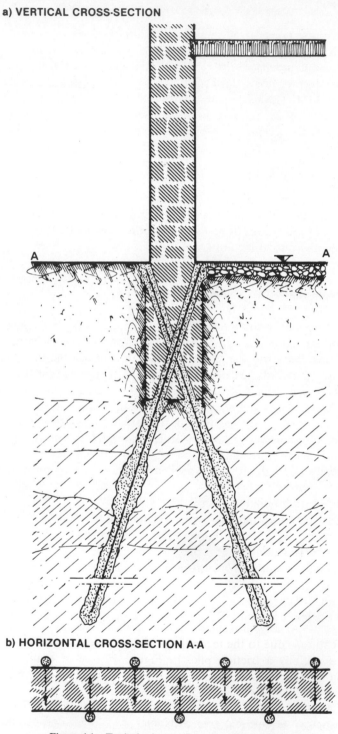

b) HORIZONTAL CROSS-SECTION A-A

Figure 4.1 Typical scheme of a pali radice underpinning.

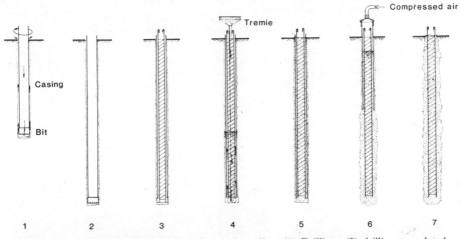

Figure 4.2 Method of construction of a palo radice. (1) Drilling; (2) drilling completed; (3) placing of the reinforcement; (4) placing the grout via tremie pipe; (5) grouting completed; (6) extraction of the casing; (7) palo radice completed.

into the subsoil; the spoil is removed by flushing water or bentonite mud introduced from the top through a rotating swivel.

(ii) Once the drilling has been taken to a convenient depth, the reinforcement is placed: a single bar for smaller diameters, (10 cm); a cage or a tube for larger diameters (up to 25–30 cm). In underpinning, the smaller diameters are generally to be preferred.

(iii) The grout is then placed by tremie pipe, the mix comprising 600 to 800 kg of cement per m³ of sieved sand. It is, therefore, a high-strength grout.

Once the casing has been filled, it is gradually extracted. At the same time, compressed air introduced from the top pushes the mix outside the pipe against the borehole. The pressure of the air is limited to 6 to 8 bars, in order to avoid ruptures of the soil ('claquages'), while being sufficient to obtain a very rough outer surface to the pile. This gives the marked adherence to the soil that is an essential characteristic of the palo radice.

4.4.2 The quick response supplied by pali radice

The most significant feature of the pali radice used in underpinning work is the quick response to any movement, however slight, of the structure. This essential feature is due to the technology of its construction in which a palo radice is essentially a friction pile. In Figure 4.3 the diagram shows the load–settlement curves of one of the first load tests for the underpinning work carried out for a school in Naples (1952). The pile, 13 m long, had a diameter of 10 cm and was reinforced by a single bar of 12 mm diameter. The subsoil, characteristic of the volcanic area of Naples, was composed of alternating

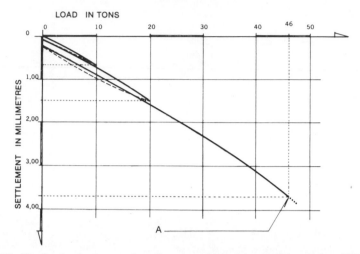

Figure 4.3 The first load test on a palo radice. *A*, crushing of the toe of the pile ($\sigma = 450\,\text{kg/cm}^2$).

layers of varying thickness of pozzolana, lapilli and sands. Generally, it may be considered a loose soil formation. It has been noticed since then that even for high loads the settlement of a palo radice is very small, in the order of a few millimetres. Being constructed as it is, pali radice underpinning does not supersede the existing foundation. From the start its function is complementary and only when necessary does it contribute to the foundation. The building continues to rest on its old foundation soil: it will call on the piles to assist only if, and to the extent which, it settles. This is the most important aspect which has made the palo radice so popular in underpinning works.

To clarify further, pali radice underpinning can be considered practically inactive at the moment of its construction. If the building has a subsequent, albeit minimal, settlement the piling responds immediately, absorbing part of the load and reducing at the same time the stress on the soil. If, despite this, the building continues to settle, the piles continue to take the load until, finally, the entire building load is supported by them.

In even the most extreme case the settlements would be limited to a maximum of a few millimetres.

4.4.3 The working load of a palo radice

The working load of a conventional foundation pile for a new building is generally a fraction of the ultimate load. In its assessment many factors have to be considered, including the desired safety factor and, above all, the extent of the acceptable settlement for the new building. For instance, while it may be acceptable to allow high settlements for the piers of a simply supported bridge, the same is not possible for a continuous structure. This consideration, which

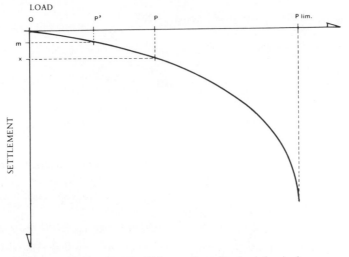

Figure 4.4 The 'working load' for a palo radice in underpinning.

is fundamental for a pile foundation, is even more important for underpinning and so cannot be neglected.

For instance, should x (see Figure. 4.4) be the maximum settlement acceptable for the structure to be underpinned (the value would be in millimetres or fractions of millimetres), the corresponding load to be supplied by the pile would be P. The fact that the ultimate load for the pile is much greater than P is of little importance. It must be stressed that the matter of importance is the acceptable settlement.

From this point of view it can be seen that a palo radice used in underpinning is not completely utilized, compared to its full bearing capacity: it could always bear much more than the assigned load. The pile, when its installation has been completed, has no immediate work to do; possibly it will never be completely utilized. As Figure 4.4 makes clear, for each intermediate settlement (m) part of the load (P') is transferred to the pile, while the remaining part ($P - P'$) continues to be supported by the soil.

4.4.4 The 'safety factor' of a pali radice underpinning

It can be seen from the above that the safety factor of the pali radice underpinning does not correspond or, better, is not limited, to the safety factor of the piling, as is the case with new buildings; it is much greater.

At the moment when the pali radice underpinning is to start, the safety factor of the existing foundation will be very low; but it is obvious that its value will not be less than one. This margin will not be cancelled by the construction of the pali radice; therefore the new factor of safety will be:

$$\eta = \eta f + \eta p$$

where:

$\eta f \geq 1$ is the safety factor of the existing foundation

$\eta p = \dfrac{P_{ult}}{P}$ is the safety factor of the piling.

(P_{ult} = ultimate load; P = working load).

4.4.5 The design of a pali radice underpinning: the ultimate load of a palo radice

Considering the above and, more, in the light of wide experience gained over many decades, one can conclude that a pali radice underpinning (or foundation) does not, beyond a modest subsoil survey, need any more sophisticated investigation and study.

Where the very wide range of case histories, in different soils, do not immediately supply sufficient data about the length and bearing capacity for the various pile diameters, the design problems can be solved by direct load tests. The cost of a load test on a palo radice is without any doubt less than that of burdensome subsoil investigations; sampling analysis of the mechanical characteristics of the soil and other data, that involve extensive documentations and are, in this instance, of very little use.

After the many load tests that have been carried out, some purely orientative empirical data can be given, simply expressed.

(i) With the exclusion of particularly soft soils, a palo radice develops its maximum bearing capacity (to the crushing limit of the grout in the cross-section) over lengths of not more than 30 m.
(ii) For soils having an average consistency, 20 m is generally sufficient.
(iii) For very stiff soils, lengths of 10–15 m are sufficient.
(iv) For compact sands and gravels, the limit varies from 6 to 10 m.
(v) For clay, the lengths can vary from 10 to 15 m depending on the compactness of the formation.

Considering the above, a simple empirical formula can be put forward, for the ultimate load P_{ult} (kg) of a palo radice:

$$P_{ult} = \pi D L K I$$

where

D is the nominal diameter (in cm) of the pile, i.e. the drilling diameter;
L is the length of the pile (in cm);
K is a coefficient that represents, in kg/cm², the average interaction between the pile and the soil for the whole length. (From the physical point of view, it can represent the pile/soil adherence, or the shear stress induced in the soil by the pile, or the cohesion of the soil, etc.)

Table 4.1 Values of K (in kg/cm^2)

Soil	K
Soft soil	0.5
Loose soil	1.0
Soil of average compactness	1.5
Very stiff soil, gravels, sands	2.0

Table 4.2 Values of I

Diameter of the pile	I
$D = 10\,cm$	1.00
$D = 15\,cm$	0.90
$D = 20\,cm$	0.85
$D = 25\,cm$	0.80

I is a non-dimensional coefficient of form, that depends on the nominal diameter of the pile.

Tables 4.1 and 4.2 give the approximate values of K and I.

4.5 Case histories of underpinning

The versatility of the pali radice system, which can be executed in any subsoil and site conditions, has prompted its extensive use. It is by now the almost universally adopted system of underpinning. A small number of case histories, to be considered only as examples, are given below.

4.5.1 Venice, Italy: Tre Archi Bridge (XVII century)

This is the only bridge in Venice to have three arches (Figure 4.5). It was constructed in the 17th century across one of the most important urban waterways. Following very serious settlement it was originally decided to demolish it. The bridge, however, was fully restored through a complete underpinning with pali radice, a reinforcement of the masonry with the 'reticolo cementato' system (network of grouted steel bars), and strengthening of the vaults by a saddle in reinforced concrete. An appropriate use of resins was made in the works; particularly, they were used in the connection between the existing vault and the saddle to improve the bond between these two elements.

4.5.2 Eure (France): monumental church of Tourny (XV century)

The historic building (Figure 4.6) was in a very bad condition, following marked differential settlements of the foundations. The underpinning with

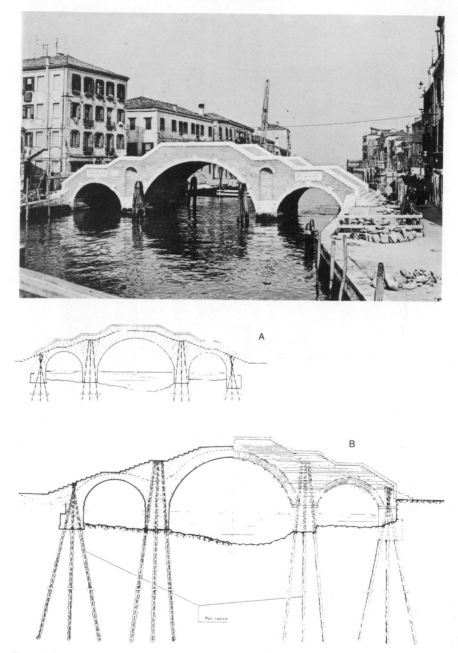

Figure 4.5 The 'Tre archi' bridge, Venice, Italy. *A*, scheme of the reinforcement of the upper structure; *B*, scheme of the underpinning.

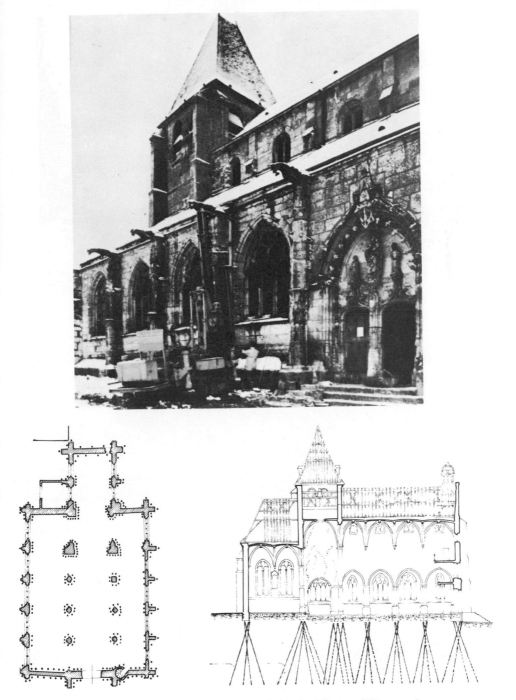

Figure 4.6   Eure, France. Monumental church of Tourny (XV century).

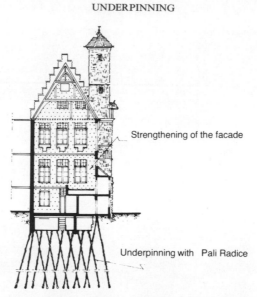

Figure 4.7   Ghent, Belgium. 'Het Toreken' (XV century).

pali radice did not cause any additional harm to the existing structure.

4.5.3 Ghent (Belgium): 'Het Toreken' building (XV century)

The very critical overall static condition of this building (Figure 4.7) demanded a full preliminary restoration of the upper masonry before underpinning with pali radice could begin.

4.5.4 Derby (UK): St. Mary's Bridge

St. Mary's Bridge (Figure 4.8) over the River Derwent, in Derby, was built in the years 1778–94, on the model of the bridge of Neuilly in Paris. It was built on the foundations of an old bridge which dated from the time of the Danish invasions in the year 800. Strengthening was required owing to foundation settlement of the two central piers, caused by extensive undermining due to scour. It was therefore carried out by first filling the cavities with bagged concrete and then underpinning with pali radice (diameter $D = 22\,\text{cm}$) installed from the bridge deck through the masonry and penetrating about 12 m into the clay soil.

4.5.5 Trapani (Italy): Pepoli Museum (XIV century)

The National Pepoli Museum (Figure 4.9), built in calcareous tuff masonry, showed evidence of stress at many points. Those most apparent could be seen in the north-west corner of the cloister porch, along the junction of the Church

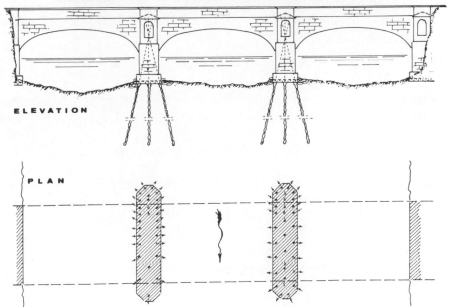

ELEVATION

PLAN

Figure 4.8 Derby, UK. St Mary's Bridge.

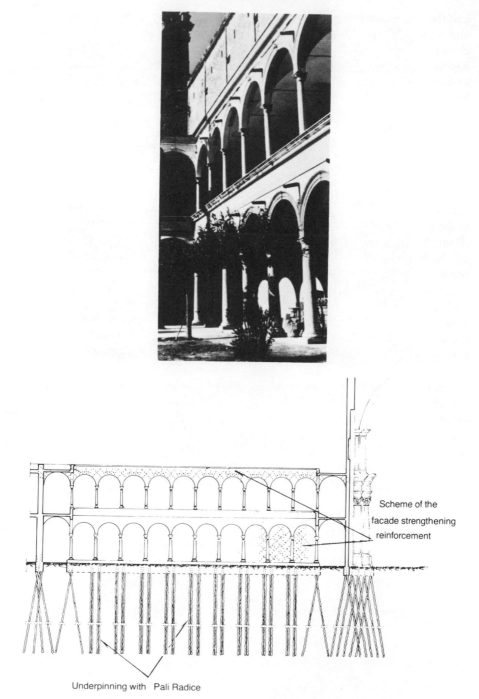

Scheme of the facade strengthening reinforcement

Underpinning with Pali Radice

Figure 4.9   Trapani, Italy. Pepoli Museum (XIV century).

and the Chapel, and along the West End. Further, it was clearly out-of-plumb, and a remarkable bulging of the four sides of the porch in relation to their central sections could be seen. A preliminary survey indicated that the edifice had been affected by the instability of the subsoil, which because of the type of soils, was particularly affected by movements in the water-table level caused by the exploitation of some nearby wells. Other disjunctions were noticeable in the correspondence of the porch arches with the adjacent structures. As well as restoration of the upper masonry the foundations were underpinned with pali radice.

4.5.6 Florence, Italy: the underpinning of the Ponte Vecchio

This job was carried out in the years 1962–63. The work was necessary owing to the precarious state of the structure, caused by age, the events of the last war (Ponte Vecchio was the only bridge that survived the systematic destruction of all the bridges during the war), and, last but not least, vibration caused by traffic.

As is shown in Figure 4.10, the underpinning is a classic pali radice type, with piles installed through the structures that have to be supported. The upper part of the bridge was not touched, because it was possible to carry out the work from under the arches, installing all the equipment there and using raking pali radice. This was a very important advantage. This underpinning underwent an exceptional and onerous test during the disastrous flood that struck Florence in 1966. The Ponte Vecchio with its small arch spans acted as a sort of dam, which had to bear the very strong impact of the current and the detritus it carried. This catastrophic event made it necessary to enlarge the flow capacity through the arch spans of the Ponte Vecchio. This was done recently by lowering the concrete floor under the arches by 50 centimetres.

Figure 4.10 Florence, Italy. The Ponte Vecchio. Scheme of the underpinning.

4.6 Reticulated pali radice (RRP)

The support of any man-made construction is the soil. But the natural soil, as it is found in the site selected for the new construction, does not always have sufficient strength for the purpose. To provide this basic requirement, several different systems have been adopted since ancient times. The first and oldest based its efficiency on enlarging the base of the walls of the new construction, in order to reduce the unit stress on the soil to within acceptable limits, consistent with its mechanical characteristics. In very soft soil, overall resistance was increased by means of small wooden piles, driven at close centres at the base of the walls, in order to obtain a tamping effect. This system, used since ancient times and with substantial success (consider the case of Venice) was, until recently, the only example of in-situ soil reinforcement. The limitations of the available means of driving the piles precluded more impressive results.

Modern systems, as stated previously, entrust the loads of the new constructions to piles deeply rooted in the subsoil. With surface soil no longer the direct support of the construction, it is the overall resistance of the subsoil, especially of its deepest strata, which supplies the bearing capacity to the indirectly supporting elements (piles). But the introduction of piling, aimed essentially at supporting indirectly only the vertical loads of the construction, did not solve all the problems which, in more recent times, have confronted the engineer. There was in some cases a need for a 'direct' reinforcement of the in-situ soil. In recent years several very interesting systems of in-situ soil reinforcement have been introduced and are, by now, widely used. The majority of these systems involve a physical, and in some cases also chemical, alteration of the natural soil, such as transformation of structure, variation of volume, variation of permeability, aggregation of particles, and introduction of intergranular materials, etc. Such alterations are normally accompanied by remoulding, etc.—in short, by a substantial alteration of the existing equilibrium of the soil.

On the other hand there are several cases in which no state of stress, alteration of the existing equilibrium, variation of the volume, or variation of permeability can be accepted on account of the presence of existing structures (natural or artificial) because of which even small excavations are not possible. The soil must remain unaltered—where it is and as it is. This is the field of application of reticulated pali radice structures.

4.6.1 Reticulated pali radice structures

A reticulated root pile structure (see Figure 4.11) is a three-dimensional lattice soil/pile structure built directly in the soil in situ according to a pre-determined plan, with many pali radice forming a special resisting network. The piles are all connected at the top by an RC capping beam. In the resistant complex, the

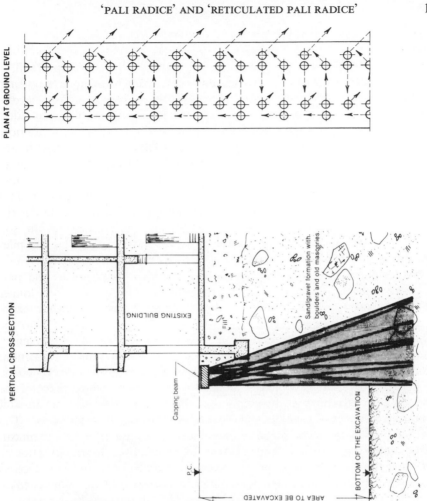

Figure 4.11 Typical scheme of reticulated pali radice (reticulated root piles, RRC). (*Right*) detail of the capping beam.

piles are the lines of force, while the soil encompassed supplies the weight, rather like a gravity wall. The whole is intended to resist compressive as well as tensile and shear forces.

In the example shown in Figure 4.11, and in the practical applications given in the following pages, the advantages afforded by this original type of structure are seen mainly in the context of the protection of old buildings, when the excavation is to be carried out in close proximity. Other applications also described relate to the prevention of landslips close to existing constructions (buildings, roads, bridges etc.). On account of the natural rigidity offered by the soil, the settlements and deformations of a reticulated pali radice structure are generally extremely small. The use of these structures is therefore of great advantage for solving problems where the utmost avoidance of soil relaxation is essential.

This structure had its origins in 1950–51, in attempts to find a proper solution to the problem that frequently occurs during the construction of underground structures in towns. The problem indicated in Figure 4.11 is that of constructing a retaining wall in close proximity to existing buildings, without previous excavation and without introducing any relaxation in the buildings' foundation soil. This may have to be done in any type of soil, including those containing boulders, old foundations or other obstructions. The first idea was to strengthen a convenient portion of soil by means of grout injections, in an attempt to consolidate it. As stated previously, however, not all soils can be injected, and even in cases where it is possible, the correct spread of the grout cannot be guaranteed. What is more, a soil, although 'treated' with grout, always lacks tensile resistance. It was therefore envisaged that reinforcing elements might be introduced into the soil according to a predetermined plan in order to strengthen it, in a similar way to which the steel bars strengthen the structure in reinforced concrete.

The basic element of the reticulated pali radice structure is therefore the palo radice, whose main characteristic, as described in the preceding pages, is exceptional adherence to the soil. It is worth noting that the system does not rely on an intergranular improvement of the soil obtained by penetration of the grout used for the construction of the piles, since, as stated above, in impermeable soils, this effect would be non-existent. (If it does exist, so much the better in such cases, as it can be taken into account by reducing the number of piles needed to construct a suitable network.) On the contrary, the system is based on the interaction between pile and soil: in fact, if a pile takes its bearing capacity from the soil, it is logical to presume that the soil, in its turn, is in a position to transfer a stress to a pile.

Provided they are not too far apart, the piles can therefore be relied upon to provide a kind of 'knot' effect. The network of piles encompasses and so supports the soil, but at the same time the piles are supported by the soil. The piles' primary purpose is that of introducing reinforcing elements into the soil.

The validity of the above assumption, at first intuitive, has been widely confirmed by experience, as will be seen below.

In the following sections different applications of reticulated pali radice are described.

4.6.2 The strengthening of the subsoil in urban areas

As stated above, the problem which first instigated the development of reticulated pali radice structures was that of the protection of existing buildings against alterations induced in the subsoil by natural causes or human action (particularly the construction of underground tunnels in urban areas). This is not a problem of protecting structures already suffering from foundation settlement, but rather one of avoiding damage to currently stable constructions. The protective structure constructed in the in-situ soil is intended to separate the foundation soil of the building from the disturbed zone of the excavation. Obviously, it is imperative that the construction of the protective structure must not introduce any alteration in the static equilibrium of the existing buildings. This means that no relaxation or reduction of resistance can be permitted in the subsoil on which the buildings rest.

This essential requirement suggested the idea of direct reinforcement of the in-situ soil, in order to improve its mechanical characteristics in view of the new states of stress set up by the execution of the new works. The basic philosophy of this reinforcement is derived from several general considerations, i.e. a vertical excavation in natural soil, presents in general the following difficulties (Figure 4.12):

(i) the crumbling of the soil from the face of the excavation, thereby losing the continuity and compactness possessed, to a greater or lesser extent, by any in-situ soil.

(ii) the sliding along possible critical surfaces, $a/a, b/b \ldots n/n$, so that even if crumbling can be prevented within a certain depth, the breakdown of an entire section of the soil is to be feared.

The vertical excavation sketched in Figure 4.12 would be possible, if the soil were appropriately strengthened to form an ideal supporting gravity wall $ABCD$, with the soil itself acting as basic material. The purpose of the pali radice must therefore be twofold, i.e.

(i) the piles must retain the soil and prevent its spoiling by any 'flow' through the network formed by the piles, causing a reduction of the continuity and unity of the gravimetric mass—it is only under these conditions that the overall behaviour of piles and soil, acting as a uniform whole, can be relied upon;

(ii) the piles must also supply a stitching and nailing of the various layers of the earth, by offering an additional resistance along the possible sliding

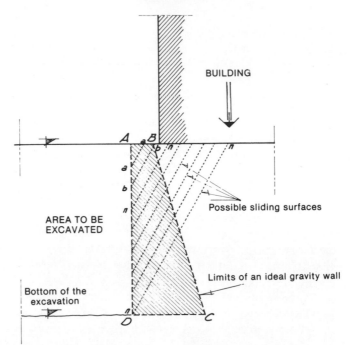

Figure 4.12 Stability scheme for an excavation close to an existing building.

surfaces. In this way the solid *ABCD* can assume a unitary behaviour as a gravity wall able to support compressive, as well as tensile and shear forces.

4.6.2.1 The protection of buildings close to excavations for underground roads or railways. A typical scheme, used for the Paris underground as well as several other underground roads and railways in urban areas (Milan, Washington and Barcelona underground, Naples Rapid Transit, Salerno subterranean railway, etc.) is shown in Figure 4.13. The reticulated pali radice structure does not impose any restriction on the building activity and, if necessary, can be carried out without disturbing the surface traffic, as shown in Figure 4.13, where the work was carried out by means of a small service tunnel constructed below the sidewalk. The reticulated pali radice wall is intended to supply a cut-off between zone *A* (above the tunnel to be excavated) and zone *B* (below the buildings); consequently the possible relaxation of zone *A* does not affect zone *B*.

4.6.2.2 The protection of buildings directly above construction site of shallow tunnels. In these cases it is impossible to prevent the soil under the building from being affected by the relaxation caused by the tunnel. It is therefore necessary to transfer the load of the structure outside the relaxed area. In

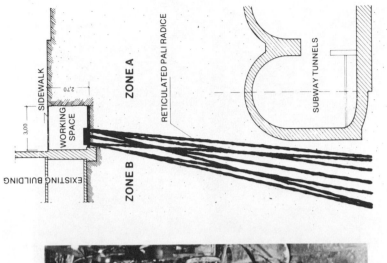

Figure 4.13 Paris Metro—protection of existing buildings during the excavation of tunnels.

Double track railway tunnel

Figure 4.14   Salerno, Italy. Protection of buildings during the construction of the new railway tunnel under the town. (*Above*) elevation; (*opposite*) plan. (1) Reticulated pali radice structures; (2) capping beam in RC connecting the reticulated pali radice with the structures above; (3) complementary pali radice for 'stitching' the soil above the tunnel.

Figure 4.14 an example is shown. As a preventive measure, a reinforced concrete structure was constructed in the basement of the building, connecting the building frame to the pali radice piling to make a solid complex. The piling, executed as a multiple reticulated pali radice structure, fulfils the two aims of underpinning the building directly and avoiding the relaxation caused by the tunnel construction, by being extended from area *A* to areas *B, B'*, outside the protective structure.

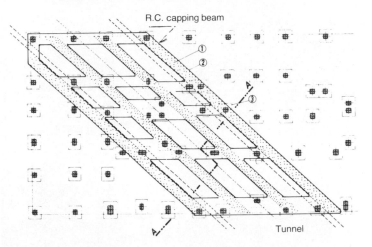

R.C. capping beam

Tunnel

4.6.3 The problem of landslides

Another solution to a problem for which reticulated pali radice structures have proved to be very effective is that of landslides. The direct or indirect protection of a construction (building, road, bridge, etc.) against the risk of landslide should be considered as a problem of underpinning, because it involves the stability of the existing structures.

Any natural surface when inclined has an inherent tendency to slide down. The potential movement is normally prevented by the combined actions of internal friction and cohesion of the soil. When these internal forces decrease in, or lose, their efficiency, the soil slides: this is the case, for instance, in clayey soil, where the increase of moisture content reduces its mechanical resistance. In this case appropriate retaining structures are necessary in order to reach firm strata and keep in place the natural soil above, especially when there are structures resting on the surface. Whenever possible, masonry or concrete retaining walls are constructed; but there are cases where the excavation necessary for placing such retaining walls is not possible without endangering the stability of the whole slope. In such cases a reticulated pali radice retaining wall, buried deeply in the soil to reach the firm strata (Figure 4.15), offers a suitable solution, because

(i) it does not require any excavation;
(ii) it can be constructed in any soil, whatever the permeability and whatever boulders or other obstructions may be present;
(iii) the network of piles does not prevent water circulation in the subsoil, so there is no risk of water accumulating at the back of the wall;
(iv) design can be arranged to counteract any pattern of internal forces.

Of course, such a solution is only possible provided some stable formation can be found at a reasonable depth.

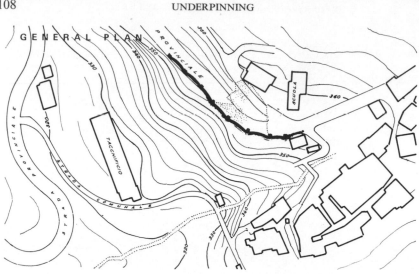

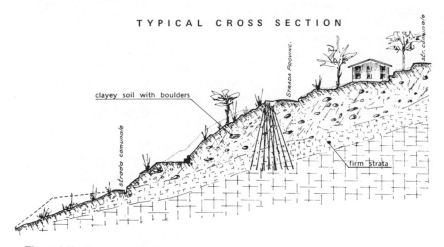

Figure 4.15   Reticulated pali radice structure for stabilizing a landslide in loose soils.

4.6.3.1 The problem of landslides in fractured rock or semi-rocky formation. The classic landslide in clayey soil, as discussed in the previous section, is not the only kind of landslide. Recently the construction of highways, dams and other large structures has involved major modifications in the morphology of the existing surface of the natural soil, thus creating a state of instability and risk even in normally stable formations. The increased

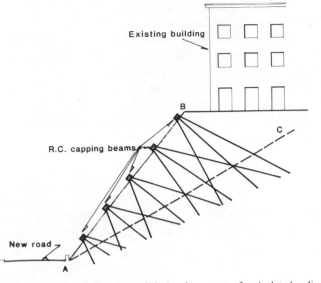

Figure 4.16 Typical example of slope consolidation by means of reticulated pali radice in a semirocky formation.

gradient of the slopes—dictated by local exigencies—has created the possibility of landslides. A typical example is sketched in Figure 4.16. The construction of the new road involves a cut $A-B$ in the existing slope. Because of the presence of existing buildings, the cut $A-B$ must be steeper than the safe inclination $A-C$. Consequently the portion $A-B-C$ of the slope needs to be consolidated.

A reticulated pali radice structure, with piles spread in groups connected by a series of small horizontal concrete beams, proves to be a most suitable solution. The three-dimensional pattern of the reinforcement gives an appropriate unity to the unstable rocky foundation, which comes to resemble a form of reinforced masonry resting on the safe inclined surface $A-C$. Additionally, the penetration of the piles for a few metres beyond the critical surface $A-C$ acts like 'nails' providing additional resistance to the sliding forces.

The scheme is similar in appearance to the system of prestressed anchoring, but it is substantially different in its philosophy.

(i) First, its purpose is not the connection of the surface with some firm and reliable strata in the subsoil, for which very long anchors are sometimes necessary. The only purpose of the reticulated pali radice structure, from this point of view, is the 'reinforcement' of the wedge $A-B-C$. It is therefore sufficient for the toes of the piles to penetrate only a few metres beyond the critical surface $A-C$.

(ii) A reticulated pali radice structure does not introduce any stress in the soil; this point, as described above, is crucial and fully in accordance with the spirit behind the underpinning of buildings. For the complete preservation of the existing equilibrium is also of paramount importance in the case of a slope in a critical state, while the introduction of forces, as with prestressed anchors, could be dangerous.

(iii) Prestressed anchors depend for their efficiency on the constraints introduced in the soil. This efficiency is completely lost by relaxation, or by interruption along their length owing to corrosion or other causes. Any pile of an RRP structure is, however, always participating over its full length in the overall resistance of the whole in taking compressive, as well as tensile, stresses, even in case of partial ruptures after a failure. This is because of the high frictional resistance of a palo radice.

(iv) Anchors require a bulky reinforced concrete structure on the surface to unite the very large loads entrusted to them. The RRP structure, based on a denser configuration of piles, requires only small horizontal connections. This is very important for the preservation of the environment that is normally required for slopes in inhabited areas.

Figure 4.17 illustrates example, as described above. The new São Paulo–Santos Highway in Brazil, had to cross a very difficult mountainous region, the Serra do Mar. Cuts in the slopes and the construction of foundation wells (after the traditional system of 'tubuloes') involved in several cases, an alteration of the equilibrium of the soil (weathered gneiss, largely fractured). A three-dimensional reticulated pali radice structure, introduced gradually, without any disturbance in the subsoil, supplied the necessary reinforcement.

4.6.4 *The reticulated pali radice structure as a reinforced soil basement*

The problem illustrated in Figure 4.18 is another example of the adaptability and versatility of the system of reinforcing the soil with pali radice. Two tunnels on a new line of the Tokyo underground had to be driven near to an existing tall construction, (the 'Panorama Tower'). The problem was the preservation of the stability of the tower.

The problem was solved in a very quick and simple way by a complete underpinning of the existing foundations with a network of piles encaging the soil. The result is a reinforced soil 'underbasement', integrated with the tower to form a single gravity system sunk deep into the soil. Indeed, so deeply rooted was the structure that the construction of the tunnels caused only minor movement. The obvious conclusion is that the integrated soil/pile basement involves a very large volume of the subsoil which cannot, as would have been the case with the existing foundations, be affected by the relaxation resulting from the construction of the tunnels.

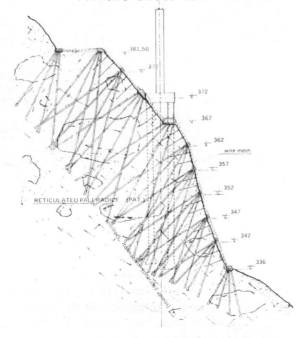

Figure 4.17 São Paulo, Brazil—Santos Highway. Landslide prevention in a semirocky formation by means of reticulated pali radice.

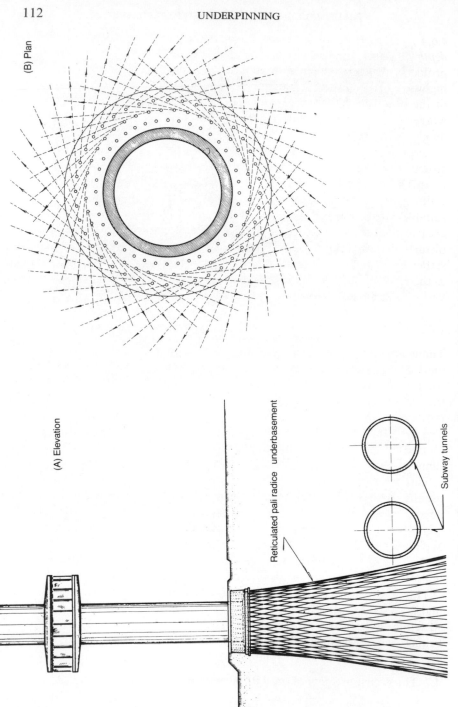

(B) Plan

(A) Elevation

Reticulated pali radice   underbasement

Subway tunnels

Figure 4.18   Tokyo, Japan—Panorama Tower. The 'reinforced soil' underbasement.

4.6.4.1 Another case of underpinning, to facilitate the construction of a medium depth tunnel beneath an existing building. Figure 4.19 illustrates one of the problems which was solved in connection with the construction of a new highway in the subsoil of the city of Naples. As soon as the excavation of one of the two tunnels approached it, the building showed signs of some very worrying differential settlement. Considering the relative position, in plan and depth, of the building and the tunnels, it was impossible to consider an underpinning of the type indicated in section 4.6.2.2, where the load of the structure is taken in the deep strata 'outside' the tunnel. The solution was the construction of a reticulated pali radice structure through the foundation walls, in order to obtain a reinforced soil sub-foundation 'above' the tunnels, suitable for absorbing the unavoidable soil relaxation introduced by the excavation of the tunnels, without apparent deformations and without disturbing the overall stability of the construction. There was, in fact, general settlement of the area, including the building which did not suffer any damage, as the RRP structure precluded the possibility of differential settlement of the various parts of the structure.

4.6.5 *Reticulated pali radice for consolidation of damaged tunnels*

Tunnelling in structurally complex formations, such as flysch (a chaotic mix of marl, clay and limestone) is still very difficult. Very frequently, the unbalanced soil thrust causes damage to the lining of the tunnels. Figure 4.20 illustrates the scheme for strengthening the outer shell of a tunnel. The pattern of pali radice forms an arch of reinforced soil reaching far into the surrounding soil. The piles have the function of homogenizing and distributing the stresses exerted by the soil, and of eventually concentrating these stresses within the tunnel lining.

This type of reinforcement should not be confused with 'rock bolting' usually carried out in rock formations to reach sound materials existing just beyond the zone disturbed by the excavation. Here in fact there is no competent material to reach; it is the unstable soil itself which is reinforced and made self-supporting. The design of the reinforced soil arch is based on an evaluation of the average mechanical behaviour of the soil surrounding the lining, which is to become the support of the composite soil–pile structure.

This scheme was successfully adopted in Italy recently to secure a number of highway tunnels which showed signs of imminent failure after their construction. A similar reinforcement was carried out for an old railway tunnel in France, where the invert was progressively suffering uplift.

4.7 The design problem of an RRP structure

One of the major advantages of pali radice used for the purpose of underpinning is, as already stated, the extreme simplicity of design, in

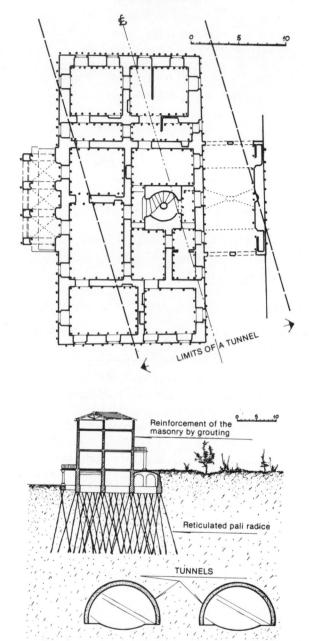

Figure 4.19   Underpinning of a building to be underpassed by a tunnel.

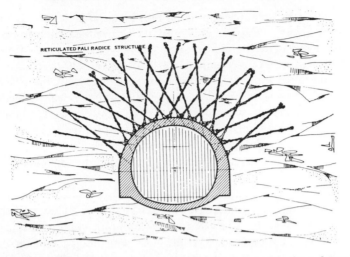

RETICULATED PALI RADICE STRUCTURE

Figure 4.20 Scheme of reinforcement of a tunnel in an unstable clayey formation.

comparison with the old systems. It is also possible to prepare a simple and reliable estimate of cost, excluding allowance for any unusual circumstances. A reliable design is not, however, so simple with a reticulated pali radice structure. In this connection, it must first of all be remembered that the purpose of the pile network is twofold:

(i) first, to encompass the soil in order to make a composite soil/pile mass — in general, this depends on the mechanical characteristics of the soil: a good internal friction and, even more, a good cohesion, reduces the number of piles necessary for the purpose;
(ii) second, to supply the necessary reinforcement to the soil/pile structure, in order to resist essentially tensile forces.

The design of a reticulated pali radice structure is therefore based essentially on the 'density' that must be given to the structure itself in order to accomplish these requirements. For this, it is necessary to determine the following:

(a) the number and diameter of the piles necessary to adequately retain the soil in order to enable it to behave as a unit;
(b) the number and diameter of the piles necessary to stitch the different layers between them and to provide the rooting in the soil beneath.

Each of these requirements, though they do not conflict, does envisage a different 'density' for the piles. It is evident that the number of piles will be that required by the prevailing conditions in each case. In general, it may also be said that it is better to use a denser distribution of small-diameter piles, rather than a more thinly scattered one of large-diameter piles.

This general rule may be departed from in specific cases, for example, when dealing with reticulated structures required to prevent landslides composed of rocky or semi-rocky fractured materials. This material in its natural condition constitutes a negative element owing to its precarious equilibrium, but if inserted into a reticulated pali radice structure may, on the contrary, become a co-operating element of very great usefulness. In this case, the general encompassing of the soil is always necessary, but even more important is the need to oppose the shear forces, which can, along the critical surfaces, reach very high levels, especially when the landslip is actually moving. In these cases (presence of rocky materials), the possibility of exploiting to best advantage the effect of the shear resistance of the piles suggests the adoption of diameters greater than those normally used, together with an adequate steel reinforcement.

The use of reticulated pali radice structures is by now quite common, and the specific requirements of each case offer the chance of different schemes and sizing. This ability to be adapted to very different situations is a unique element of reticulated pali radice. It must be remembered that the sizing of such a structure—that is, the 'density' to be given to the piles—is primarily a technical problem, in as much as it directly affects the safety factor; but there is also the problem of economics, since a reticulated pali radice structure with too dense a pile layout would be very expensive, and its practical application would therefore become very restricted. The encouraging results of the work already carried out, however, suggest that safety margins adopted may perhaps have been excessive. Since the beginning, therefore, the need has been felt to check the behaviour of the structure in model tests and at full scale, by measurement and instrumentation, to derive suggestions for future applications.

4.7.1 Model tests on reticulated pali radice

The essential purpose of several tests, carried out to full scale and in model reticulated structures, has been to check, at least on a qualitative basis, the interaction between the piles through the soil. The mutual influence between piles located at close spacing (the 'group effect') is well known. In order to check the soil/pile behaviour as a whole, it is necessary first to verify, at different spacings, the mutual influence of parallel piles. It is very difficult to carry out such an investigation on a theoretical basis only, on account of the heterogeneity of natural soils. Some contribution to the understanding of the problem was therefore supplied by tests carried out in artificially made homogeneous soil with reduced-scale model piles.

The scheme of one such test is indicated in Figure 4.21. The soil was coarse sand. The full experiment consisted of four series of tests, with piles respectively 50, 100, 150 and 200 diameters long. Each series was formed of 6 groups of 3 piles each, spaced from 2 to 7 diameters, plus an additional single pile. The results of the tests are summarized in the diagrams showing spacing against efficiency. The term 'efficiency' is indicative of the loadbearing capacity of a pile in a group, compared with the similar loadbearing capacity of

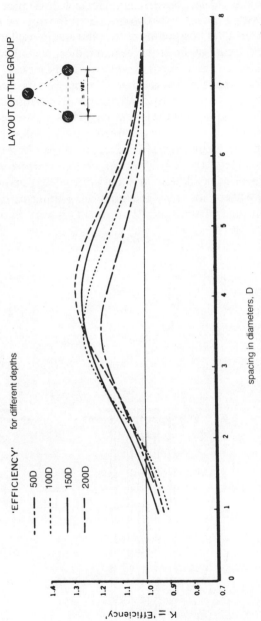

Figure 4.21 'Efficiency' of piles in groups. K = 'efficiency' = (loadbearing capacity of the pile in group)/(loadbearing capacity of the single pile). Soil, sieved coarse sand.

a single pile—practically, the 'group effect'. From the diagrams it can be seen that spacing between 2 and 7 diameters, the loadbearing capacity of the piles in groups is higher than the loadbearing capacity of a single pile. This result is not in agreement with what is currently considered the normal behaviour of piles in groups, where closer positioning of the piles is supposed to reduce their 'efficiency'. But, in the case of the group of pali radice, one must consider the great length of the piles as compared with their diameter. The test demonstrates, therefore, that the load is carried not only by the single piles, but also by the soil they encompass. Obviously the results correspond to the soil and to the particular conditions of the test; nonetheless, full-scale experiments have confirmed that the interaction between parallel piles is effective at spacing well beyond the conventional limit of the three diameters.

This 'group effect' is not the only effect on which a reticulated pali radice structure relies. There is in addition the 'network effect', derived from the three-dimensional pattern in which the piles are arranged, to encompass the soil to make it part of the soil/pile whole. This very important effect

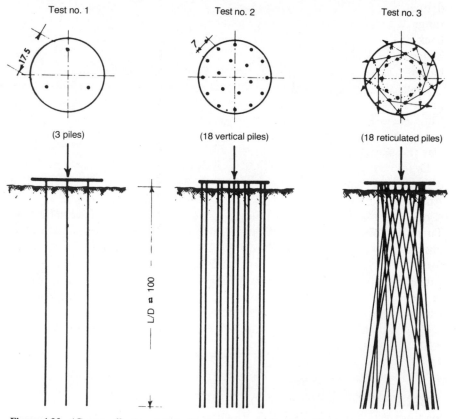

Figure 4.22 'Group effect' and 'net effect'. Layout of the tests. Spacings (*s*) and length (*L*) expressed in diameters, *D*. Soil, sieved coarse sand.

has been checked by field and model tests. One model test is described in Figure 4.22. The soil was coarse sand. Tests were carried out on three groups of piles: one formed by three vertical piles, spaced at 17.5 diameters; the second formed by 18 vertical piles, spaced at 7 diameters; and the third formed by 18 piles again spaced 7 diameters, but arranged in a network, like a basket. The increase in the loadbearing capacity, taking 1 as the value for a pile belonging to group No. 1 (piles widely spaced), was 68% for the piles in group of 18 vertical piles and 122% for the piles in the 18-pile network. Similar results, although not with the same percentages, were found in different soils.

4.7.2 Full-scale tests carried out on reticulated pali radice

The first official test on a full-size structure was carried out in 1957 on behalf of the Milan Underground (Figure 4.23). A full-scale reticulated pali radice retaining wall, 12 m deep, was installed in the Milan subsoil (essentially sand and gravel). The wall consisted of 16 piles (60 mm nominal diameter, each reinforced with a 12 mm steel bar) per running metre of wall. The 60 mm diameter was exceptionally small, as normal minimum diameters are in the range of 100 mm. An RC capping beam connected the piles at the top. On the back of the reticulated pali radice structure, an RC wall, supporting heavy ballast, was intended to represent the action of a building. The load of the ballast was approximately 40 tonnes per running metre of wall.

Once the installation was completed the front face of the wall was progressively excavated to a maximum depth of 8 m, over a central section of 8 m. The deformation of the reticulated structure was accurately checked during the excavation (first phase), and during a second phase when the load was transferred from the back of the wall directly on to the wall itself.

Despite the size of the applied load, the wall did not show significant deformation, and although this encouraged the Milan Underground Authority to adopt this type of structure for several other difficult jobs (Loggia dei Mercanti, Corso Buenos Aires, Via Boccaccio, Molinello and Turro Viaducts, etc.) it did not contribute significantly to the evaluation of the ultimate resistance of the reticulated structure. The doubt remained, therefore, that the structure had, perhaps, been overdesigned. On other jobs strain gauges were installed on some of the piles to check the presence of stresses, and in these cases as well, although the structure fully satisfied the purposes for which it was adopted, no significant stresses have been detected.

This particular aspect (rigidity of reticulated pali radice structures) will be dealt with in the next section.

4.7.3 The reticulated pali radice structure from the physical point of view

The experience gathered from both the many works carried out and the direct loading tests explains the true physical meaning of the behaviour of a reticulated structure.

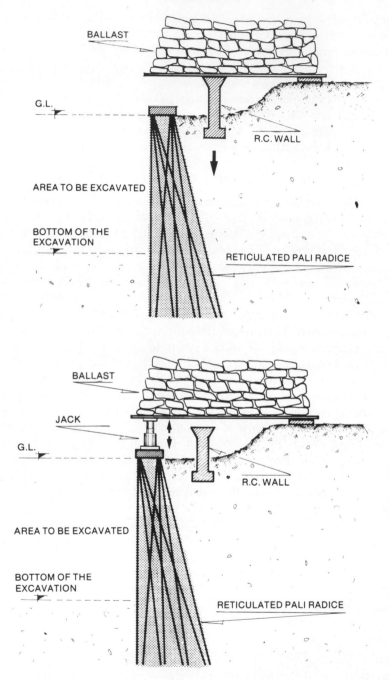

Figure 4.23 Scheme of the load test on a reticulated pali radice retaining wall. (*Left*) the scheme: top, first stage, bottom, second stage. (*Above*) the site.

The central factor in this structure is the soil with its mechanical properties (density, internal friction, cohesion, etc.) and also its fragility and very limited deformability. A network of piles alone without the soil has, in practice, no resistance at all and a potentially infinite deformation. If inserted through the soil, the network retains it and makes it 'homogeneous' by connecting the various parts and so allowing a full collaboration by supplying, where required, a resistance—even if a small one—to tension and shear forces. This resistance is available only within very small limits of deformation, since the limiting factor is the failure of the soil. At this stage it may appear that the contribution of the piles is not very significant, since their full resistance is not developed. This is true, but the small contribution they make is nonetheless essential.

One cannot expect significant deformation to precede the final failure of a reticulated structure built in a natural soil. A soil reaching a deformation near the maximum rate allowed by its mechanical characteristics becomes fissured, loses its continuity and fails without being supported by the reticulated structure: similarly in reinforced concrete, if the concrete is crushed the stability of the structure can no longer be supplied by the reinforcement alone. In looking for experimental confirmation of the way a reticulated pali radice structure works, therefore, it would be necessary to use exceptionally sensitive measuring instruments, capable of checking even the minimal movement of the encompassed soil, as well as the smallest deformations and stresses arising in the piles.

4.7.4 The design of a reticulated pali radice structure

Considering the above, the design of a reticulated pali radice structure is not an easy task. In the very complex soil–pile interaction, there are many factors whose influence on the final behaviour of the structure cannot be conveniently assessed. There is the soil, with its heterogeneity at different levels, each of which is characterized by different geometrical and geotechnical parameters (cohesion, internal friction, specific gravity, modulus of elasticity, subgrade reaction, etc.). There are the piles with their geometrical patterns and their characteristics of resistance, modulus of elasticity, skin friction etc. Apart from the fact that the nature of the relationship between so many different parameters is practically unknown, there is also the difficulty of collecting correct values for the parameters themselves.

On the other hand a design may be considered reliable only when different designers come to the same conclusions for the same problem. It is well known that this cannot be expected in some geotechnical problems. It is therefore preferable to base the design of a reticulated pali radice structure on some simple assumptions based on the concept of 'reinforced soil', and so similar to those currently used for reinforced concrete. Two typical cases will be considered: the reticulated pali radice gravity retaining wall, and reticulated pali radice for general soil reinforcement.

4.7.4.1 The pile–soil amplification factor. The pile–soil amplification factor is a key parameter whose value has a great influence on the results of numerical calculations. It can be assumed as:

$$m = \frac{E_p}{E_s}$$

where
  E_p = modulus of elasticity of the pile
  E_s = modulus of elasticity of the soil.
Alternatively it can be assumed as

$$m' = \frac{W}{K}$$

where
  K = subgrade reaction of the soil
  W = ratio between the unit stress on the cross-section of the pile and the corresponding settlement, as can be checked by a direct load test on a pile.
  Obviously, the two values are not likely to be equal; it is up to the expert to choose the most suitable value.

4.7.4.2 Design of a reticulated pali radice gravity retaining wall. This scheme is most suitably applied in cases where conventional systems are impractical or impossible, such as in 'cut and cover' constructions for subways where the stability of nearby buildings has to be fully protected, and where, owing to difficult subsoil conditions, other solutions—such as diaphragm walls—cannot be used; or for landslide prevention in loose soil, where it is absolutely impossible to excavate for the construction of conventional retaining walls.

Figure 4.24 illustrates the typical arrangement of a reticulated pali radice gravity retaining wall. The forces acting on the structure are

S_a = active pressure from the back
S_p = passive pressure at the foot
P = gravity.

On a horizontal cross-section $A-A$, the forces can be reduced to

V = vertical force (load)
H = horizontal force (shear).

For the design, different assumptions can be made depending upon the particular soil characteristics in order to collect several ultimate values for the soil and pile stresses. Table 4.3 shows a possible calculation, with reference to a reticulated pali radice retaining wall.

Geotechnical data

angle of internal friction:	$\phi = 30°$
unit weight of the soil:	$\gamma = 18\,\mathrm{kN/m^3}$
cohesion:	$c = 0$
surcharge:	$g = 20\,\mathrm{kN/m^2}$

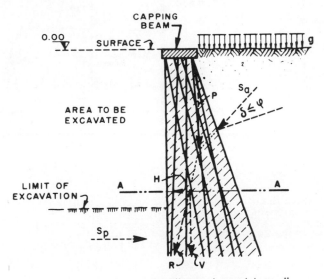

Figure 4.24 Reticulated pali radice gravity retaining wall.

Table 4.3(a)

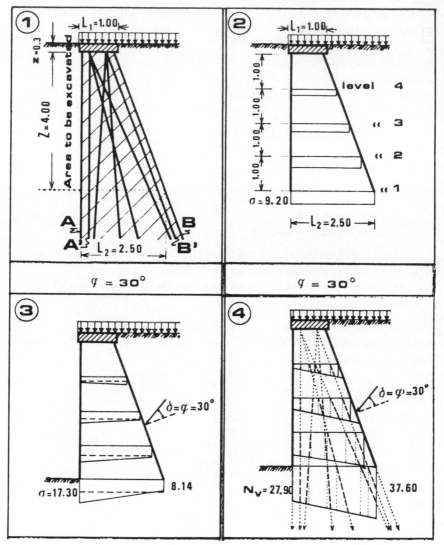

Pali radice data

diameter:	$b = 150\,\text{mm}$
steel reinforcement: one bar, diameter:	$d = 18\,\text{mm}$
number of piles (linear metre of wall):	$n = 10$
Pile–soil amplification factor:	$m = 40$
Vertical unit stress on the soil:	$\sigma(\text{N/cm}^2)$
Load on piles (vertical component):	$N_v\,(\text{kN})$

(1) shows the scheme of the reticulated structure; (2) shows the gravimetric stresses on the soil before the excavation; in (3), the vertical load as well as the

Table 4.3(b)

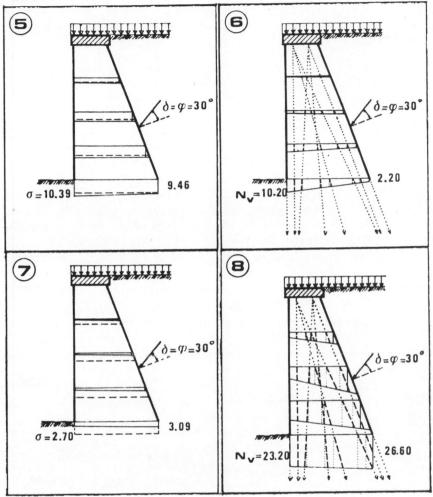

forces introduced by the active pressure, after the excavation, are assumed to be supported by the soil only (no piles). The maximum values for the unit stress on the soil, σ, are obtained. In (4), the same forces as for (3) are assumed to be supported by the piles only. The maximum values for the load on the piles are obtained. In (5) and (6) the forces introduced by the excavation are assumed to be supported by the combined action of soil and piles according to the amplification factor, m. Some intermediate values are obtained, both for the soil and the piles. In (7) and (8) it is assumed that, ultimately, all forces, including the dead weight before the excavation, are supported by the combined soil–pile action. Some reference values are obtained.

It is up to the experienced geotechnical engineer to decide the most acceptable values, considering that a very efficient soil–pile interaction can be

more easily obtained in stiff soil. As for the resistance to sliding of the structure
due to the thrust produced by the active earth pressure, it is resisted, normally,
by the soil only, through the frictional resistance and the cohesion, if any.
Therefore the condition of stability is:

$$Ptg\,\phi + Ac \geq S_0$$

where

$P =$ total vertical load acting on the horizontal section;

$A =$ area of the section

$S_0 =$ horizontal component of the thrust.

Only in the case of a semi-rocky fractured formation is the shear
resistance entrusted mainly to the pile reinforcement.

*4.7.4.3 Design of a reticulated pali radice structure for general soil reinforce-
ment in stiff or semi-rocky formations.* This is the scheme generally adopted
for soil reinforcement to stabilize a landslide in stiff or semi-rocky formations
(Figure 4.25). In addition to the normal geotechnical parameters of the soil (at
least as an average), and the geometrical, structural, and mechanical data of
the elementary palo radice, it is also necessary to collect data on the possible
external forces acting on the proposed reticulated structure as a whole. Once
the above elements are collected, the design of the reticulated structure may
proceed. The problems to be solved are generally related to the behaviour of
the composite soil–pile structure as subjected to compressive (and tensile), as
well as shear, stresses. In all cases, the problem is to calculate the contribution
made by the piles to the resistance of the natural soil.

The first step is to determine the 'critical' sliding surface, i.e. the surface
which has the minimum factor of safety. Several methods are in use, but

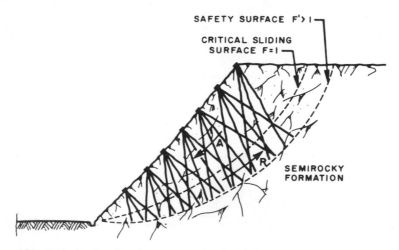

Figure 4.25 Reticulated pali radice structure for landslide prevention in stiff or semirocky
formation.

analysis by an experienced geotechnical engineer is absolutely necessary. The purpose of the network of pali radice is twofold: first, to encompass the soil portion above the 'critical' surface, and second, to 'nail' this surface, so supplying additional shear forces. The design of this 'nailing' can be carried out as follows: once the factor of safety F_x has been assessed, the design of the reticulated structure (number and diameter of piles, reinforcement etc.) is obtained by the following formula:

$$F_x = (R + R')/A \geq 1$$

where
  R = total resistive forces on the 'critical' surface
  A = motive forces on the same surface
  R' = the additional shear resistance provided by the piles.

This additional resistance depends on either the shear resistance of the piles or the resistance of the soil to be 'cut' by the piles, whichever is the smaller. In semi-rocky or very stiff soils the shear resistance of the piles is more important than in loose soils, where the resistance of the soil is the limiting value.

4.7.4.4 Reticulated pali radice structures in rocky formations. This case occurs more frequently than might be expected, because the instability of such natural formations involves serious problems of safety. The main principle in the use of reticulated pali radice structures in these situations is very simple: the object is to form a strengthening three-dimensional network of sufficient thickness to produce a kind of cyclopean masonry wall, in which the connecting element is supplied by the piles (Figure 4.26). No surface capping structures are necessary, except for some wire mesh, reinforced by cables to guard against the fall of small pieces of rock.

4.7.5 The design of a reticulated pali radice structure—conclusions

In the absence of a more reliable theoretical approach, calculations roughly based on the concept of 'reinforced soil', and so similar to those currently used for reinforced concrete, may be used. A better guide, however, can now be obtained by an extensive examination of works carried out. Reflection upon the facts, and the collection and selection of results to obtain some data of general validity is, at the moment, the best way to determine future designs. In addition, the advantages and opportunities offered by the modern systems of calculation must be fully encouraged in order

(a) to explore the influence on the final result of the several different parameters of the problem;
(b) to investigate the possible forces, as well as the possible deformation of the structures, according to the different hypotheses.

A computer could be of great help in a survey of this kind, since the problem

128   UNDERPINNING

TYPICAL CROSS SECTION

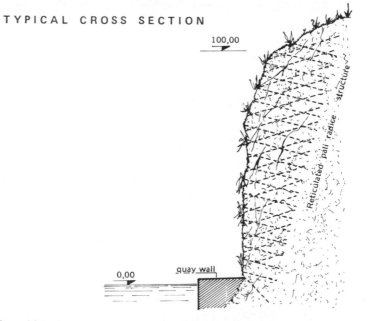

Figure 4.26 Capri, Italy. Reticulated pali radice for consolidation of a rock face.

could be posed as a logical matter of analysis and synthesis, supported, if possible, by more and more appropriate instrumentation.

It must be concluded that for this, as for many other geotechnical problems, it is not possible to have at one's disposal an exhaustive system of calculation ready to be applied with complete safety. The design of a reticulated pali radice structure, therefore, requires the attention of a qualified expert. It is to be hoped that the interest raised in this particular structure will lead to some improvement in future design approaches.

4.8 The problem of stability of a tower

The reinforcement of the foundations of a tower is a unique problem in the field of the consolidation of ancient monuments. The stability of a tower is always extremely delicate and the risk of a disastrous failure arising from its uncertain stability during the reinforcement works must always be borne in mind, besides which, the erection of preventive shoring is not very simple, for two fundamental reasons. Firstly, with masonry shoring (buttresses) there is the risk of increasing the unit stresses on the soil adjacent to the tower, resulting in a possible consequent failure. Secondly, a metal shoring, on the other hand, is subject to variable stresses induced by variations in temperature. In the following sections some further case histories are illustrated, in addition to the reinforcement of the foundations of the Panorama Tower in Tokyo, already described in section 4.6.4. To describe a case still pending, some notes will be given on the Tower of Pisa.

4.8.1 The Burano Bell Tower, Venice, Italy (XVI century)

The consolidation of the foundations of this famous tower (Figure 4.27), a well-known feature in the landscape of the Venetian lagoon, was a very difficult problem which involved the following (Figure 4.28).

(a) Preliminary preparatory work. Owing to the very poor quality of the soil and, even more, the extreme urgency, it was not possible to study and carry out adequate preparatory work. The tower was in danger of imminent collapse. The problem of an emergency safeguard was solved by means of two opposing groups of a few provisional pali radice, prestressed respectively in compression and in tension, in such a way as to create a stabilizing moment. For this purpose the piles were drilled, as usual, through the existing foundation masonry, but were not connected to it. Instead, they could slide in their holes under the action of two series of jacks, one for introducing compressive forces on the leaning side, the other for introducing tensile forces on the opposite side. The jacks acted against a sturdy steel frame constructed in the base of the tower.

Figure 4.27   The leaning Burano Bell Tower, Venice, Italy.

(b) Underpinning. Once a reasonable stability of the tower had been obtained the underpinning, by means of pali radice, was carried out. The aforementioned provisional piles were not taken into account. The pali radice underpinning, on account of the close spacing of the piles, may be considered also as a reinforced soil basement, gravimetrically associated with the tower. The system of pali radice can be easily compared to the root structure of a tree. It is connected to the structure in such a way as to react both to tensile and compressive stresses. This is extremely important. The centre of gravity of this gravimetric complex is very near to the level of the soil, the advantages of which are obvious.

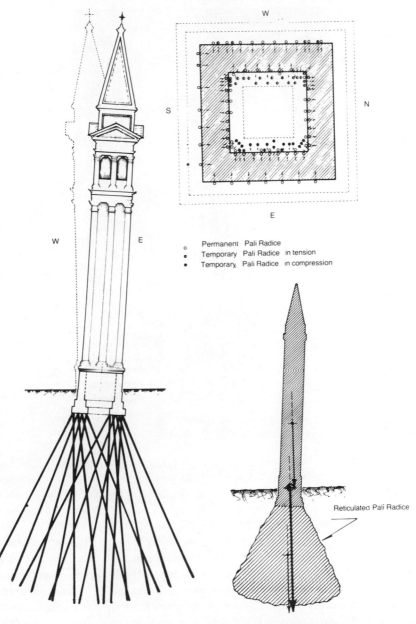

o   Permanent   Pali Radice
   Temporary   Pali Radice   in tension
   Temporary,   Pali Radice   in compression

Reticulated Pali Radice

GRAVIMETRIC SCHEME

Figure 4.28   Burano Bell Tower—scheme of the underpinning by means of pali radice.

Figure 4.29   Mosul, Iraq. The Al-Hadba leaning minaret.

4.8.2 The strengthening of the Al-Hadba Minaret, Mosul, Iraq (XII century)

Dating back to the 12th century, this minaret (Figure 4.29) has always, for both historical and religious reasons, been a famous monument beloved of the Iraqi people, who have often taken it as one of the very symbols of the cultural heritage of their nation. Like the majority of other minarets of the area, exposed as they are to the northwest winds, the Al-Hadba has shown over the years a marked tendency to lean towards the south-east. This phenomenon had resulted in an ever-increasing and decidedly dangerous swaying in recent years, introducing extra compressive stresses on the leaning side and tensile stresses on the opposite side. The precious architectural brickwork ornamentations were crumbling and becoming detached from the main structure. The original masonry could not resist such phenomena, made as it was of poor-quality, chalky-based bricks and mortars, due to which it had undergone a slow and progressive deterioration.

As may be seen in Figures 4.30 and 4.31, a complex and systematic intervention was made, both above and below ground level, yet this was completed in only nine months of effective work.

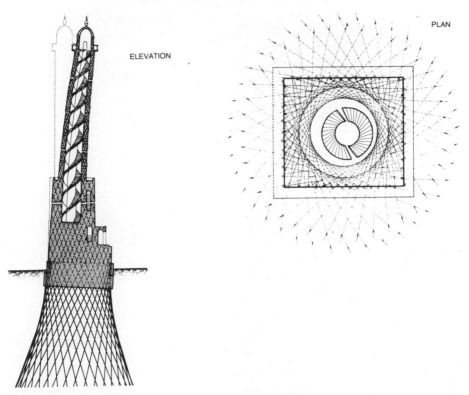

ELEVATION

PLAN

Figure 4.30 The Al-Hadba leaning minaret. Scheme of the underpinning by means of pali radice.

4.8.3 The Tower of Pisa

The fact that the problem of the consolidation of the Leaning Tower of Pisa is still waiting for a solution, after more than eight centuries, is just as amazing as the problem itself. Thousands of proposals collected during this time cram the archives of the authority in charge of the preservation of this world-renowned monument. Nevertheless, up to now no decision has been taken, although, in recent years, an international invitation resulted in the submission of a substantial number of proposals from all over the world, from Mexico to Japan, to the special International Committee.

It must be recalled that, in that past, some minor restoration works carried out in the immediate subsoil of the tower led to an abrupt and unexpected increase in the inclination of the monument. Perhaps this alarmed the authority in charge and suggested the need for the maximum of prudence. Yet, apart from the unique historic and artistic renown of the Tower of Pisa, its problems of stability are probably no more complex than the two analogous problems illustrated above (Burano Bell Tower and Mosul Minaret).

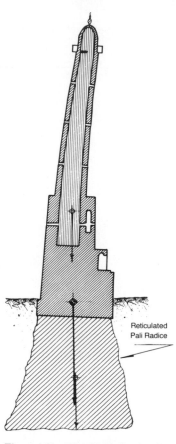

Reticulated
Pali Radice

Figure 4.31 The Al-Hadba leaning
minaret. Gravimetric scheme.

Figure 4.32 shows the three structures side by side to the same scale. The reader will note, in the ratio between height H and minimum base dimension B, the greater slenderness and greater instability of the Burano Tower and the Mosul Minaret, when compared with the Tower of Pisa. But what is more important is that the movement of the first two towers at the commencement of the strengthening contracts were extremely active, while the movement of the Tower of Pisa is almost negligible, and can be detected only by very sophisticated instruments.

Figure 4.33 illustrates the design proposal submitted by Fondedile S.p.A. It was designed by a group formed by the author (F. Lizzi), and by E. Giangreco, J. Kerisel, and R. Morandi, with the collaboration of G. Carnevale and F. Grasso. The most significant aspect of the proposal is the fact that it is based on techniques and technologies (such as pali radice) which have been widely tested over thirty years of experience. Here the concept emphasized above

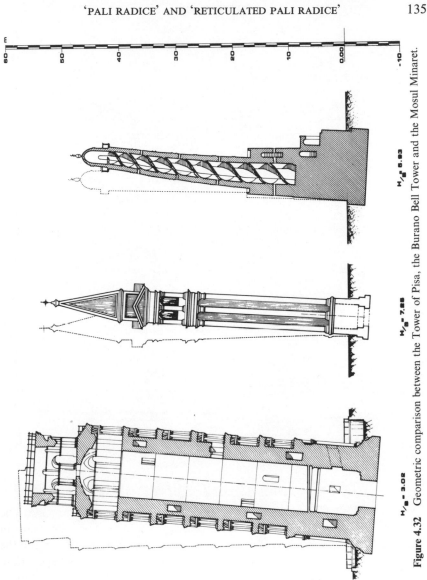

Figure 4.32 Geometric comparison between the Tower of Pisa, the Burano Bell Tower and the Mosul Minaret.

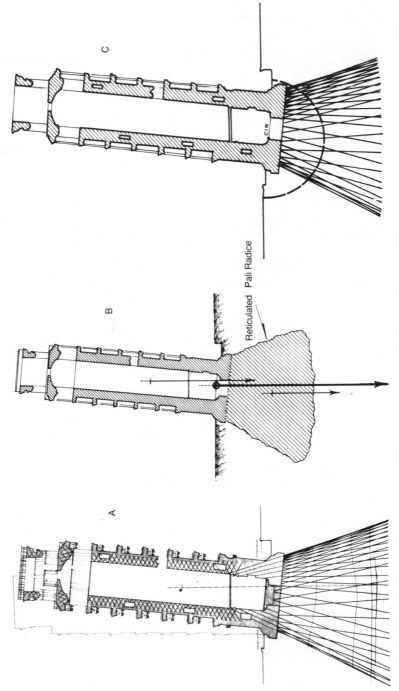

Figure 4.33 (*over*) The Fondedile S.p.A. project for the consolidation of the Tower of Pisa. (*A*) Scheme of the works; (*B*) gravimetric scheme; (*C*) the 'Knee-cap'; (*D*) the temporary strutting.

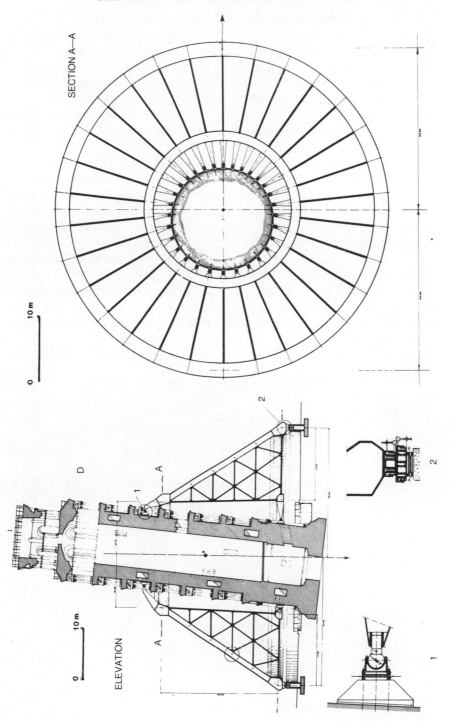

SECTION A—A

10 m

0

2

D

A

1

2

ELEVATION

10 m

0

A

1

must be recalled, in which a dense pali radice underpinning, in addition to being a true foundation, may also be considered as a soil–pile 'reinforced soil' basement, closely bonded to, and associated with, the upper structure, with the resultant overall centre of gravity very close to the ground surface.

There is, however, another way of looking at it, namely that proposed by Professor J. Kerisel: the 'root pile' underpinning makes a positive crossing of the critical sliding surface (a kind of 'knee-cap'), which, on the basis of the available data, may be supposed to be under the Tower.

4.8.3.1 Temporary strutting for the Tower of Pisa. An important part of the project concerns the temporary strutting. In fact, in addition to the project for consolidation, the International Invitation asked for a preliminary structure to be installed before the execution of any work, to obviate the risk of any movement, however minimal, of the tower during the phase of underpinning and strengthening.

The structure proposed by Fondedile is a reticular steel 'bell', having the form of a child's playpen, which surrounds the tower (Figures 4.33, 4.34). The reaction between the building and the propping structure is induced automatically, in case of emergency, by the reaction between the tower and two solid metal rings, belonging to the 'bell' and situated at different levels.

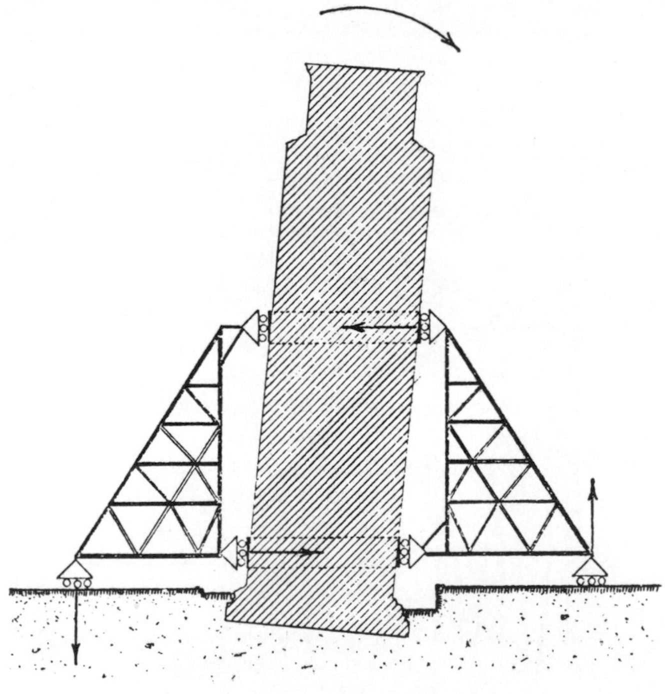

Figure 4.34 Layout of the temporary struts.

Under normal conditions, the two rings have simple contact with the tower, by means of bearings, which slide vertically along the surface of the tower; there is therefore, no transmission of stresses. In the case of emergency (a sudden increase in inclination), the tower reacts against the two rings, developing a stabilizing couple (only a couple), that prevents the tower from leaning further. Besides the advantages of not increasing the load on the soil, therefore the support offers immediate relief to the instability of the monument.

As well as the above-mentioned vertical bearings, the 'bell' is supplied with sliding horizontal bearings set on the outer base ring. They ensure that any variation of temperature gives rise only to an expansion (or contraction) of the steel structure as a whole; so, as the vertical as well as the horizontal bearings allow for such deformation, no action occurs against the tower. This insensitivity to temperature would exist also if the 'bell' were actually supporting the tower, because the reaction between the building and the 'bell' would not hamper the free expansion (or contraction) of both the vertical and horizontal bearings.

In short, the provisional safeguard structure proposed is characterized by the following essential points:

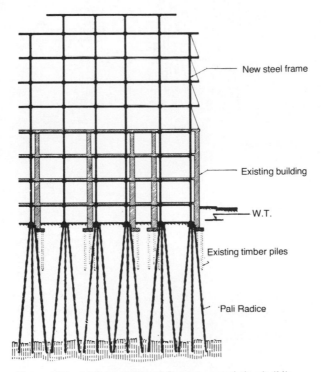

Figure 4.35 Adding additional floors to an existing building.

(1) No applied external forces.

(2) Quick response.

(3) Reaction in proportion to the degree of disturbance.

(4) Minimum stresses on the masonry and the soil.

(5) Insensitivity to variations in temperature.

(6) Possibility of reaction in all directions.

(7) Simplicity and safety. Automatic reaction.

(8) Reaction by means of a stabilizing couple and not by external forces. No

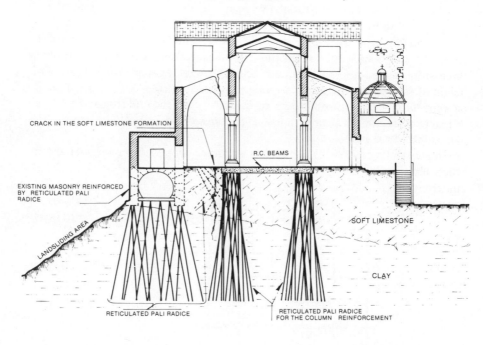

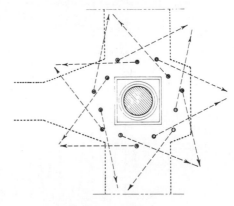

Figure 4.36 The Cathedral, Agrigento, Italy. (*Top*), consolidation works (*Bottom*) scheme, in plan, of the column underpinning.

increase in the load on the subsoil of the tower; but, on the contrary, an immediate decrease.

4.9 Special case histories

Some further case histories, described below, may illustrate better the adaptability of the pali radice systems.

4.9.1 Adding new storeys to an existing building in Naples

As shown in Figure 4.35, the existing building was originally built with only three storeys, besides the basement floor. It was necessary to increase the height of the building by five additional storeys; but the existing offices had to be kept in operation throughout the work.

The problem was solved by constructing foundation beams supported by pali radice in the basement floor, adjacent to, but neatly separated from, the existing foundations. Steel columns were then erected, starting from these beams and passing through the existing floors up to the roof. This work was quickly carried out in the evenings after office hours. The working site for the construction of the five additional storeys in steel frames was then installed on the roof of the old building, without hampering the activities of the offices below. Once the construction of the five additional storeys had been completed, it was possible to transfer the offices to the new floors and then demolish the old structures, incorporating the relative floors as part of the new structure.

4.9.2 The consolidation of an old monument in Sicily, in a landslide zone

The ancient Cathedral of Agrigento is founded on a soft limestone layer of varying thickness, resting on a clay formation. The limestone was fractured in all directions and a large crack had appeared in recent years along the entire length of the floor of the left aisle, and also outside the church. The clay, being subject to slow plastic deformation in the area of contact with limestone, and exposed to a marked landslide movement outside the monument, tended to slide down, leaving the upper limestone almost suspended in a cantilever state: hence the large crack and the differential settlement of the various parts of the church.

Owing to the extreme delicacy of the situation, the work was divided into two contracts separated by some years (Figures 4.36 and 4.37).

4.9.2.1 Prevention of landslide. The first phase of the work had the aim of stopping the landslide movement. The novelty of this first part of the work lies in the fact that the retaining structure (reticulated pali radice) was executed

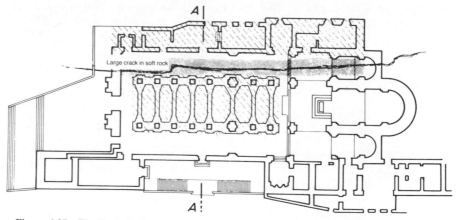

Figure 4.37 The Cathedral, Agrigento, Consolidation works. (*Top*) the entrance; (*bottom*) zone of intervention, in plan.

from a previously strengthened underground chamber. These reinforced structures became, therefore, the capping beam of the system. The underlying reticulated pali radice structure behaves like a retaining wall, the weight of which is supplied by the soil and the overlying masonry, while the resisting frame is formed by the pali radice, founded in the deep clay well beyond the unstable area. This reticulated pali radice wall also serves as underpinning for the external columns of the left aisle. Also included in this first phase of the

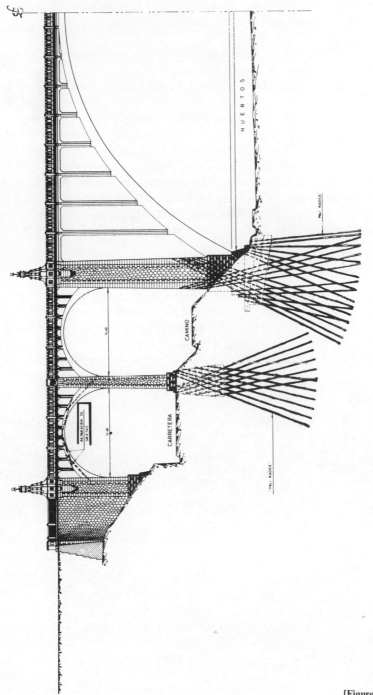

[Figure 4.38

work were the stitching and strengthening of the large fracture in the church floor, by means of cementitious pressure grouting.

4.9.2.2 Underpinning of the central nave. After some years during which the Cathedral was kept under observation, the effectiveness of the retaining wall was confirmed, so the second phase of the work, involving the underpinning of the central nave, was carried out. Figures 4.36 and 4.37 show the details of this underpinning. The characteristic layout of the piles in *doppia rigata* (double helical rows) must be mentioned. This arrangement is normally adopted for pali radice in the underpinning of towers and slender structures having limited cross-sections (see the case of Panorama Tower in Tokyo, section 4.6.4.) To improve the connection between the reinforcing structures the piles were linked below the floor level, by horizontal reinforced concrete beams. It was an essential feature of these works that they allowed complete protection of the environment, as well as of the church and the slope on which it is built.

4.9.3 The underpinning of an old bridge in Spain

In the late sixties, the Teruel bridge (Figure 4.38), subjected over a long period to foundation settlement and to some slow landslide phenomena, suddenly became an emergency that demanded prompt remedial measures. The underpinning by means of pali radice has proved very suitable for the gradual improvement of the stability of the abutments. At the same time, the dense

Figure 4.38 Teruel, Spain. The old bridge.

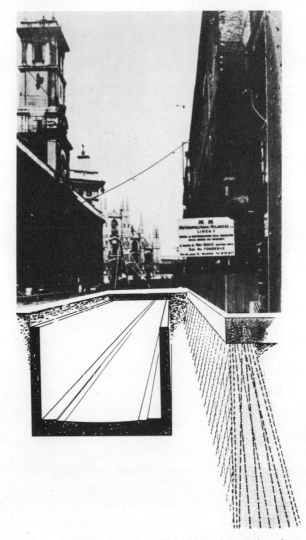

Figure 4.39   Milan, Italy. Consolidation of an old building close to the subway cutting to be excavated.

complex of piles required for the underpinning formed a reticulated structure well rooted in the soil. The scheme adopted, therefore, satisfies at the same time the exigencies of both underpinning and landslide prevention.

4.9.4   Another case of underpinning and RRP retaining wall— the Milan Underground

The construction of a cutting so close to an existing, and very important, historical building raised concern about the stability of the edifice. It was

Figure 4.40 Stabilization and partial straightening of a building in South Italy subject to differential settlement during its construction.

feared that the digging of the cutting, although carried out with much care, might produce relaxation of the subsoil, with dangerous consequences for the overall stability of the building. The edifice was already in a precarious condition, and therefore not in a position to withstand even a minimal alteration of equilbrium. This condition necessitated a precautionary reinforcing of the foundations, and their protection against possible relaxation caused by the excavation works. To these ends, the foundation masonry was locked into a reticulated pali radice structure, executed through the masonry and extended to well beneath the lower excavation level. In this way, the reticulated structure performs the twin functions of underpinning the edifice (to give it a stable new foundation), and acting as a gravity retaining wall.

4.9.5 Stabilization and partial straightening of leaning edifices by means of pali radice

There have been several cases in which the use of pali radice in two phases proved to be successful, first straightening and then stabilizing buildings leaning in consequence of differential settlement. This is the case illustrated in Figures 4.40–4.42 where the foundation structure of a huge building in South Italy is illustrated. A minor building is located adjacent to the main construction.

The soil, of very poor strength, was not suitable for the building, which started to settle during its construction, and when approaching the fifth floor reached the rate of about 20 mm per week on the north side, and a smaller amount on the south side. Consequently there was a marked progressive inclination towards the north end. Fortunately the upper structure was

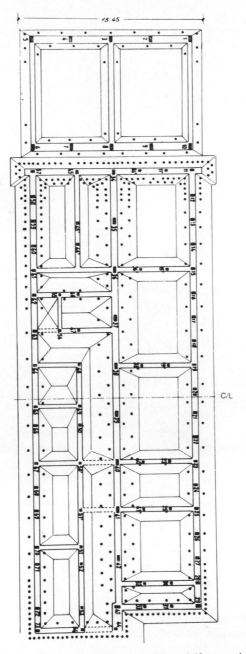

Figure 4.41 Plan of the foundation of the building of Figure 4.40, strengthened with pali radice.

F

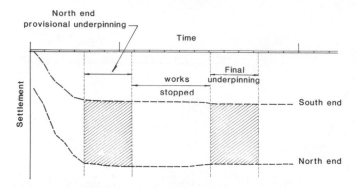

Figure 4.42 The leaning building of Figures 4.40–4.41. The settlement.

Figure 4.43 Santos, Brazil. Leaning buildings.

formed by a sturdy RC frame, which supported the serious deformation of the foundation level without any damage.

The contract, which had to be carried out quickly, was divided into two phases.

(i) In the first provisional phase, the north end only was underpinned with some 30 pali radice. This first phase was sufficient to stop this end moving. In the meantime the south end continued its slow settlement, with consequent partial straightening of the building.

(ii) After a period of six months the underpinning was resumed at both ends

Figure 4.44   York, UK. Bootham Bar—the underpinning.

LAYOUT OF BRIDGE PIERS AND ABUTMENTS

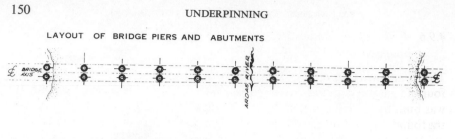

LAYOUT OF PIERS AND ROOT PILES

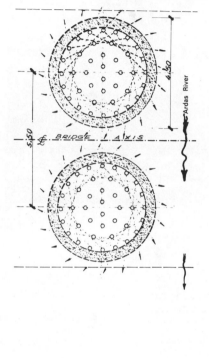

CROSS SECTION SHOWING PIER
AND ROOT PILES

Figure 4.45 Bridge on the River Ardas, Greece. Caisson foundations in difficult soil strengthened with pali radice.

(including additional piles at the north end to replace the 30 first-phase piles, which were no longer considered reliable) and carried out towards the centre of the building.

A similar job was carried out in Santos (Brazil) where, on account of the poor-quality subsoil some tall buildings were subject, after construction, to differential settlement (Figure 4.43).

*4.9.6 A case of foundation settlement owing to traffic—
Bootham Bar, York, U.K.*

This is an ancient monument of great historical importance. It is one of the four old gateways to the city of York, which was founded by the Romans. It was built by the Normans in the late Norman style in the twelfth century, on the foundations of the old Roman gate. The subsoil consists of silty sands. The work was necessary owing to serious foundation settlement, caused by vibrations induced by traffic and variations in the water table. The underpinning was carried out by 114 mm nominal diameter pali radice having a working load which, owing to the delicacy of the situation, was limited to only 10 tonnes, even though the test loads gave results above 50 tonnes without failure.

*4.9.7 Integration of an inadequate foundation in difficult soil—
the bridge on the River Ardas (Greece)*

This is a very long bridge of 10 spans. In the original project each pier was intended to be supported by a pair of RC caissons (4.50 m diameter). But, on account of a very difficult layer of weathered rock and boulders, the caissons could not be sunk to the fixed depth. The foundation was then completed by a network of pali radice, drilled through the caissons and extending in the subsoil like the 'roots' of a tree.

Bibliography

1. Lizzi, F. (1964). Root pattern piles underpinning. In *Symposium on Bearing Capacity of Piles*, Roorkee, India.
2. Zanetto, L. (1975). Aspetti tecnologici della costruzione dei micropali. In *6° Ciclo Annuale di Conferenze Dedicato ai Problemi di Meccanica dei Terreni*, Politecnico di Torino.
3. Lizzi, F. (1976). Pieu de fondation à 'cellule de précharge'. In *Revue 'Construction'*, June 1976, Paris.
4. Lizzi, F. (1977). Practical engineering in structurally complex formations. In *International Symposium on the 'Geotechnics of Structurally Complex Formations'*, Capri.
5. Lizzi, F. (1978). 'Reticulated root piles' to correct landslides. In *ASCE Convention*, October 1978, Chicago.
6. Lizzi, F. (1981). *The Static Restoration of Monuments*. S.A.G.E.P. Publisher, Genoa.

5 Micropiling

F. LIZZI

5.1 The diffusion of pali radice

When pali radice were first applied, early in the fifties, the regulations then in force for piling (in particular the German DIN), prescribed a diameter of not less than 40 cm for cast-in-place piles. This created problems when the palo radice was introduced as it was difficult to believe that a pile having a diameter of only 10 cm could bear loads of up to 30–40 tonnes or more. Fortunately a load test for values in the order of fifty tonnes involved only very modest expense, but supplied a convincing, definitive proof of the effectiveness of the system.

Pali radice made a name for itself in Italy and abroad, although in the USA there were some difficulties, as cast-in-place piles are not very popular in that country. After about twenty years (in the 70s), with the expiry of the first patents of pali radice, other similar piles were proposed. They were generically called 'micropiles'. Some of them in practice conform to the characteristics of pali radice, while others have been characterized as steel piles, cemented into the soil.

5.2 Steel pipe micropiles, cemented into the soil

It has been said before that the high bearing capacity of pali radice, compared with their small diameter, is their most favourable characteristic. But in a palo radice, as in any concrete pile, the bearing capacity has its limit in the crushing resistance of the cross-section of the shaft.

The tendency therefore arose to increase the steel reinforcement to obtain more resistant sections. Finally micropiling, consisting substantially of very heavy metal pipes (or structural beams), which could bear considerably higher loads were proposed. They are securely cemented into the subsoil.

One such micropile ('Tubfix') is illustrated in Figure 5.1, where the phases of construction are depicted.

(1) The drilling is carried out with any system suitable for the particular soil, including flushing of the spoil with bentonite mud.
(2) Once the fixed depth is reached, a steel pipe (reinforcement) is introduced.

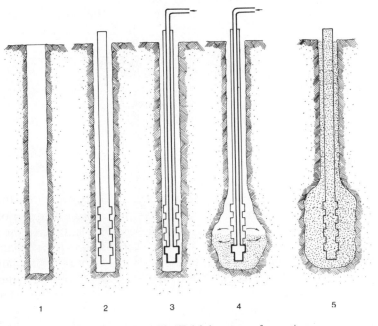

Figure 5.1 Micropile 'Tubfix'—stages of execution.

At its lower end, the pipe is provided with a series of holes protected by rubber sleeves (valves).

(3) Through these valves a cement mix is injected to fill the annular space between the hole and the pipe.

(4) Before the complete hardening of the mix, the lower valves are pressure grouted in order to form a kind of bulb. These special valves allow for some regrouting, if necessary.

The high strength of the steel offers an increased loadbearing capacity. On the other hand some other points must be considered.

(a) The adhesion between the pipe and the soil, in metal piles, is obtained by means of fluid cement grout, injected through the pipe. Obviously, the thin cement grout crust so obtained cannot ensure a very effective adhesion between steel and grout or in turn, between the grout and the soil. It is necessary to inject in the lowest part of the pipe, where it is possible to obtain higher pressures. The bearing capacity is obtained in practice by a kind of point bearing supplied by the deeper layers, instead of by skin friction as is the case with pali radice. Figure 5.2 shows two typical curves of load transfer from the pile to soil, for a palo radice and a metal micropile respectively. For this reason, the settlement of a metal micropile is in the order of some centimetres, and not millimetres as in the case with a palo radice. Figure 5.3 shows the load–settlement graphs for a

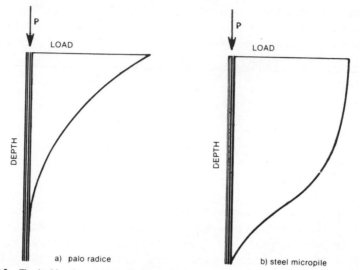

Figure 5.2   Typical load transfer curves from the pile to the soil, for a palo radice and for a steel micropile.

palo radice and a steel micropile. Both were constructed on the same site for a building that needed underpinning and a partial reconstruction with additional new structures. The same figure shows the characteristics of the subsoil. The diagrams demonstrate that metal micropiles, even if (owing to the resistance of the steel) they are potentially fit for supporting greater loads, cannot be used for underpinning, because of their high settlement. In fact, for the underpinning of the building, pali radice were used, while the steel micropiles could be used as foundations for the new structures.

(b) The risk of corrosion in steel pipe micropiles cannot be ignored.

(c) Buckling, which is not normally taken into consideration in the case of very slender piles, cannot be ignored in the case of steel micropiles which are heavily loaded and not adequately supported by the soil in the upper layers. For this reason, such piles are only installed vertically.

5.3 The preloading on micropiles

As shown above, the palo radice, if used carefully within well-defined, and not excessive, load limits, is able, with its prompt response, to give a definitive and rational support to foundations incurring problems. But, as has also been shown, the bearing capacity of a palo radice in the absolute sense can be very high, much higher than required: it cannot be utilized, because the corresponding settlements would not be acceptable for a building in distress. This has sometimes suggested the idea of preloading the micropiles, in order to make better use of their bearing capacity without exposing the building foundation to the corresponding greater settlement. This tendency must be decisively rejected (except, of course, for temporary use in particular cases) for the following reasons.

(a) The pre-loading introduces into both soil and building stresses which constitute a striking disturbance to the existing stability, the consequences of which can be very severe.

(b) The factor of safety of such an underpinning is no longer

$$\eta = \eta f + \eta p \quad \text{(see 4.4.4)}$$

but only

$$\eta = \eta p.$$

That is, it has to rely only on the bearing capacity of the piles, without the essential contribution of the existing subsoil.

(c) The building is transferred on to the piling, losing its contact with the soil. Freed from the building load, the soil sooner or later loses its high degree of consolidation, reached, sometimes, after centuries. Should the building settle again, pressing anew on the soil, this would create conditions leading to consequences more serious than were possible before the building was so imprudently detached.

(d) The connection between the piles and the structure has to be postponed until the time when the piling is complete, at least in part, and in a state of preloading. Instead of a progressive improvement of the piling, as in the case with normal pali radice underpinning, a long period of distress would occur, terminating only with the completion of the structures above ground level.

What could happen in the meantime to the building? Very probably. shoring or other supporting structures would be necessary.

5.4 Recent types of pali radice

The palo radice described previously has, with time, developed from its original form. This has allowed better adaptation to the demands of specific problems, always remembering, however, the fundamental principles which inspired its creation.

Among these developed forms, the recently patented 'pali radice a base espansa' (root pile with expanded base) must be mentioned. The innovation consists basically of a vacuum 'cell' at the toe of the reinforcement, made of a resistant deformable cell, which remains empty during the grouting of the pile (by the usual system of a tremie pipe). After hardening of the grout, a neat cement grout mix is injected into the cell through a grout pipe. As indicated in the figure, a single steel pipe can generally be used for reinforcement as well as grouting. The cavity allows the formation of a fluid 'bubble' which, breaking the walls of the cell produces a uniform pressure on the soil and creates a base

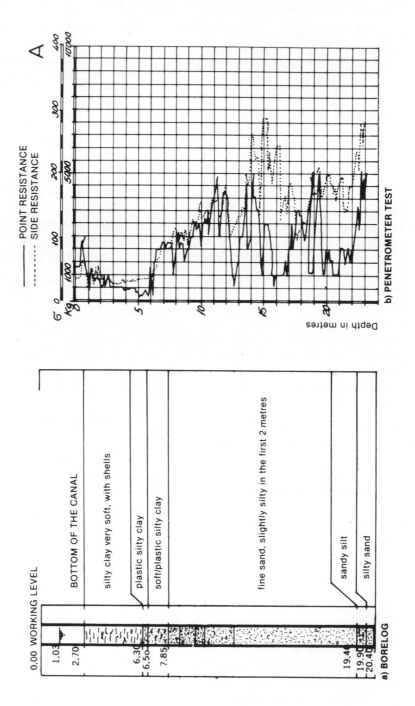

a) BORELOG

b) PENETROMETER TEST

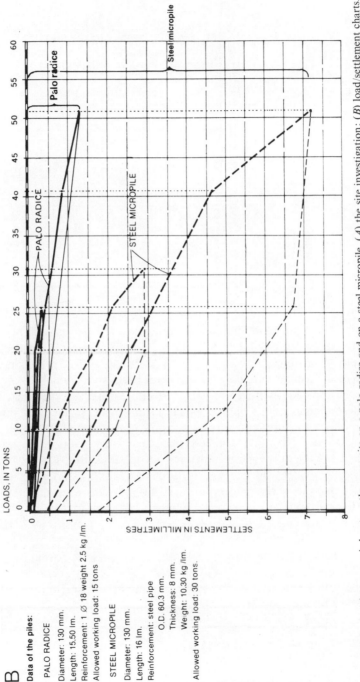

Figure 5.3 Load tests carried out on the same site on a palo radice and on a steel micropile. (*A*) the site investigation; (*B*) load/settlement charts.

B

Data of the piles:

PALO RADICE

Diameter: 130 mm.

Length: 15.50 lm.

Reinforcement: 1 Ø 18 weight 2.5 kg /lm.

Allowed working load: 15 tons

STEEL MICROPILE

Diameter: 130 mm.

Length: 16 lm.

Reinforcement: steel pipe

    O.D. 60.3 mm.

    Thickness: 8 mm.

    Weight: 10.30 kg /lm.

Allowed working load: 30 tons.

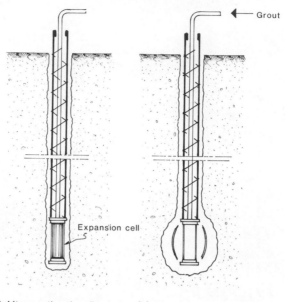

(a) After casting the pile shaft   (b) After injection in the cell

Figure 5.4   The palo radice with expanded base.

bulb. This applies in any type of soil, whatever its permeability.

In outline, this system recalls the procedure of injection in steel micropiles using valved pipes. However it is substantially different, because the grout injected, instead of going through rubber valves which allow a limited, irregular passage with a noticeable loss of pressure, is first collected in the cell, where it forms a fluid 'bubble' which acts on a wide surface (the side surface of the cell) with full pressure (which can be controlled at the surface). Also, as stated above, the system can be applied in any soil, not only the granular ones, which are the only types suitable for normal injection. The formation of this 'bulb' provides an increase in end bearing resistance to the essential characteristic of the palo radice, i.e., its high skin friction.

The palo radice with expanded base is also used in those situations where the pile must react to tension as well as compression—as is the case, for instance, with towers for electricity transmission lines.

In the most recent form of pali radice, the bars are covered with a special, very thin layer of sand–resin mortar, after a patented procedure. This treatment is intended to increase the skin friction and supply an additional protection against corrosion.

5.5 Micropiles for new foundations in difficult soils

Conventional foundation piles, especially large-diameter piles cannot be drilled easily in any soil. Sometimes the presence of boulders, old foundations

Figure 5.5 Reticulated root pile foundation, in difficult soil, for a tall viaduct in Naples, Italy.

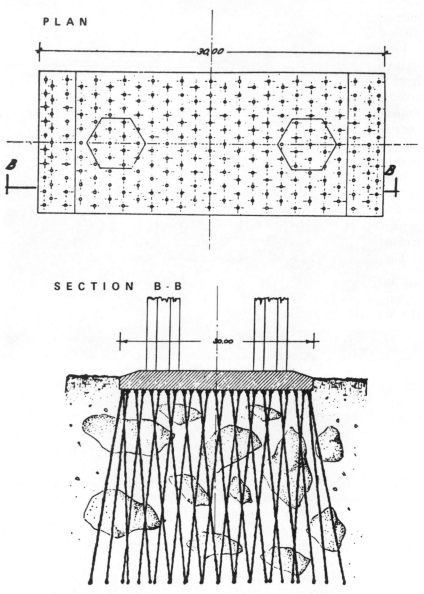

Figure 5.6   Scheme of the foundation for the viaduct of Figure 5.5.

or other obstruction in the subsoil makes the drilling of such piles difficult or impossible. But the penetration of, for example, large boulders present in the subsoil to make way for large-diameter concrete piles seems illogical, due to the waste of time and energy involved. It would usually be much more convenient to substitute for the large-diameter piles an adequate number of micropiles, which on account of their more flexible technology, can be more easily drilled through any obstruction.

Figures 5.5 and 5.6 illustrate the foundation of a very high modern highway viaduct. The ground comprised old quarry fill, including large boulders, so the large diameter piles adopted along the other sections of the same highway could not be constructed in this particular section. Instead, a micropile foundation proved to be very efficient and easily executed. The boulders were penetrated without any difficulty, so becoming part of the foundation. As in the case of landslides, once reinforced with root piles, the boulders became a positive element instead of a negative one.

It is worth noting the pattern adopted for the piling: it is a reticulated pali radice scheme, in which the loadbearing capacity of the single piles is increased by a 'group effect'—owing to the density of the piles (one per square metre approximately)—and by a 'network effect', owing to their mutual inclinations.

The foundation can therefore be considered from two aspects:

(a) As a normal pile foundation relying on the loadbearing capacity of the single pile. This was the basis of the design, derived from load tests.
(b) As a 'reinforced soil foundation', where all the structure (piles, soil, boulders etc.) is contributing to the loadbearing capacity of the foundation. This is a result of the reinforcement introduced by the piles, which connect and, as it were, 'integrate' the different ground conditions.

The loadbearing capacity of the 'reinforced soil' according to this second viewpoint is greater than the loadbearing capacity of the total piles acting individually as in (a). This was clearly demonstrated in practice, when the settlement of the foundation (once of the viaduct had been completed) gave results of practically zero, instead of the few millimetres that could be expected after the load tests carried out on single piles.

This result looks much more important than the problem that brought it about. It demonstrates once more that the modern tendency to increase more and more the diameter of foundation piles, in order for them to support greater loads in the range of thousands of tonnes, is perhaps a mistake. Such piles, spaced widely, are generally very long—sometimes 50 metres or more— because they have to rely essentially on the deep strata, neglecting (at least in terms of safety) the possible contribution of the upper layers of soil. A denser pattern of smaller-diameter piles (not necessarily micropiles), however, of not exaggerated length, is probably more suitable for involving the collaboration of the soil, so returning to it its essential role as principal support of any man-made construction.

6 The Pynford underpinning method

J.F.S PRYKE

6.1 Introduction

This chapter seeks to describe the Pynford stooling method of underpinning by reference to practical examples. As the years pass an ever widening range of civil engineering techniques are invented and refined, and then gradually become part of the engineer's 'toolkit'. This applies as much to underpinning, strengthening and shoring techniques as to other branches of civil engineering. Thus often more than one effective solution to a problem is available (references 1, 2). The choice is then determined by cost. It is important to compare the total cost to a client of different methods. Thus, lintel beams may be inserted in brick or stone masonry walls by a number of methods (reference 3) and the amount and cost of temporary shoring and of repairing incidental damage to the building will vary depending upon the method chosen, the particular location of the beam in the building, the quality of the finishes, and whether or not it is necessary to replace them. The cost at any particular time will also depend upon the workload and location of particular specialists in relation to the general contractor using older and more widely understood and practised methods. The total cost to the client is the sum of the cost of the prime construction, that is the lintel with associated shoring, and of the secondary work, that is the necessary incidental repairs and reinstatement.

The scene is continually changing as methods evolve and new ones are introduced. For example, Pynford reduced the manhours required to construct identical beam and pier underpinning schemes by a factor of three between 1947 and 1970. The process continues and the cost to the client has continued to fall in real terms since then, due partly to continuing innovation and partly due to the growth in number of specialist contractors in the UK since 1970.

It should also be noted that this chapter is primarily about the use of the Pynford stooling method to construct cast-in-situ RC Pynford beams in existing loadbearing masonry walls, of either stone or brick. A wide range of problems, arising from the failure of foundations of masonry structures or from the need to alter them, and that were solved safely and effectively using Pynford beams, are described to explain the method and encourage innovative applications by the reader. Thus the chapter discusses underpinning

162

at high level as well as at foundation level. If an RC beam or slab in a masonry wall or pier can assist in the solution of a problem, then it can be constructed safely using the method. In the years from 1940 to 1984, when this chapter was written, no wall or has been encountered by Pynford in which beams could not be safely constructed using the techniques which will be described in this chapter.

The reader is not advised to read this chapter without first reading the Preface to this book and Chapter 1, which emphasize the advantage of acquiring a basic knowledge of civil, structural and geotechnical engineering theory and practice before seeking to develop the specialist skills required to understand older structures and to design and supervise underpinning. No book can be a substitute for experience, but perhaps careful reading can help the newcomer to underpinning problems to approach them with more confidence, and the experienced engineer to extend and develop his or her thinking.

Understanding the structure to be underpinned is crucial. The loadbearing structures of all Ancient building, to use Thorburn's categories, and of many Recent and Modern ones, are constructed with the traditional 'craft' materials, that is stone, brick and mortar to carry compressive loads, and timber and small amounts of iron used as ties and connectors, where tensile and bending strength are required. Materials were laboriously hand-crafted before steam power spread in the mid-19th century, and were thus expensive, and often re-used. Buildings were also continuously changed and adapted as one generation of owners succeeded another. In some cases too many changes, each small and safe in itself, accumulate to bring the old buildings near collapse and make them difficult to alter. Where walls or piers are seriously overstressed, the building must be strengthened temporarily before it can be altered. The engineer must be especially wary when evidence of alteration exists. Chapter 1 emphasizes the causes of stress concentration, especially in stone masonry buildings.

The engineer must understand how a building and the supporting soil 'work' to carry the imposed loads. He should have a three-dimensional stress model in his mind and consider at all stages of the work the effects upon this stress model. Amongst others, Heyman has done valuable work in understanding the engineering of masonry, and his book *The Masonry Arch* (1982) (reference 4) is strongly recommended to engineers unfamiliar with his work.

Force (stress × area) causes deformation (strain), and the engineer should also seek to imagine the deformations under load of his stress model and particularly the effect of widely differing material moduli. For example, a flexible beam under a stiff brick wall will not carry a uniform load. Work on composite action such as that by Wood (references 5, 6) highlights the enormous differences between theory and reality that can occur. There is a major discontinuity in both material strength and potential deformation when building loads pass into the supporting subsoil. Foundations are designed to

reduce the high stresses in the building materials to the lower stresses that the
subsoil can safely support, to reduce subsoil movement and consequent
deformation of the structure to acceptable levels, and to reduce cracks, if any,
to acceptable sizes.

It is now practicable and economical to introduce forces into a building of
the same order of magnitude as the building weight using hydraulic jacks.
Thus, major modification of the stress patterns in a building can be made, or
the anticipated deformation of the new permanent underpinning structures or
temporary shoring can be cancelled out to maintain existing stress patterns. A
detailed discussion of shoring and jacking falls outside the scope of this
chapter and book.

Underpinning cannot be sensibly conceived or safely achieved without
considering in detail how it is to be done. This puts engineers at a disadvantage
in countries such as the UK, where the contractual arrangements tend to
separate the designer from the contractor, and where the system can impose a
cost penalty on designers who seek to control the method of working after a
contract has been let. At the commencement of a project the designer must
clearly define the objective of the work and select in broad principle the
preferred and most economical solution, perhaps after negotiation with a
number of specialists. Then, once the team is chosen, the detailing should take
account of the techniques to be used and of the sequence of working.

Finally, it should be remembered at all times that buildings have always
been assembled by people, often working in cold and uncomfortable
circumstances, subject in all ages to the same need to survive and earn a living
that drives us today, tempted to skimp and take 'short cuts' just as we are,
getting the same thrill of achievement which rewards us when the task is
completed. Those who have little interest in and respect for what our forebears
achieved should not seek to underpin and adapt their work to our needs.

6.2 Design

The sizes of completed permanent underpinning work will be checked for
stress and deformation using the design aids and Codes of Practice, familiar to
structural and geotechnical engineers, and normal safety factors. However,
the designer should also check stresses and, where there is doubt, deformations, at all stages of the work. It should be assumed that at any stage the
work may stop, and no sequence of operations should commence that it is not
safe to delay for an extended period at some intermediate stage. Work can be
delayed by many factors outside the control of the designer, such as weather,
accidents to personnel, materials failing to meet specifications or legal
injunctions applied for by neighbours. At all stages it should be possible to
make the work safe with a minimum of further work. For example, a small
hole cut for a needle can quickly be filled in or wedged up if the hole reveals an

unexpectedly weak wall that cannot easily be supported without further work, and the necessary materials for such temporary packing should be available on site before the hole is cut.

The safety factors used when designing components should take account of their importance and contribution to overall safety. There is ample precedent for such an approach. For example, the ratio of working loads to failure loads of chains and cables varies depending upon the use, with the smallest percentage, and thus highest safety factors, being set when people are being carried. Thus if the removal of a member could lead to a major collapse of part of a building, then that member must either be made extra strong or, if possible, the sequence of operations should be revised to avoid the need for the critical member or operation. Design calculations are based on sometimes highly idealized models of structural behaviour. Codes of Practice which incorporate safety factors give satisfactory results for new work, but the stress distribution assumptions should be used with caution when designing underpinning and shoring. There are, of course, limits to the load that individual members may carry that can easily be identified. A hard spot in a stone masonry column will not be called upon to carry more than the total load on that column. A part of a foundation will never need to carry more than the whole building weight. It is helpful in this context to think of all the structure beneath a particular level as the 'foundation' for all that is above that level. Such exaggerations would overestimate the maximum, but they help to create a realistic attitude to temporary works.

In very rigid structures, such as brick buildings, constructed with strong bricks and mortar, small deflections can dramatically alter the load pattern and increase stresses by factors of two or more. When the 2500-tonne Sjommanshjemmet in Norway was moved and raised in 1983 (reference 7) it was carried on 42 jacks linked in ten operating groups. Increasing the pressure from the average working pressure of 365 bars to about 540 bars raised the building about 6 mm above the jack group being operated without visible sign of distress or cracking in the building and, in some cases, halved the pressure in adjoining jack groups up to 5 m distant. The only way to be certain of the load in support members in a building is to measure it. If the forces in permanent or temporary support members are critical they should be applied by jacks and the pressure measured. This is particularly important if there is a critical maximum force that must not be exceeded.

Conventional calculations for the settlement of supports under continuous beams reveal dramatic changes in stress when small deformations occur. It is usually assumed that these changes do not occur, without detriment to the performance of most structures. However, large load changes do occur and must be designed for, particularly in the intermediate stages of projects for underpinning rigid buildings. Underpinning is potentially dangerous and labour intensive. Material costs are usually small in relation to total costs. The cost of increasing the strength of critical members is small in relation to overall costs. It dramatically reduces risk, and may even contribute to overall economy by increasing confidence on site, and thus the speed at which the work can be completed.

   Some simple rules and checks are also helpful when devising schemes for underpinning and alterations. The designer should first consider what would have been designed to fulfil the need if the building were being newly constructed. For example, it might be decided that a house on a shallow strip foundation that is subsiding due to a patch of poor ground beneath part of the foundation would have remained stable if the original foundation had been a frame of ground beams supported by mass concrete piers of different depths to suit the changes in level of the stable stratum. One should treat with considerable suspicion a remedial underpinning proposal very different from this in concept and anticipated performance. Widening the shallow foundation would be much less likely to succeed than deepening it. Increasing the foundation depth beneath those walls where the poor ground was deeper than the shallow foundations could be achieved by traditional continuous underpinning, beam and pier underpinning, beam and pile underpinning, or micropiling without a ground beam (reference 8) and the choice will be governed by overall cost. Another general rule is that the most fragile or doubtful areas of the structure are best tackled early in the project. A building usually has much strength added by 'non-loadbearing' partitions and other 'non-structural' members such as door and window frames or infill panels. This is well known but the magnitude of the effect is often underestimated. Strain gauges fixed in the steel frame of the Air Ministry building in Whitehall in the early 1960s revealed stress levels between 10% and 20% of those designed for (reference 9), a finding which triggered off much of the work on composite action since that date. By starting with the weakest areas one maintains these secondary load paths and increases safety factors, although designers should not take account of the benefit. A corollary of this is that demolishing 'non-loadbearing' elements in an old building can shed load back on to deteriorated or modified main loadbearing walls and make them unsafe. Emergency work was required on a major central London site recently for just this reason.

   Any alteration or underpinning project will require parts of the structure to be undermined or cut away. Most brick or masonry walls are designed either to avoid excessive slenderness, or to keep out the weather, or both, and the compressive strength at foundation level may exceed the weight of a building by a factor of ten or more. Thus holes can be cut through the foundations to remove a significant portion of the wall without any risk of crushing failure. This is not always the case, particularly where brick- or ashlar-faced walls have weak cores. Thorburn suggests grouting as one method of strengthening a wall before underpinning. Another solution is to clamp the wall with plates or timbers on either side bolted together, thus changing the structural condition from unconfined to triaxial compression, and raising the strength.

A third solution is to bond in ties using epoxy resin or cement grout; epoxies set faster and bond better to clean stone or brick surfaces, but they are more expensive. A fourth solution for highly stressed walls or piers is to relieve the load before cutting away, usually by propping floors or beams carrying load on to the pier or wall. It is most important to appreciate that if the whole load imposed upon a pier is to be relieved, then all the beams carrying load to the pier above working level must be independently propped, unless very careful calculations are made of the upward support that the beam can give acting as a cantilever tailed down by the floor dead load only. Such calculations may indicate that some of the beams at highest level may not need to be propped.

A final and most important rule is that great care must be taken when excavating around or beside existing foundations to ensure that removal of lateral restraint does not weaken the soil beneath the foundations and initiate subsidence or collapse.

6.3 The Pynford underpinning method

To construct a beam in a loadbearing wall a horizontal slot must be formed in the wall into which the beam is either placed in one piece or assembled in segments which are then joined together. 'Beam slots' cannot be simply cut without supporting the wall above as it will collapse. If the beam is to be placed in one piece, which would be the case if a steel 'I' section were chosen, the wall above is usually supported by needles, that is short beams projecting through holes cut in the wall above the beam slot and propped on either side (Figure 6.1). Thus the whole wall load is carried on narrow sections of packing or wedging on top of the needles which would typically be placed at 1 m to 1.5 m centres, raising the local peak crushing stresses by a factor of between 5 and 20 if the load is equally divided by careful wedging, and by even more if it is not. The needles may bend under the load and the props on either side of the walls will rest on independent pads or a bearer beam, in turn supported on unloaded ground or even on paving or floors propped from level to level. Small wonder that some cracking and 'settling down' is expected when such work is carried out. Supplying, fixing and removing needles will be fairly expensive even if the beam is near ground level, and the wall will be damaged by holes cut above beam level which ultimately have to be rebuilt. However, the beam will be a cheap length of RSJ.

Alternative solutions, such as forming the beam in sections subsequently fixed together, result in dearer beam construction but avoid the needling and repair work above beam level (reference 3). Holes can be cut at intervals and segments placed in position along the line of the beam. The segments will need to be accurately bedded down and then packed or pinned up above. The segments may be of precast concrete, placed with small gaps between them which are packed prior to threading tendons and post-tensioning the blocks to

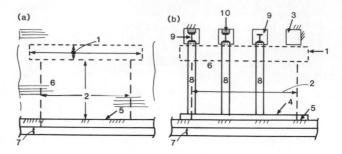

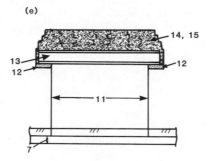

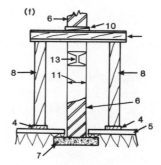

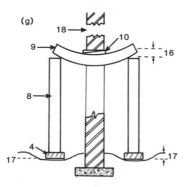

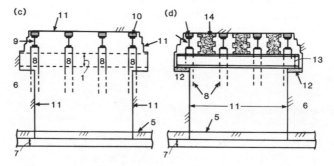

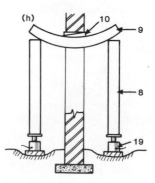

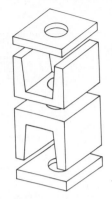

Figure 6.2   The Pynford Stool—inventor Fordham Pryke.

form a prestressed concrete beam, or they may be steel sections assembled and pinned in place in sequence and bolted together. Segmental beams have not proved very effective commercially, perhaps mainly because there is not a large market for a standard product, and thus each beam needs to be individually designed and produced.

The Pynford beam system is similar to the segmental beam in many respects. The wall loads are supported along the line of the beam slot by stools which are assembled from a small number of standard parts which can be manufactured in large numbers. The original Pynford stool (Figure 6.2) was assembled from a pair of standard precast RC U-blocks and two or more precast RC plates, bedded together with mortar joints. By adding plates in the middle, the depth of the stool can be varied to match the required depths of beam. A variety of different stool designs are now used, the main difference being that the U-blocks and centre plate(s) are replaced by some form of steel strut. These stools are built into holes about 0.3 m wide cut in the wall, generally at 0.9 m centre to centre. The gap over the stool is then pinned up with a strong earth damp mortar, 1 : 1 portland cement and sharp sand, well rammed in. The stool replaces the support given by the brickwork to be cut away. When the mortar and pinning up has hardened the brickwork between the stools is cut away leaving the wall load to be transferred across the beam slot by the stools (Figure 6.3).

The beam is completed by threading reinforcement through and alongside

---

Figure 6.1   Needling. 1, dotted outlines of beam to be inserted; 2, proposed new opening; 3, holes cut through wall *above* new supporting beam; 4, temporary bearer plate on existing solid floor; 5, existing solid floor; 6, wall in which opening is required; 7, foundation; 8, temporary props supported by 4; 9, temporary needle beams; 10, temporary wedging on needles; 11, wall cut away to provide space for the new beam and to form the required opening; 12, padstones to support new beam; 13, new beam; 14, new brickwork built in and pinned up between needles; 15 needles and props removed and brickwork and pinning up completed; 16, needle may bend; 17, prop foundation may sink; 18, crack; 19, jacks preload shoring and cancel out deflections thus preventing distortion of structure being underpinned.

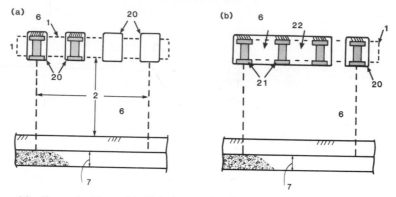

Figure 6.3 Key as for Figure 6.1. 20, holes cut *along line* of required beam for Pynford stools; 21, Pynford stools built into holes and pinned up; 22, brickwork between stools cut away to form *beam slot.*

the stools, attaching shear reinforcement, which is generally assembled from pairs of U-shaped bars, placing formwork on either side of the wall, concreting to within about 50 mm of the underside of the wall above, and finally pinning up between the stools (Figure 6.4). The stools are cast into the beam, which thus directly carries the load on them without a second load transfer sequence of operations when the supporting wall is cut away beneath the beam to form the opening which the beam will have been designed to bridge.

Stresses are raised by a factor of about 4 immediately above and below the stools but will be virtually unaltered more than 0.6 m above and below the beam slots. Settlement caused by transferring the building load to the stools is negligible. It is primarily that due to direct compression of the stool assembly, as the method prevents the brickwork from loosening before the stools are pinned up in position.

The stooling method is successful because it is easily adapted to the endless variety of beam depths and widths required in practice. Nibs and piers can be underpinned by placing extra stools beneath them and widening the beam and intersections and corners can easily be arranged thus allowing frameworks of beams to be constructed at no more cost per metre run than simple straight lintels. In thicker walls top and bottom plates can be enlarged, and in very thick walls two or more stools can be placed side by side to support the full width of the wall. If the wall is weak or crumbling, stools can be placed at closer centres and/or the top and bottom plates can be made wider to reduce the stress raising factor to two or less. In very thick walls the first stools can be pinned in position before the full width of the wall is cut away. The work can be carried out from one side of a wall, thus reducing disturbance to a minimum, and in masonry of a reasonable quality the beams may be narrower than the wall, leaving a protective skin of brickwork or stonework undisturbed in order to reduce disturbance and reinstatement costs (Figure 6.5). When used for underpinning foundations, Pynford beams are usually positioned just below dpc level (Figure 6.6). If the foundations are very

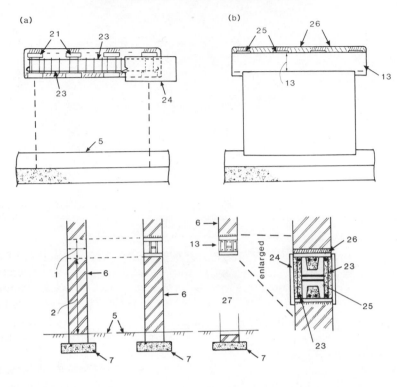

SECTION   SECTION

Figure 6.4 Key as for Figures 6.1, 6.3. 23, reinforcement threaded through and around stools and shear reinforcement placed; 24, formwork fixed on either side of the wall; 25, concrete poured around stools and reinforcement to form RC beam; 26, gap above beam and between stools pinned up; 27, wall cut away to form opening after concrete has hardened.

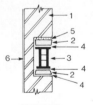

SECTION

Figure 6.5 The 'beam slot' does not occupy the full width of the wall. 1, wall; 2, concrete plates; 3, steel Pynford stool; 4, mortar joints; 5, pinning up; 6, surface to remain undisturbed.

shallow there will be insufficient sound construction beneath the stools to distribute the load on then, and precast or cast-in-situ RC pads are then used bearing directly on the ground, which will have already been consolidated by the building load (Figure 6.7).

The fact that the stooling system maintains the existing load paths and stress patterns until the new structure is complete is a very important feature

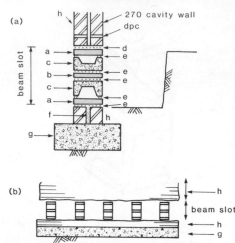

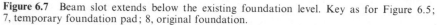

Figure 6.6 (a) Pynford stool assembly in beam slot. (b) Pynford stools at 900 c/c a, RC top and bottom plates; b, optional centre plates to increase beam depth; c, RC U-blocks; d, pinning up; e, mortar beds; f, cavity filled; g, concrete foundation; h, brickwork above and below beam.

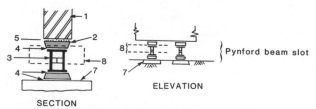

Figure 6.7 Beam slot extends below the existing foundation level. Key as for Figure 6.5; 7, temporary foundation pad; 8, original foundation.

and enables the engineer to guarantee that the parts being supported will be virtually undisturbed by the work.

A number of illustrated case studies selected from Pynford archives follow to illustrate the use of the method in practice. They cover a range of problems chosen to illustrate the versatility of the method. No doubt the reader will be able to imagine others, for if an RC beam can be inserted in a loadbearing masonry wall with advantage as part of a solution to a problem, then the beam can be constructed at a reasonable cost with minimal disturbance using the Pynford stooling method.

6.4 Case studies

Case Study no. 1: Underpinning at Imperial College, London

A good example of the use of the stooling method of constructing RC beams as part of a major underpinning project was the work at Imperial College, London. Imperial College was constructed, with heavy loadbearing brick

Figure 6.8

walls, in the 19th century as a major centre for teaching and research in science and engineering (Figure 6.8). The College was completely reconstructed in the late 1950s and the first stage was to excavate a very deep basement at the rear of the existing buildings. Away from the building the basement excavation was sheeted with contiguous bored pile walls to minimize vibration and noise, but the very heavy surcharge loads generated by the building persuaded the engineers to underpin the main building walls directly. On the left of Figure 6.8 it will be noted that the walls divide into a series of heavily loaded piers each approximately 1 m thick × 2 m wide. In the centre right of the picture the staircase tower wall is seen to be over 35 m high, with brick work at the base 560 mm thick. The most heavily loaded pier carried approximately 4000 kN and the staircase wall loading was approximately 250 kN/m. The depth of the basement excavation was required to 9 m below existing basement floor level and the walls were underpinned to a depth of 11 m using hand excavation methods. The subsoil was 6 m of river terrace gravel overlying London Clay, and the water table stood at approximately 2 m below basement floor level.

The underpinning wall required to retain the site beneath the building was formed in pits approximately 3 m² on plan, and the Pynford stooling method was used to construct a strong horizontal beam just below existing basement level to distribute the wall loads uniformly over approximately 3 m length of foundation on either side of the primary underpinning piers, which were

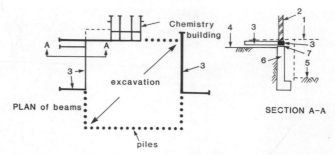

Figure 6.9 Imperial College. 1, basement level; 2, wall to be underpinned; 3, Pynford beam; 4, existing foundation; 5, bottom of excavation; 6, underpinning; 7, pinning up beneath beam.

positioned at about 8 m centres, that is beneath the main loadbearing piers of the lecture room block wall, and at a similar spacing along the staircase wall and the low rise link block (Figure 6.9) between these sections. Return beams at corners adjoining the work and inside the building beneath crosswalls carried the loads of these walls partly away from and partly on to the top of the underpinning, thus both relieving heavy surcharge loads close to, and tieing back the top of, the underpinning.

The beam was reinforced with a roughly equal area of steel rods top and bottom as the moments that are generated when the main piers are constructed reverse when the panels between them are excavated to complete the underpinning. This is typical of beam and pier underpinning schemes, that is, the beams act as temporary shoring to carry the building loads over the underpinning excavations using the existing foundations on either side as temporary support, and the moments then reverse when the excavations are concreted and pinned up and the ground between either continues to sink or is excavated, as in this case, to complete the underpinning.

When the work was complete the beam was continuously supported in this case and thus the function of the beam is entirely one of temporary support during the excavations. A simple approach to the design was made. A point of contraflexure was assumed at mid-point of the support zone, thus allowing the moments to be easily calculated for the initial condition. Simple continuous beam theory was used to check the bending moments after the main piers had been constructed. The excavation sequence was controlled so that no two piers closer than 16 m apart were excavated at one time.

The main underpinning piers were reinforced and designed to be strutted from a central dumpling except in the corners where diagonal strutting was used between the penultimate piers (see Figure 6.25).

It is clearly vital that the excavation technique used should eliminate the loss of ground during excavation, and that the excavations should be closely and securely timbered. This is referred to later.

Figure 6.10 shows an early stage in the beam construction. A series of holes

Figure 6.10

Figure 6.11

have been cut beneath the staircase walls, and Pynford stools built in. They bear upon the existing foundation and are assembled with precast concrete plates above and below a steel strut comprising six legs welded into top and bottom steel plates with bracing at intervals. Note the pinning up above the stool assembly. The far right stool has not been pinned up. Clearly the brickwork remaining between the stools could not carry the full wall load. The sequence in which the stools are fixed is arranged so that there is always ample support for the wall. In this case every fourth stool was fixed in the first phase of the stooling sequence followed by intermediate stools. At this stage every other stool would have been inserted and pinned up to carry a full load. The stool fixing sequence is then repeated following a similar sequence. Thus at no time is more than approximately 12% of the wall support cut away. Figure 6.11 shows reinforcement fixed between the stools and the formwork partially constructed. Note that the beam is slightly wider than the wall and that the shear reinforcement is closely spaced on either side of the stool, but that there are no stirrups in the stool position. The stool construction provides adequate shear reinforcement as the vertical legs are welded into top and bottom steel plates to form continuous shear loops.

It will be noted that there is ample space for pouring concrete between the stools and beside them, and that the arrangement of the top bars is designed to allow for adequate concrete compaction using poker vibrators. Figure 6.12 shows the beam concreted. The stools can clearly be seen projecting above the

Figure 6.12

Figure 6.13

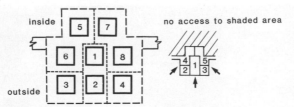

Figure 6.14 (Left) Plan of brick pier showing fixing sequence for Pynford stools. (Right) Plan of pier showing five stages in which beam slot was cut out. Arrows show access positions.

upper surface of the concrete. To complete the beam construction the gaps between the stools will be pinned up. Figure 6.13 shows the base of a main pier bearing upon a main concrete foundation 1.5 m deep. The pier was underpinned with a group of 8 stools, and the stool strength and fixing pattern was designed to ensure that the pier was adequately supported at all times (Figure 6.14). Figures 6.15 and 6.16 show the stooling-up sequence well advanced. Four stools have been fixed and the workman is cutting away for the fifth and sixth stools. It will be evident that the beam depth must be chosen to allow adequate working space. The nominal beam depth was 675 mm and the overall beam slot was 825 mm, that is the equivalent of 11 courses of brickwork. Note the two-pin stool beside the shovel, which has yet to be

Figure 6.15

Figure 6.16

Figure 6.17

Figure 6.18

Figure 6.19

Figure 6.20

pinned up to carry the light infill panel. These figures emphasize the dangers inherent in underpinning operations and the importance of properly designing the stools and the stooling sequence. Figure 6.17 shows the stooling sequence complete and the working area tidied in preparation for fixing the reinforcement. The simplicity of the method and the absence of needles and shoring enables tidy working and assists the supervisor to ensure a high standard of workmanship and safety. In Figure 6.18 the reinforcement has been partially fixed. Reinforcing bars and shear reinforcement have been placed and tied at the rear, and stirrups are being placed in position for the front reinforcement. Clearly, the main bars must be threaded into position by sliding in and working backwards and forwards in some cases. Thus, careful detailing is essential. It is important to ensure that bars are not bent into

Figure 6.21

position as there is a danger that the workman may use the steel stools for this purpose thus applying lateral leverage and possibly dislodging them. Figure 6.19 shows the completed beam with the gaps between the stools being pinned up. In Figure 6.20 reinforcement is being fixed at a beam intersection. The importance of good detailing if the work on site is to proceed with minimum difficulty will be readily appreciated. Figure 6.21 shows the formwork in place prior to concreting the framework of beams beneath the main staircase.

In one part of the building a substantial change in level of the beams returning into the building was required, in order to follow a change in basement level. A diagonal beam was constructed in the wall for this purpose and the stool holes were staggered downwards, to facilitate this. A similar

Figure 6.22

Figure 6.23

condition would occur if beams were required to follow the line of a staircase. Figures 6.22 and 6.23 show stools positioned for this diagonal beam construction. The sloping beam slot can clearly be seen. The horizontal stool head clearly acts to prevent any tendency for shearing between the sloping beam and the brickwork being supported.

The underpinning excavations beneath the Pynford beam were close-boarded and well-strutted. As the depth increased pumps were installed. Ample room was provided for the men working in the hole to stand clear of the bucket being used to remove the spoil. The excavation was carried out through waterlogged sandy gravel in which normal planking and strutting methods are impossible. Pynford developed an effective excavation shield for this project which enabled excavation without loss of fines, checked by

Figure 6.24

pumping through settling tanks. Gaps are left at intervals in the timbering and filled with a filter medium. This produced a large drainage surface as the piers were excavated, and reduced the velocity of groundwater flow into the excavations and thus the tendency to move fines.

The completed underpinning is shown in Figure 6.24. The heavily strutted bored pile wall can be seen to the right. The Pynford beam is seen to be in proportion to the magnitude of the loads being carried. Note the diagonal strutting in the centre of the picture, and the struts to right and left sloping down to the dumpling. Figure 6.25 shows the strutting in more detail. Note the splayed struts just beneath the crane jib tied at wall level. The main piers and infill panels can be clearly seen. Figure 6.26 shows 4 no. Pynford shoring jacks tightened against $200\,mm^2$ timber walings, supporting the trench sheeting confining the dumpling.

Approximately 90% of foundation problems affecting domestic dwellings occur on the shrinkable clay beds of the south-east of England[9]. One of the driest spells recorded in England ended in September 1976. Figure 6.27 compares the number of problems reported to Pynford during 1976 with the average of the numbers reported in preceding years. It will be seen that 1976 was between two and four times worse than the average of the previous ten years in south-east England. Stated differently, this means that the

Figure 6.25

Figure 6.26

	0	1	2	3	4	5
NW						
London and Home Counties						
NE						
Midands						
Wales						
SW						
Scotland						
East Anglia						
Bristol and Welsh Border						
South Coast						

Figure 6.27   The extent of the subsidence problem—1976 compared with previous years. o, 1966–76; ● 1972–76.

exceptional year of 1976 was no more than the accumulation of about three 'ordinary' years. 1976 subsidence damage claims are reported to have been in excess of £100 m. The average annual cost of unacceptable differential movement of house foundations is very large. Most domestic foundation failures are caused by ground movement in the upper two metres or so of the subsoil and can be cured by underpinning to a depth of between 2 m and 3 m.

Hand excavation is relatively simple in clay soils and the most economical method of underpinning to this depth is generally to construct continuous

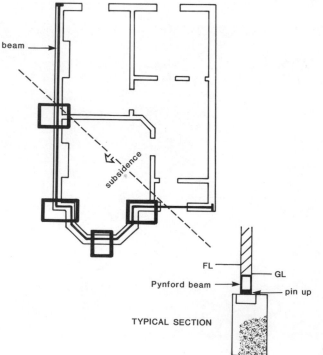

Figure 6.28]

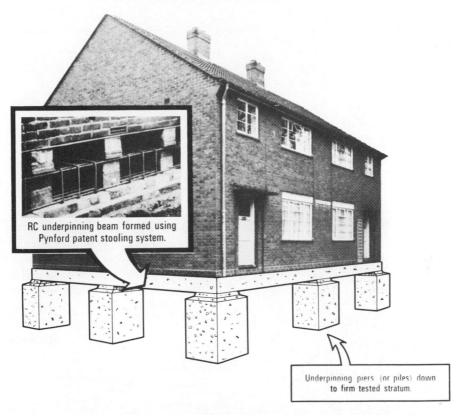

RC underpinning beam formed using Pynford patent stooling system.

Underpinning piers (or piles) down to firm tested stratum.

Figure 6.28

beams just below ground level, supported on mass concrete piers spaced at intervals. A typical underpinning scheme for the corner of a house is shown in Figure 6.28. Subsidence of the foundations of external walls of the front left-hand room has been identified. A Pynford beam extends from the rear left-hand corner to the front right-hand corner and 4 piers support the unstable walls. The Pynford underpinning beam is extended on to stable foundations to support the wall during excavation and to form transition zones where the deep underpinning changes level to the original foundations.

In Chapter 1 criteria for assessing damage are discussed. It is important that cracks are not judged in isolation but that the total cracking pattern is assessed. Figure 6.29 shows a small crack beneath a window in a low-rise factory development (see Case Study no. 4). This crack, which is less than 1 mm wide, was part of an extensive pattern of cracking, in which some cracks were significantly larger. Figure 6.30 shows a very distorted arch in Carlisle Cathedral in the north of England. Severe subsidence of the right-hand pier has caused the damage, but the adaptable nature of the masonry and repairs carried out over the centuries have enabled the movement to continue until it

Figure 6.29

stabilized without structural collapse. Clearly, such excessive movement is undesirable and could have been prevented by underpinning at an earlier stage. Equally clearly, underpinning was not necessary to prevent collapse, and it should be recognized that much underpinning is carried out to maintain acceptable serviceability limits of distortion in the superstructure and to protect the value of the owners' investment. This is particularly relevant for privately owned houses which are difficult to sell if foundation movement is evident and which cannot then be fully insured.

Case Study no. 2: Underpinning a house in Wimbledon, London

Figure 6.31 shows the front elevation of the property, which stood on sloping ground near a road junction. The ground level to the left of the picture had

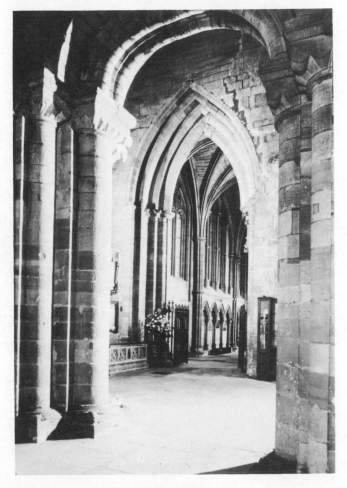

Figure 6.30

been lowered three metres for the construction of a block of flats without adequate strutting. The ground began to slip and at the rear of the house the garden collapsed into the excavation. Cracks over 5 mm wide appeared in the left-hand walls of the house and smaller cracks appeared towards the right. The foundation was stabilized by forming a frame of Pynford beams just below foundation level beneath all the external walls and the internal walls of the garage. The plan lent itself to the design as the walls could all be approached from outside or from the garage, thus eliminating disturbance to the ground floor of the house. The loadbearing cross-wall to the left of the front door was considered to be sufficiently far from the adjoining excavation to be buttressed at front and rear by the external underpinning. Figure 6.31b is a plan of the work. The piers supporting the underpinning beam were dug to a

(a)

(b)

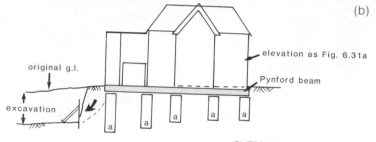

original g.l.

excavation

elevation as Fig. 6.31a

Pynford beam

a: mass concrete piers

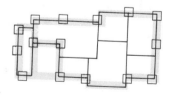

——— Pynford beams

☐ underpinning piers

Plan of house

Figure 6.31

Figure 6.32

depth of 4 m at the left-hand end of the property and those further to the right were progressively reduced in depth. Figure 6.32 shows the underpinning beam being constructed within the garage. Note the access trench approximately 1 m wide alongside the walls and stools in position. The brickwork between has been cut away in readiness for the reinforcement to be fixed.

Note the steel stool on the right-hand side of the garage to facilitate reinforcement in two directions where the underpinning beam beneath the return wall of the garage intersects with the main beam along the front, and also note that in the left foreground the beam has been concreted. On the right of the picture, stools have been built in and the brickwork between has not been cut away. Figure 6.33 shows the next stage of beam construction on another property. The reinforcement is fixed in position prior to fixing formwork and concreting. Beam sizes are generally chosen to minimize the need for shear reinforcement. Construction of support piers can proceed soon after the Pynford underpinning beams have been cast and before the pinning up has been completed between the stools. Pinning up between the stools is rarely necessary for structural reasons because the stools are cast into the beam.

Case Study no. 3: St Nicholas' Church, Charlwood, Surrey

The Church of St Nicholas was constructed in four stages between 1080 and 1480. The external walls of the church are about 900 mm thick, and mainly

Figure 6.33

constructed of irregular flat stones in weak mortar with larger tie stones at random to strengthen the construction, and dressed stonework surrounding doors and windows. The internal walls are of similar construction as they were first built as external walls.

The Church has a double pitched roof, partly of stone and partly tiled, with a central valley gutter. Rainwater is collected in gutters and discharges via downpipes into an open brick channel around the church walls which drains into a nearby brook. The south side of the church was suffering long-term continuing subsidence of the foundations, and severe lateral movement of the south wall had occurred at eaves level.

Site investigations identified clay shrinkage due to natural atmospheric conditions and the extraction of moisture by tree roots as the principal causes of foundation movement, compounded by outward thrust from the roof and by the shallow depth and poor quality of the foundation construction. The foundations consisted of a 1 m-deep layer of random stones set in a matrix of grey/brown clay, bearing upon a 3 m deep firm brown clay over dense dry shale. The foundations and the clay just beneath them were heavily colonized to a depth of 2 m by the roots of a large conifer tree growing near the south-west corner of the church.

There was an ancient and very valuable wall painting on the inner face of part of the south wall. The Parish Church Council (PCC) naturally required that there should be no damage or cracking whatsoever to this wall painting as

Figure 6.34

Figure 6.35

a result of the underpinning works. To ensure this, the sequence of stool fixing was very carefully planned and added protection was given by temporary raking shores set against the part of the wall that was inclined most severely.

The PCC also required that there should be no disturbance inside the church. The Pynford stooling system of underpinning enabled all the work to be executed from an external access trench, and normal church services and functions were able to continue throughout the period of underpinning.

Pynford beams extended alongside the whole of the south wall, around the porch and returned 8 m along the west wall and 10 m along the east wall, and were supported by four mass concrete piers positioned along the south wall and two more at the corners of the porch bearing upon the dense shale at a depth of 3.2 m below ground level. As has already been stated, when only part of a building is being underpinned using a beam and pier system, it is good practice to extend the beams well beyond the piers at each end of the section that is being refounded. These extensions are termed 'transition beams' as they reinforce the foundation at the junction between deep and shallow

Figure 6.36

foundations. They are designed as if they were supported by 'virtual' piers at their ends. The underpinning is illustrated by Figures 6.34 to 6.36.

The sequence of work was to erect the shoring against the most tilted section of the south wall, to cut away for and fix the stools, to cut away between the stools, to fix the reinforcement and formwork, concrete and pin up between the stools and to excavate, concrete and pin up the piers and finally to remove the shoring. The beams were stooled up and concreted in four sections as an additional precaution in view of the importance of the wall painting.

After the underpinning was completed, cracks in the walls were repaired by epoxy resin injection and tie bars were fixed at high level to provide additional lateral restraint for the tilted south wall.

Case Study no. 4: Beam and pile underpinning for a factory near Nottingham

The factory had been constructed on a raft on a site that had been backfilled with a high proportion of domestic refuse. Before construction the ground and filling had been improved by the installation of a pattern of stone columns using the now well established vibratory technique. After a few years differential settlement began to develop. The cause was identified as decomposition of organic material in the filling resulting in a loss of confinement of the stone columns and progressive collapse. One consequence of this particular case was that, as a general rule, columns are no longer installed as a means of improving sites containing a high organic content. However, the ground improvement method offers very high cost savings, and on another Pynford project a raft has been installed with provision for jacking should differential subsidence develop. This project has proved very successful and to date no jacking has been required.

The failure of the Nottingham foundation resulted in a claim being made against the ground improvement contractor, and the building was underpinned using Pynford beams supported by bored piles. Figure 6.37 shows the caisson piling rig in position in preparation for boring a cast-in-situ RC pile. Figure 6.38 shows a corner of the building. To the left a section of concreted beam can be seen. The corner stands on stools and reinforcement has been fixed. Note that the beam cantilevers beyond the corner to bear directly upon the pile. The pile reinforcement can be seen bent over just beneath the top reinforcement. Figure 6.39 shows an internal corner. Formwork is fixed on the left-hand side of the picture and is being fixed at rear right. An internal cross-beam is shown projecting beyond the wall on to a pile.

Piles may be used in a number of ways to support underpinning. These include piles placed in pairs, one in compression and one in tension, to support cantilever caps. Piles may be used in pairs on either side of a wall to carry a simple pile cap or a cross-member formed as part of the underpinning beam frame. This requires internal piling and all the disturbance that this causes.

Figure 6.37

For light structures piles may also be installed singly with cantilever caps, provided that they can be adequately reinforced for bending. However, a minimum number of piles is usually required when the arrangements are similar to those shown in this case. If piles can be installed in doorways or openings, one then approaches most nearly to the ideal case, that is, the 'open site' beam and pile foundation with the piles installed directly beneath the walls.

Case Study no. 5: Pynford beam used for shoring a brick pier

A particular problem was posed when the site adjoining a multi-storey London warehouse building (Figure 6.40) was to be developed. A multi-

Figure 6.38

Figure 6.39

Figure 6.40

storey steel frame building was to be erected on the site and one new column stood close to the brick pier in the bottom right of the illustration. The pier measured approximately 2 m × 0.6 m on plan and carried over 2000 kN. A substantial column foundation was to be constructed close to, and much deeper than, the pier foundation which was 2.6 × 1.2 m on plan and less than 1 m deep on firm gravel. The foundation pressure loading was substantially in excess of recommended practice, although the foundation was performing satisfactorily.

The problem of excavating the column foundation could not be solved by propping the beams on either side of the pier as the prop foundations had either to be carried deeper, which would have undermined the pier, or left at high level and thus vulnerable to the column foundation excavation. Pynford proposed that a beam should be constructed just below ground level along the line of the wall to needle the pier and thus enable it to be underpinned to a greater depth than the proposed new foundation column.

The plan area of the pier was divided into eight and one corner at a time was cut away and stooled up. With four stools in place the centre section of the brickwork was cut away in sequence to place the other four stools. It will be noted that practically the whole area of the pier was supported when the stooling was complete and that not more than 12% of the pier was cut away at any one time. The underside of the beam was just below the very shallow existing foundations and the stools were supported by cast-in-situ foundation pads which were then extended beneath the beam on either side of the pier to form an inverted 'T' construction designed to spread the load on either side of the pier before excavating for the underpinning.

Figure 6.41 shows the eight stools beneath the column, rods upstanding from the spreader pad beneath the proposed new beam and main beam reinforcement being threaded into position. Figure 6.42 shows the beam reinforcement complete and formwork fixed. Note the shear reinforcement placed at close centres immediately beside the pier and at wider centres further away as the load beneath the column is distributed on to the ground on either side. Care must be taken to ensure that the reinforcement cage is designed to allow for adequate compaction during concreting.

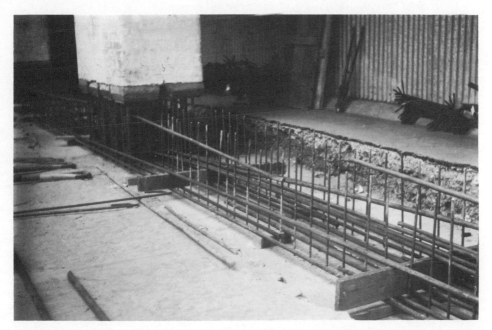

Figure 6.41

Figure 6.42

Case Study no. 6: Redeveloping major retail premises,
Oxford Street, London

Another example of the use of the Pynford stooling method for shoring is illustrated by Figure 6.43. Very large numbers of flues are found in the cross-walls of 19th-century buildings which were heated by numerous open fires. A

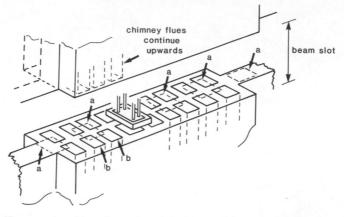

Figure 6.43   *a*, stool positions shown dotted; *b*, chimney flues; *c*, bag pushed down flue to block it; *d*, concrete filling flues; *e*, special Pyford stool; *f*, channel as top plate; *g*, concrete lintels; *h*, pinning up; *j*, mortar beds.

typical flue size is 350 × 225 mm, and adjoining flues are generally separated by half brick walls, 112 mm wide. At high level the void ratio in thick walls may be 30% or more.

The project required the removal of a length of wall approximately 10 m high at the bottom of a cross-wall, formed entirely of chimney flues, over 7 m long and over 25 m high. A conventional prop and needle scheme had been designed and was being installed when it was realized that the brickwork would be heavily overstressed above the needles.

To enable the work to proceed, Pynford designed and constructed a beam just above the needles which could safely transfer the wall loads to the needle positions. To construct the beam slot it was clearly necessary to ensure that the network of slender walls could be fully supported by the stooling process, as a significant increase in stress levels could not be allowed. It should also be noted that it is inherently more difficult to maintain the integrity of the brickwork above a beam slot than below it. This is of particular importance when dealing with Recent buildings, and particularly those constructed with relatively soft lime mortar. The brickwork is strong and tight when under compression, but when the compression forces are relieved the brickwork can easily be loosened, thus stool holes must be kept narrow if the brickwork above the beam slot is to be supported. It is clearly much less of a problem to avoid loosening the brickwork below the beam slot as it is held in place by gravity.

In this particular case it was decided to provide total support above the beam slot and to use conventional stool and pad detailing below the beam slot. This was possible and practicable because the chimney construction below the beam slot could be strengthened by filling the flues with concrete, whereas this could not be done above the beam slot. A stool was designed with a steel channel replacing the upper steel plate (Figure 6.44a) and a series of small precast concrete planks replacing the upper concrete plate (Figure 6.44b). The stools were positioned at the intersection of alternate cross-walls between the

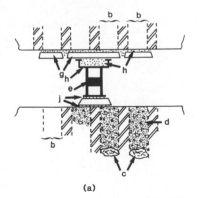
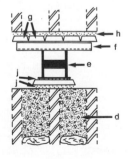

(a)   (b)

Figure 6.44 Key as for Figure 6.43.

Figure 6.45

flues. The upper concrete plate was changed to a set of lintels to make it possible to ensure that all the narrow walls separating the flues were completely
supported. Finally, the gap beneath the lintels in the channel was pinned to
relieve the load on the edges. The wall was successfully stooled up in this way,
reinforcement was fixed and the beam was concreted. It was then possible to
needle and prop safely to carry the load of the wall down to basement level.

Case Study no. 7: Pynford beams used for shoring

When altering larger buildings of recent origin it is often the case that beams
or columns are found passing through the position in which it is desired to
construct the Pynford beam.

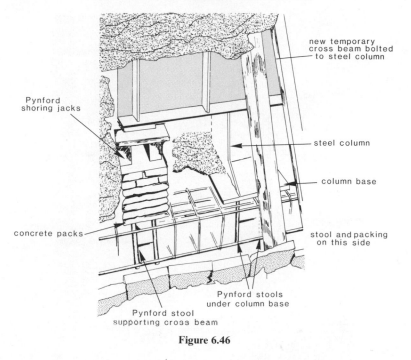

new temporary
cross beam bolted
to steel column

Pynford
shoring jacks

steel column

column base

concrete packs

stool and packing
on this side

Pynford stools
under column base

Pynford stool
supporting cross beam

Figure 6.46

(a) Case 7A. The base of a substantial steel column was found to be just above the top of the proposed underpinning beam. In such a case the base of the column is too small for a significant proportion to be cut away for a stooling sequence. The column load must first be relieved, and this was achieved by bolting a steel beam to the column shaft just above beam level. This was propped by Pynford stools on either side of the column at a safe distance from the column base so that the holes cut for the stools would not disturb the column support. Figures 6.45 and 6.46 show this in detail. The stooling operation is complete and reinforcement is fixed prior to concreting the beam. One supporting stool can be seen on the left-hand side of the picture, and the gap in which shoring jacks are installed can be clearly identified. To the right of the picture, beside the stabilizing props, the column can be seen. This has two stools fixed and pinned up between the base.

(b) Case 7B: a column beside a wall. In this example the basement in a shop unit in a terrace of properties was being deepened. The adjoining property had been reconstructed with new floors supported by columns ranged alongside the party walls and closely abutting them (Figure 6.47). The columns adjoining the party wall that was to be deepened were founded on bases above the level of the underpinning. There was a restaurant at ground-floor level with a serving counter immediately beside the wall and it would have been

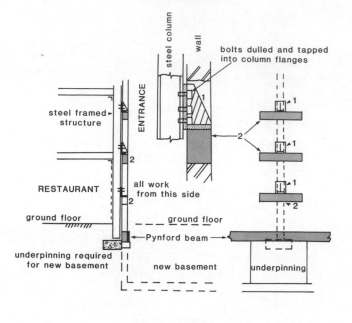

SECTION   ELEVATION from working side

Figure 6.47 Case 7*B*. 1, new steel bracket fixed to column; 2, Pynford spreader beams distribute column load on brickwork.

impossible to screen off a working area around the columns without closing the restaurant and paying heavy compensation. The columns were screened with vitrolite panelling and the problem was solved by transferring the column load to the party wall, spreading it at three levels on Pynford beams formed on the working side. The load was transferred to the beams by cutting carefully positioned holes immediately behind the columns, drilling and tapping the flange closest to the wall and fixing a bracket. With the load relieved it was then possible to underpin the column from the opposite side of the wall.

(c) Case 7C: the treatment of steel beams running into the 'beam slot'. In this typical case a frame of beams and columns was being constructed to remove a wall at ground-floor level to extend a banking premises. The beams could not be propped down to basement floor level as the disturbance in the basement could not be tolerated. Tetrahedral shoring was designed to prop the first-floor level beams from the spreader beam forming the bottom member of the frame. The general arrangement is shown in Figure 6.48. Figures 6.48, 6.49 and 6.50 show the tetrahedral shoring. Pynford shoring jacks were used to preload the shoring before the padstone supporting the beam was removed. The jacks are tightened until the beam is seen to just lift off the seating, thus

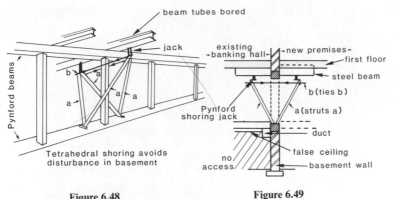

Figure 6.48   **Figure 6.49**

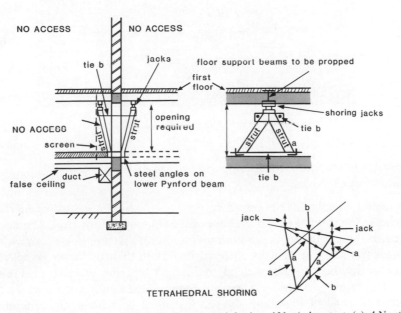

Figure 6.50   (See also Figures 6.48, 6.49). Tetrahedral shoring: 4 No timber struts (*a*); 4 No steel tines (*b*).

ensuring that the actual load is exactly matched. Where the web would obstruct the reinforcement, holes are cut with an oxyacetylene torch to allow reinforcing bars to pass through. In some cases it may be necessary to fix additional brackets to the web to reduce bearing pressures on the concrete to acceptable levels.

Figure 6.51

Case Study no. 8: Strengthening medieval stonework at
Winchester Cathedral

A number of columns developed vertical splits between the springing of the
arches in the main nave and the base of the column at floor level. These splits
occurred in each face of the column which was roughly square on plan with the
diagonals following the axes of the cathedral. In the worst case the split had
widened to about 80 mm wide at mid-height tapering upwards and downwards. Figure 6.51 shows a general view of the column with scaffolding
erected around it. Plumbing showed a distinct barrelling outwards of the
column at mid-height. Figure 6.54 shows a view of another column where a
crack can be clearly seen.

To strengthen the column, reinforced concrete discs were placed at
approximately 3 m centres within the height of the column. In the worst
column, three discs were inserted, and in other less severely damaged columns
the number was reduced. Figures 6.52 and 6.53 show plans of a typical column
supporting the nave walls. The cathedral was refaced in Perpendicular style in
the 14th century. Figure 6.52 shows clearly the new stone facings, the 14th-
century mortar behind the facings, and the Norman core. The quality of the

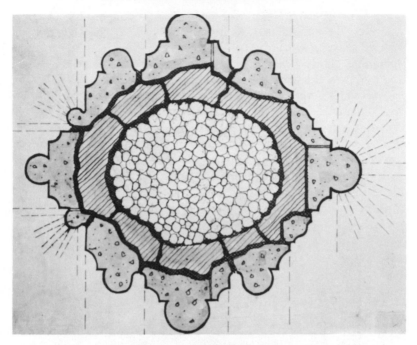

Figure 6.52

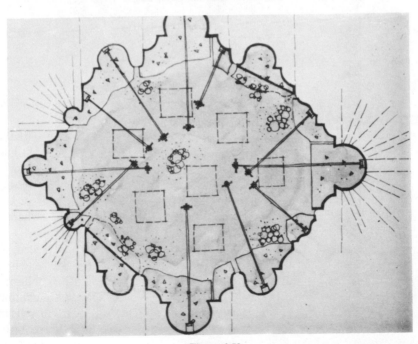

Figure 6.53

cores was variable and in some cases the load of the columns had clearly been transferred to the stone facings. Remedial work had been carried out by Nash in the 19th century on nearby columns, and this work was being extended.

Figure 6.53 shows a plan of the concrete discs. The disc was formed by cutting a hole in the side of the column and then cutting away the core in stages, replacing it with stools as the work proceeded. The position of the stools is marked. The stonework was then bonded into this core with phosphorbronze bolts anchored into the stonework and embedded in the concrete disc. This work was carried out in the early 1960s, before modern epoxy resin bonding and grouting techniques had been developed. It is a clear example of the way in which stooling can be used to insert reinforced concrete into loadbearing masonry.

Figure 6.54

Clearly holes could not be cut in a column in this way safely even to remove part of the plan area, unless the column were first strengthened. Nash constructed fairly elaborate shoring for this purpose, a model of which is still to be seen at the cathedral. For the purpose of the Pynford operation, the columns were strengthened by steel bonds secured tightly around the columns at distances varying between 0.3 and 1.5 m. Pairs of bonds were arranged immediately above and below each beam slot. This can be clearly seen in Figure 6.54. It should be appreciated that cutting out and refixing stones in columns and walls is a common masonry practice. In this case the columns were strengthened by banding and the cutting away was extended into the core using the stooling technique. Figure 6.55 shows a workman inside the column, cutting out more core. A stool has been fixed and pinned up and can clearly be seen just in front of the man. In Figure 6.56 the reinforced concrete disc with reinforcement completed is ready for concreting. The ends of the phosphor-bronze tie bolts can be seen together with reinforcing cages. In this particular

Figure 6.55

Figure 6.56

Figure 6.57

case the disc was formed in two sections. The foreman can be seen through the column at the back of the picture.

Case Study no. 9: Strengthening medieval stonework,
Cathedral Close, Winchester

Another example of strengthening work at Winchester was that carried out on the King's Gate Arch leading from just beside the Cathedral Close into College Street. This medieval gateway is one of only two existing where a church at first floor level stands above a medieval gateway.

The gate had been weakened by pedestrian arches constructed on either side of the original central arches. The piers between the side and central arches were then undermined by excavations for sewers running through the gateway. The inside wall had gradually developed a substantial inclination, leaning outwards at the top over 200 mm. The church roof trusses were not tied, and to avoid altering the appearance of this unique building a reinforced concrete skeleton was buried in the wall, including cantilevers projecting upwards to a reinforced concrete plate at roof level. This skeleton was tied just below the church floor level to restrain the wall and the roof truss.

Figure 6.57 is a general view of the work in progress. Note the horizontal timber clamping the flint facing to the wall and the raking struts providing additional vertical support. Figure 6.58 shows the frame during construction. The concreting work has been completed to line the right-hand pedestrian arch, and the column has been continued up to springing level. Formwork is in position for the beam arching over the central gate, and slots have been cut on the right- and left-hand side for the upward cantilever. A particularly interesting problem was supporting the masonry at the intersection of the pedestrian arch, the column and the beam over the main arch. The solution was a star-shaped 'stool' which supported the hanging corner on the right-

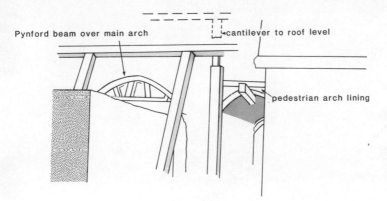

Figure 6.58

hand side of the column over the pedestrian arch. The integrity of the core was maintained in the column slot about first-floor level by fixing horizontal stools, one of which can just be seen in the photograph. Figure 6.60 is a view looking down the sloping beam slot over the main arch. Two vertical stools

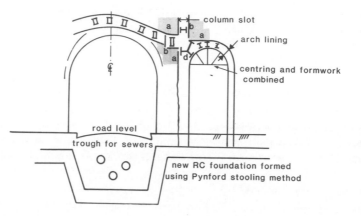

Figure 6.59

Figure 6.60

stepped down can be seen. Also note an inclined stool on the far left of the photograph set at right angles to the line of the arch at that point. One leg of the star-shaped stool can be seen between the scaffolding pole and the raking shore. The top of the photograph is framed by the horizontal timber clamping on the flint facing during the work.

Should the reader chance to be in Winchester it can be noted that the reinforced work is completedly concealed within the walls. The only visible evidence of the strengthening is the tie bars which can be seen from the roadway tucked up at a high level just beneath the first floor on either side of the traffic opening.

It is hoped that the foregoing text and illustrations will have clearly explained the Pynford stooling methods. Once the principle of containing the masonry by steel struts acting along the lines of stress, which are normally vertical, is understood, then it will be appreciated that reinforced concrete elements can be inserted in loadbearing brick and stonemasonry structures with a great deal of freedom. The method has been used on many occasions to form reinforced concrete frames or lintels in buildings that are to be altered.

Clearly good design, detailing, and workmanship are of paramount importance. Should the site team not be familiar with the method, very close attention must be paid to the work by the engineers. Clearly site supervision requirements are reduced as the site team gains experience. The very repetitive nature of the fixing of stools and pinning up operations assists in reducing the training period necessary.

It should be noted that in many cases foundation problems can be avoided by forming rectangular frames, sometimes simple rectangles, sometimes elongated rectangles propped along their length by new reinforced concrete columns. An cxample of such work is now briefly described.

Case Study no. 10: Altering a Tudor structure—Trinity College, Cambridge

When the senior combination room at ground-floor level beneath the Master's Lodge at Trinity College, Cambridge, was extended in the early

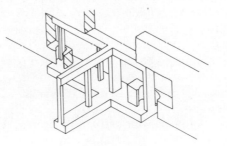

Figure 6.61

Figure 6.62

1960s, a reinforced concrete framework was inserted using the Pynford stooling system. Figure 6.61 shows the framework in isometric view. Figure 6.62 shows the stooling and reinforcing complete for the foundation level beams just prior to concreting. The work was being carried out to remove the walls at the rear and on the right between ground- and first-floor level. The top of the frame was 75 mm below first-floor level. The alternative method of constructing the frame in structural steelwork would have required needling of the rear wall above first-floor level. For this purpose the unique Tudor panelling in the Master's Lodge at first-floor level would have had to be removed and the very heavy cost of doing this work was saved by using the stooling method. Figure 6.63 shows construction of the beam slot at first-floor level nearly completed. It is interesting to compare the very small area of steel carrying the rear wall, that is 28 no. 25 mm diameter circular steel legs, with the much larger area of Tudor stone masonry that has been cut away. This dramatically illustrates the discontinuity in construction methods and materials that occurred when steel was introduced as a new building material. In Figure 6.64 the reinforced concrete frame is complete. Some of the walls have been cut away to form the column slots. In Figure 6.65, the masonry between the columns has been removed and the building work is in progress.

Moving brick and stonemasonry structures can be readily accomplished using modern cranes or rolling and sliding gear, and Pynford have completed many operations of this type. It is important to have a rigid and stiff chassis

Figure 6.63

Figure 6.64

Figure 6.65

Figure 6.66

Figure 6.68

Figure 6.67

beneath the structures that are being moved, and the final cases included in this chapter illustrate three very different examples of such work.

Case Study no. 11

A small brick counting house in a cattle market near Birmingham was removed to a nearby historic building site to make way for a supermarket development. A reinforced concrete slab, 225 mm thick, was constructed just below ground level and the building was then lifted by crane on to a heavy transporter and carted five miles to the proposed new site. It has been put back into use as a ticket office. Figure 6.66 shows the building with work about to commence. Figure 6.67 shows stools being constructed in preparation for formation of the supporting slab by which the building was lifted. Figure 6.68

Figure 6.69

shows the work nearing completion. The building has been transported to the new site and is being lowered into position. The lifting cables are clearly to be seen attached to the corners of a lifting frame from which the building and supporting reinforced concrete slab are suspended.

Case Study no. 12

The historic old school house at Warrington is another example of a brick structure that was moved on a Pynford reinforced concrete chassis. This 800-tonne Georgian brick building, which was of considerable historic importance to the city of Warrington in Lancashire, was moved over 15 m to make room for a road widening improvement scheme. The building was strengthened using

Figure 6.70

Figure 6.71

Figure 6.72   Masonry in positions *a* held in position by vertical stool, horizontal stool and star-shaped stool.

epoxy resin techniques, and some tie bars attached to timber plates. A reinforced concrete frame was then constructed just below foundation level. This is clearly seen Figures 6.69 and 6.70. A second reinforced concrete frame was the constructed beneath the first, leaving a gap within which the sliding gear was installed. This lower frame was extended to the new site, and the beams were infilled to form a raft foundation. Figure 6.69 shows the building just prior to the move, with the River Mersey in the background. Figure 6.70 shows the move at halfway stage, with the building sliding on grease skates and towed by winches (see reference 10).

Case Study no. 13

To conclude the chapter, some illustrations are given of the removal of some Romano-British masonry to a museum in Hertford. These fragile flint walls were underpinned below foundation level with a reinforced concrete slab and transported to the museum by lorry, using a technique very similar to that described in Case Study no. 11. The walls were first exposed during site stripping for gravel extraction, and Figure 6.71 shows the walls further exposed by archaeologists. Stooling is carried out (Figure 6.72), the walls are packaged ready for transportation (Figure 6.73) and the structure is loaded for transport to the museum. (This project has also been described in technical literature—see reference 11).

Figure 6.73

References

1. International Association for Bridge and Structural Engineering, *Proc. Symp. September 1983*. IABSE, London.
2. Institution of Civil Engineers (1982), *(Proc. ICE Conf.) Repair and Renewal of Buildings*, Thomas Telford, London.
3. Pryke, J.F.S. (1982) Underpinning, framing, jacking-up and moving brick and stone masonry structures. In Ref. 2.
4. Heyman, J. (1982) *The Masonry Arch*. Ellis Horwood, Chichester.
5. Building Research Establishment, Research Paper No. 13.
6. Wood, R.H. Composite action of brickwork supported by beams.
7. Norwegian hotel moved in biggest ever lift. *New Civil Engineer,* 2nd June 1983.
8. Pryke, J.F.S. (1983) Relevelling, raising and re-siting historic buildings. In Ref. 1.
9. Pryke, J.F.S. (1979) Differential foundation movement of domestic buildings in south-east England. Distribution, investigation, causes and remedies. Adapted from *Proc. Conf. on Settlement of Structures*, Cambridge, April 1974. British Geotechnical Society, London.
10. Stables, A.A.J. A Moving Experience. *Industrial Nottingham*, March 1984.
11. Pryke, J.F.S. (1976) Underpinning system in Romano-British Corndryer removal. *Concrete*, October 1976.

7   Ground freezing

J.S. HARRIS

7.1 Introduction

Artificially frozen ground is used by civil and mining engineers alike as a means of ground stabilization to provide support and to exclude groundwater. Since first used in South Wales in 1862, the process has become recognized worldwide as a reliable method of dealing with adverse ground conditions for both temporary and permanent applications.

As a temporary expedient, freezing has been used for excavations (shafts, tunnels, foundations and storage), stabilizing ground slides, underpinning buildings, sampling weak soils, constructing temporary access roads over boggy ground, and the exploitation of ore reserves in lake bottoms.

Permanent freezing systems are rare outside the arctic regions of the USSR and North America, but include control of Young's Modulus in gravels beneath radar sites, maintenance of frozen soil beneath heated buildings and overhead pipelines founded on permafrost, and in-ground storage containers for cryogenic liquids.

Whereas the principal uses of the method are associated with shaft sinking or tunnel headings, the dramatic increase in strength that is achieved as the temperature is lowered is of particular advantage for temporary load support purposes.

As it is transient in nature and does not affect the water table or groundwater quality, the process finds favour when environmental considerations are significant.

7.2 The method

The artificial ground freezing (AGF) process is one of the more versatile geotechnical methods available to engineers, there being few limitations on account of scale, site conditions, soil type or the presence of groundwater. Figure 7.1 indicates the versatility of AGF over a full range of soil types so long as they contain (or can be made to contain) water. Unless there is a heat source (e.g. fast-moving water) in the immediate neighbourhood of the ground being refrigerated, the outcome is predictable and certain even in mixed strata.

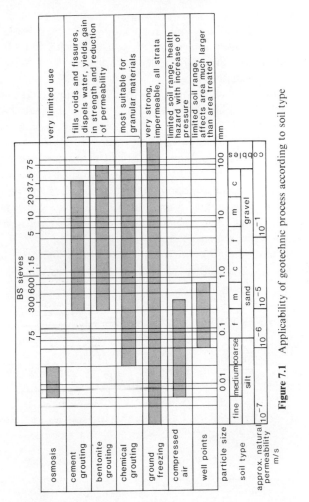

Figure 7.1 Applicability of geotechnic process according to soil type

In the freezing process the pore-water is converted into ice which then bonds the soil particles together, rendering the strata both strong and impermeable. A twentyfold improvement in mechanical strength is common, while the creation of an enclosing frozen membrane offers cofferdam (water-exclusion) performance too.

Frozen conditions are usually created by circulating a cold fluid through a series of coaxial pipes. These freeze-tubes are so disposed that, when the individual ice-cylinders associated with each merge, either a continuous membrane (ice-wall) is formed around the volume to be protected or excavated, or a supporting column of desired area is created.

The configurations of the site and the existing and/or future structures will determine the shape of the ice-body needed, and therefore the number and orientation of the freeze-tubes. Some examples are given in Figure 7.2 and further referred to in section 7.6. A circular or elliptical shape is preferred if an excavation is to be protected.

Conventional rotary drilling or soft ground boring methods are normally used to form holes into which the sealed freeze-tubes can be introduced.

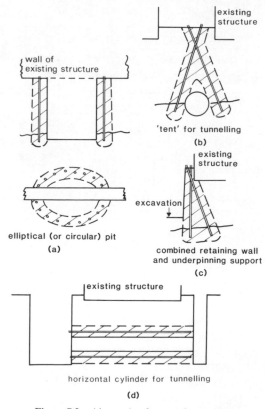

Figure 7.2   Alternative freeze-tube patterns

Alternatively, the freeze-tubes themselves may be drilled or jetted directly into place. It is often necessary to survey the course of the boreholes to ensure that a regular pattern has been maintained over the depth of penetration.

The several attributes of AGF are considered when assessing its relevance as a constructional aid in particular circumstances; once selected, the planner can usually make economies in his temporary works. Thus the significant increase in soil strength enables excavations to proceed without the need for any further support, while the encumbrance of walings and struts is avoided. It should, however, be noted that if the permanent structure/lining is not being constructed immediately following excavation it may be necessary to insulate the exposed ice-wall to prevent its deterioration.

Similarly, the impermeable nature of frozen ground avoids the need for groundwater lowering over a wide area and, when the total cofferdam has been created, the trapped water can be pumped away to leave a dry stable excavation. Settlement problems that often arise from vibrations during sheet piling, or from the removal of fines during groundwater lowering, are eliminated. The freezing and thawing cycle is simply a physical transformation—a reversible change of state. There is therefore no contamination of aquifers, nor is the level of the groundwater affected. Medical hazards and non-productive time associated with compressed air working do not arise.

Limitations are few, being mainly related to water movement. A flow of water across a zone being refrigerated is a continual source of added heat which at best will require added effort to overcome, or at worst will preclude the use of the method. For this reason extraction of water from nearby wells must be limited or avoided during the currency of refrigeration. It is generally accepted that groundwater velocities should not exceed 2 m per day, particularly if mechanical refrigeration is being used (see below).

7.3 Methods of refrigeration

7.3.1 On-site mechanical plant

The most commonly used plant consists of a reciprocating or screw compressor operating with ammonia or freon. The refrigeration achieved is used to chill a brine-based heat transfer medium (or secondary refrigerant) which is circulated through the freeze tubes before being returned to the plant to be rechilled in a closed-circuit system. The heat removed from the rock or soilwater is dissipated to the atmosphere via a cooling tower or an evaporative condenser or to a convenient water source, e.g. lagoon or river.

The component parts of such a plant—the compressor, motor, heat exchanger(s), expansion valves, pumps, switchgear and instrumentation—are usually all packaged on a common base and installed in a container (see Figure 7.3), or on a trailer, for ease of assembly on site.

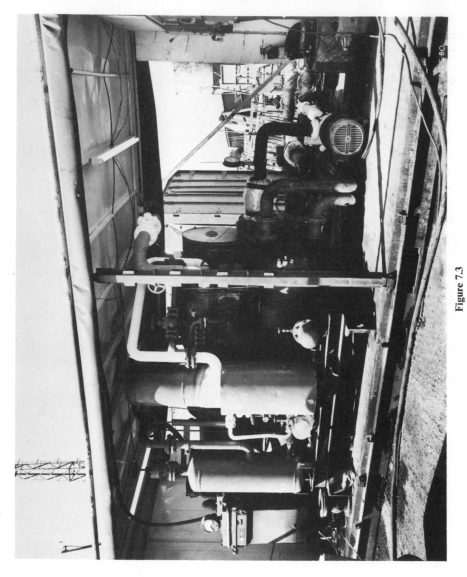

Figure 7.3

With two-stage compound compressors, using ammonia as the primary refrigerant and calcium chloride brine, temperatures down to $-35°C$ or even $-40°C$ can be achieved when required. A usual design value is in the region of between $-25°C$ and $-30°C$ to create the required frozen conditions in a period of only a few weeks.

7.3.2 Off-site-produced expendable refrigerant

Cryogenic liquids—those substances which evaporate at very low temperatures unless stored under pressure in insulated vessels—may be used as refrigerants. Of these, liquid nitrogen and liquid carbon dioxide are produced in bulk for commercial distribution and sale. Both are inert and can be vented safely to atmosphere after their work cycle. Liquid nitrogen is available from many more distribution points than is liquid carbon dioxide, boils directly to gas within the pressure range experienced, and is therefore generally used. With closely-spaced freeze tubes a rapid primary freeze period of only a few days is easily attainable in most situations.

With cryogenic refrigeration site plant requirements are simple, a power supply is not necessary, and the system is silent as well as fast. However, as the refrigerant is exhausted to atmosphere after only one cycle, it being impracticable to recondense it, the cost advantage of fast freezing can rapidly be lost if the frozen state has to be maintained for a long period.

These features often restrict choice of cryogenic refrigeration to remedial works where action is urgently required, or to smaller-scale applications including short tunnels, sealing of damaged sheet piles and underpinning.

7.4 The properties of frozen ground

7.4.1 Strength and creep

The frozen strength of any soil or rock type is dependent on its moisture content and the temperature below freezing point to which it is subject. In general, at a given sub-zero temperature, sand will be stronger than silt, and silt will be stronger than clay. Typical strength/temperature relationships for some generalized soil types have been published from time to time (Figure 7.4).

Frozen sands and soils with large pore spaces develop reasonably high compressive strengths at temperatures only a few degrees below freezing point, but in silty and clayey soils very substantial proportions of the total moisture content may remain unfrozen at temperatures as low as $-10°C$. The more clayey the soil the greater the proportion of unfrozen moisture, and this has a marked influence on strength.

Lovell (1957) has shown that the compressive strength of clay–silt soils increases three- to fourfold as the temperature is reduced from $-5°C$ to

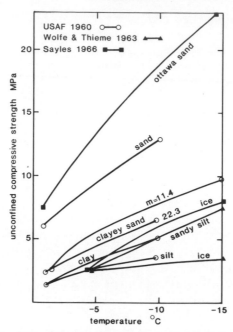

Figure 7.4 Unconfined compressive strength

− 18°C. Furthermore the unconfined compressive strength increases exponentially with the relative moisture frozen. As an example, for a silty clay studied, the amount of moisture frozen at − 18°C was only 1.25 times that frozen at − 5°C, but the compressive strength at the lower temperature was over four times as high as that at the higher temperature.

As with unfrozen clays, ice and frozen soils behave in an elasto-plastic manner, and under steady load will exhibit creep (time-dependent strain). The mechanical parameters are all both temperature- and time-dependent. The characteristic deformation–time curve at constant temperature and constant load follows firstly a decreasing, then a rapidly increasing, strain-rate with time characteristic (Gardner *et al.*, 1984), the inflection being defined as the failure point (Figure 7.5).

From tests on a sample of organic silty clay Sanger and Kaplar (1963) have shown that, at 80 psi (0.6 MPa) this failure occurred after 17 hours when the sample was maintained at just below 0°C, yet that failure point had not been reached after 60 hours when tested at − 2.5°C.

A combination of high ground pressure and small negative temperatures may, in some frozen soils, lead to measurable creep. A high rate of creep dictates special techniques and monitoring. Consideration of creep does not generally become important in freezings of shallow to medium depth, and is usually confined to formations such as plastic clays or organic silts.

The strength and creep properties are measured in the laboratory on

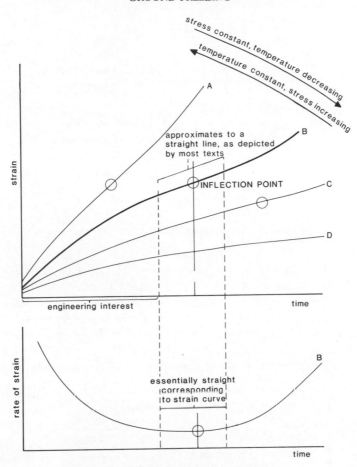

Figure 7.5 Characteristic creep curves

specimens recovered from in-situ frozen locations or on specimens frozen in the laboratory under simulated in-situ conditions.

Specialist testing facilities are required, which include a cold room whose temperature can be controlled to within $\pm 1°C$ for storage of field-frozen samples, creation of laboratory-frozen specimens, and workshop-type activities when the specimens are prepared and conditioned for testing.

In the field freezing does not occur triaxially, but as the freezing front advances. To simulate this in the laboratory, the specimen is frozen uniaxially. Another process associated with freezing is moisture migration, as described later (section 7.4.2). A single apparatus, illustrated in Figure 7.6, satisfies these various conditions: the water contained in the brass pot is well insulated and is therefore the last component to be frozen when the apparatus is placed in the cold room. At this stage the specimen is chilled from the top, the zero isotherm advancing steadily from top to bottom, until totally frozen. During

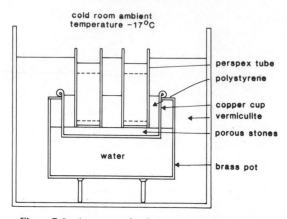

Figure 7.6   Apparatus for frozen sample preparation.

this time the surface of the water is free to find its own level according to any volume changes that may arise. The specimen is then released from the apparatus and stored until the test is to be conducted.

Strength is determined by testing at a constant rate of strain, while creep parameters are measured by tests performed at constant stress. The refrigerated compression equipment illustrated in Figure 7.7 has been built to perform either type of test. A microcomputer program controls the loading

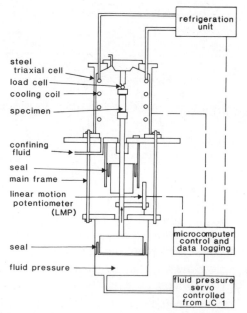

Figure 7.7   Refrigerated triaxial compression apparatus

applied at any time and, in the case of creep tests, takes account of change of cross-sectional area as the sample shortens.

7.4.2 Frost heave

The change in the volume of water as it is chilled is well known. Much of this volume increase is dissipated by expulsion of water ahead of the freezing front, and is a function of the degree of saturation and the permeability of the ground. The remaining volume increase creates a pressure which may result in compression frost shattering of the bounding strata, or ground heave, or remains as a stress, according to the overburden pressure. Such heave as does occur at this stage is very small, and usually insignificant.

Ground heave of an order likely to cause distress occurs at sub-zero temperatures when a so-called frost-susceptible soil has access to a plentiful supply of water. It has been observed, in respect of a surface layer of soil which is subject to climatic freezing, that the soil must have an open system (a condition in which free water in excess of that originally contained in the voids is available to be moved to the freezing front) if segregated ice is to form, i.e. for it to be a frost-susceptible soil (Arvidson and Morgernstern, 1977). Such conditions usually occur in silts or fine sandy silt where the mechanism of upward water movement is attributed to capillary forces acting in the pore spaces of a soil near to the groundwater table within a medium of reasonably high permeability which permits mass movement while freezing conditions apply. The ice lenses so formed displace the ground above and heave is observed at the surface.

Jumikis (1966) conducted a series of experiments to illustrate and explain the upward migration and freezing of moisture which can in some cases result in appreciable rise in ground level. These experiments were directed mainly at the behaviour of road subgrades but the conclusions are relevant in some instances to artificial ground freezing. Freezing as a constructional aid usually involves the creation of vertical boundaries between frozen and unfrozen material, primary water migration therefore being essentially horizontal. Another differing feature is that the temperature gradient across the interface is very much greater than with climatic freezing, thus reducing the conditions which favour bulk migration of water.

In general, heave is not a serious problem, but must be expected and allowed for in unfavourable conditions.

7.4.3 Concreting

When pouring concrete against frozen ground, a principal concern is that the concrete should not itself become frozen before achieving the initial set (Altounyan et al., 1982). Generally the heat of hydration will be sufficient to prevent advance of the freezing isotherm for several days. Increased heat of hydration can be achieved by the use of rapid-setting cements, by using additives such as calcium chloride, by preheating the aggregates and/or by mixing with hot water. Additionally an insulating layer may be placed against the exposed ice-wall, such that a considerable time can elapse before the temperature of the setting concrete falls to freezing point. During this time a limited thawing of the innermost part of the ice-wall will occur as the temperature gradient from the hot concrete distorts the location of the zero isotherm. Care must, of course, be exercised to ensure that overheating does not occur.

7.5 Design

7.5.1 Structural

For shallow excavations the calculation of an adequate thickness of a cylindrical or circular icewall to withstand earth and hydrostatic pressures is commonly based on the Domke formula using strength parameters. An extension of the Lamé approach to thick cylinders, the Domke formula was the first to recognise and take some account of the plastic behaviour of frozen ground, and can be usefully expressed in the form

$$S_x = a\left[0.29\frac{P}{Q} + 2.3\left(\frac{P}{Q}\right)^2\right]$$

where S_x = icewall thickness
a = radius of excavation
P = external (ground) pressure
Q = compressive strength of frozen ground.

The failure criterion is simple, and the formula only allows calculation to be carried out on the basis of strength with no check on deformation.

Later work by Vialov (1966) and others based on the Mohr–Coulomb plastic shear criterion, and in some cases taking account of end restraint, has generated many formulae. A useful one for shallow frozen ground structures may be conveniently written as

$$P = \frac{2cN^{1/2}}{N-1}\left[\left(\frac{b}{a}\right)^{N-1} - 1\right]$$

where N = flow factor $\dfrac{1+\sin\phi}{1-\sin\phi}$
ϕ = limiting angle of shear resistance of frozen ground
b = radius of outer face of icewall.

For small-diameter, shallow pits as required for underpinning purposes, the simplest check by Domke will normally be sufficient to determine the minimum thickness required.

When frozen ground is to be utilized as a loadbearing element it is also necessary to check its bearing capacity. The Terzaghi formula is appropriate (Andersland and Anderson, 1978). But, because the strength is both temperature and time-dependent, the value used in estimating the allowable bearing capacity must take due account of the thermal regime that will apply during the working life of the ice-body. Likewise it is necessary, during the execution of the works, to ensure that the design temperature of the ice-body is attained and preserved.

For tunnels and deep shafts the Finite Element Method (FEM) allows the deformation and stresses to be analysed. This is particularly useful in soils subject to creep, as the changes in deformation and stress with time can also be computed and presented in easily interpreted, diagrammatic and graphical form. Although computer time is expensive, FEM modelling represents the ground behaviour more accurately than elastic analysis and is therefore to be preferred for sensitive cases.

7.5.2 Thermal

Having established the volume and average icewall temperature needed structurally, the thermal properties of the formations and the refrigeration capacity are equated with freeze-tube dispositions and freezing periods to establish the scope of the projected freezing operation.

As heat is abstracted from the ground, cooling proceeds in three distinct regimes: ground already frozen is being further cooled, water at the freezing front is being frozen by removal of its latent heat, and the ground beyond the freezing front is being cooled below its natural temperature. The many variables at any given location, which are rarely measured, make a full and rigorous analysis impossible. As with permeability, thermal conductivity varies with the direction of heat flow and with the phase and temperature of the wet material. The moisture content and the velocity of any groundwater flow will affect refrigeration demand.

In practice the designer correlates theoretical calculations with data collected from previous work in this field. Theoretical design methods have been given in the literature by many workers, e.g. Jumikis (1966), Collins and Deacon (1972), Shuster (1972), Sanger and Sayles (1978), but all require refinement based on the experience of the major practitioners, much of which remains their in-house know-how.

7.6 Applications

7.6.1 Open pits and shafts

The common feature of shaft work is that excavation takes place within an icewall—usually circular or elliptical—which encloses the construction volume and isolates it from the groundwater. This principle is also applied, at reduced scale, to gain access beneath foundations of existing buildings to facilitate their underpinning. The position of the freeze circle—the pattern of the freeze-tubes in plan—is located such that the line of the footing is a chord, as shown in Figure 7.2(*a*). When the enclosed space has been excavated to a stable stratum, the underpinning support which will transfer the load of the building to the stable stratum can be constructed. Once this support is secure the frozen ground is allowed to thaw. During the operation it may be necessary to introduce a bridging beam beneath the original footing to prevent degeneration; if so, the icewall will act as a temporary loadbearing support for that beam, although this has not been shown on the figure.

The permanent underpinning support may be constructed as a simple extension downwards of the original foundation, i.e. to a similar width, followed by backfilling of the remaining void; alternatively it may be cheaper to erect a single shutter to isolate the underpinning area and the smaller sector and backfill that volume with concrete, utilizing the icewall itself as the remainder of the form.

7.6.2 Tunnels

As with pits and shafts, freeze-tubes can be installed parallel to the tunnel axis, as in Figure 7.2(*b*). Excavation can then take place within the enclosing icewall although, with time, the ice-front will advance into and across the trapped space; with tunnel diameters of 3 m or less the core is likely to be totally frozen within three weeks of the zero isotherm crossing the excavation line.

Alternatively the freeze-tubes can be installed from the surface to straddle the line of the tunnel (unless there is no cutoff stratum, when additional freeze-tubes may be needed through the tunnel space to ensure ice closure across the base). Where there are space restrictions at the surface, as in Figure 7.2(*c*), angled freeze-tubes to create a tent-like cross-section may be appropriate.

7.6.3 Structural support/retaining wall

Figure 7.2(*d*) illustrates a possible freeze-tube pattern to combine the functions of temporary support to the existing building foundation and a retaining wall to the soil under the building while the neighbouring site is excavated. It may be necessary, additionally, to install freeze-tubes from within the existing building to create a wider bearing area and thicker icewall, and/or to install ground-anchors as excavation proceeds, and/or to buttress the icewall if the excavation is particularly deep.

7.7 Examples

The number of published descriptions of frozen ground underpinning applications that satisfy the definitions 'to provide new support beneath a wall or column without removing the building' or 'to facilitate the construction of foundations for a building that exists' is small. In order to illustrate the versatility of the ground freezing method for this purpose, the following accounts include some examples which do not in themselves truly satisfy the definitions, yet in principle could do so in appropriate circumstances.

(i) At Timmins in Northern Ontario, Canada, exploitation of an ore-body was commenced at the surface by open-pit mining, and also underground from a 900 m-deep shaft sunk within the only outcropping rockhead in the neighbourhood.

There being no further outcropping stratum capable of providing an adequate foundation for the 1500 m-deep number 2 shaft headframe, a deep excavation had to be made through the overburden of fill, muskeg (peat) and soft silty clay. The bedrock dipped from 10 m to 17 m depth across the diagonal of the required 21 m × 16 m headframe (see Figure 7.8).

A frozen enclosure through the overburden, comprising four arcs in plan, was establishing using a double row of freeze-tubes to 12 m depth, and a triple row at greater depths. Excavation of the unfrozen central core was undertaken by digger/backactor plant and the spoil pushed to one corner by dozer for removal to tipper trucks by crane-operated grab. After preparation of the rock surface, headframe erection was commenced using slipform methods. Then shaft sinking could proceed conventionally.

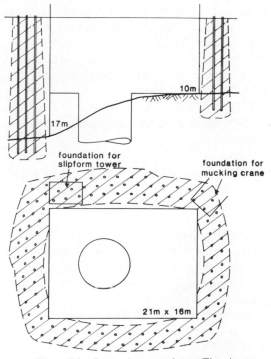

Figure 7.8 Open pit excavation at Timmins

Without ground freezing such an excavation would have needed extensive temporary support by sheet piling, framing and strutting with consequential interference to mucking and construction operations. Besides safeguarding the excavation the icewall also served as the stabilized support for the mucking crane at a shallow corner, and for the Alimak slipforming tower where the icewall was at its thickest.

(ii) In Washington DC (Anon., 1979), excavations for the foundation of a new office tower caused cracking and other damage to neighbouring property. Shoring, which was erected to brace the building, was not completely effective.

The whole length of the exposed sidewall was therefore temporarily supported by a frozen-ground retaining wall extending 11 m in depth, in the manner of Figure 7.2(c). Some 63 freeze-tubes were installed vertically and at various angles to freeze mixed strata comprising soft clay, silt and loose fine sand using a 26 TR trailer-mounted freeze plant, chilling calcium chloride brine.

(iii) At Blackpool (Maishman, 1973), on the other hand, it was feared that excavations to be made within a frame building, supported on shallow square footings to each column, would cause unacceptable distress to that structure.

The ground conditions consisted of 3.5 m of sand underlain by 2 m of peat, then a further 8 m of soft sandy silt to the basal stiff clay formation. Bored cast-in-situ piles were first constructed through the overburden to the stiff clay bearing stratum; the concreting was carried out to the eventual 6 m-below-surface pit floor level only. A frozen-ground icewall was then created around the intended excavation, extending down to the stiff clay, thus ensuring that the weak sandy silt (and the piles it then contained) could not be disturbed, e.g. by heave/buoyancy of the pit floor as the excavation reached its full depth. Once the freezing had been effected, the excavation could proceed over the full 12 m diameter until the prebored piles were exposed in the pit bottom. After casting of the pit structure had been completed, the frozen ground was allowed to thaw. The whole exercise was completed without affecting the existing frame structure.

(iv) In Gibraltar (Harris and Woodhead, 1978) large diesel-driven generating sets supported by shallow foundations and constructed on reclaimed land had suffered differential settlement in service. The requirement, when replacement of the generating sets became due, was to transfer their load through the fill to bedrock some 7 m below floor level. The foundation design called for twin piles, 2.4 m diameter under each 9 m × 4 m foundation block.

The filled ground consisted mainly of limestone rubble from the many tunnels driven in the rock, mixed with sands dredged from the seabed, a material too permeable to achieve dry conditions by pumping methods. The original foundation was first removed to just above the water table (sea level). Fourteen freeze-tubes were then installed by drilling to 6 m depth, giving 1 m penetration into the new foundation stratum, a mudstone bedrock. Refrigeration for each pile occupied 3 to 4 weeks of the whole 12-week programme.

The same principle could have been applied to create say eight piles of equivalent total load-carrying capacity beneath the original footing, had removal/replacement of the generator sets not been required.

(v) Near Wrexham, one case is recorded (Gregory and Maishman, 1973) where the process was used to safely abandon an old structure before new construction was commenced over the same site. This arose when a bypass to motorway standards was scheduled to traverse an old colliery site. Twin 300 m-deep mineshafts had stood open since mining ceased there in 1926; one of these shafts lay within the fencelines of the proposed new road. The standing water level in the flooded workings was only a few metres below ground level and coincided with the general groundwater level of the 40 m-thick alluvial overburden deposits.

Thus, to isolate the mineworkings from the effects of any subsequent fluctuation of the groundwater table, it was necessary to construct a reinforced concrete plug within a strong impermeable stratum below the saturated overburden. The shallowest suitable stratum occurred at 60 m below the surface.

To achieve this, the shaft was first backfilled with broken stone to the 60 m level. Twin 0.8 m-diameter sealed steel tubes were then floated into the shaft to rest on the stone filling; after placing freeze-tubes between the twin tubes and the shaft wall, the remaining annular space was filled with sand. Refrigeration of this saturated sand then excluded the groundwater from entering the shaft, and permitted the use of the twin tubes as access, mucking, service and ventilation shafts while excavation for and casting of the reinforced plug took place.

(vi) Metro construction in Antwerp and Brussels involved tunnelling beneath streets, buildings and other structures of various ages and descriptions. At several places the building foundations and the roof of the intended tunnel were in superficial deposits, often of unsaturated sand.

In open locations the sidewalls of the rectangular-section tunnels could usually be constructed as diaphragm walls, followed by cut-and-cover methods to excavate the tunnel space and construct the floor and roof without the need for ground treatment. Where this was not practicable due to the presence of occupied property, the strata above the tunnel roof and flanking the sidewalls were stabilized by ground freezing. From headings constructed in non-vulnerable locations, or within the protection of frozen ground, horizontal freeze-tubes were drilled over the intended roof. One or two arrays of parallel or fanned freeze-tubes were provided according to the thickness of frozen ground canopy required, the thickness necessary being a function of span and loading to be catered for—see Figure 7.9(a).

It had been established by tests that the frozen strength of the sand varied according to both its moisture content and the sub-zero freezing temperature. For example, at optimum moisture content the strength at a particular temperature was three times that at its natural moisture content (less than

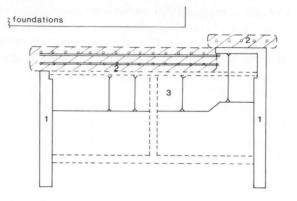

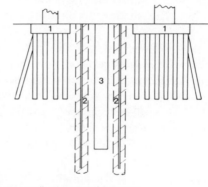

(a) Frozen roof over construction formed in headings

(b) Diaphragm wall constructed between
existing sensitive foundations

Figure 7.9 (*a*) Frozen roof over construction formed in headings. 1, flanking walls constructed under bentonite; 2, frozen roof (canopy); 3, excavation in headings with propped supports. (*b*) Diaphragm wall constructed between existing sensitive foundations. 1, piled foundations to existing railway bridge; 2, twin icewalls; 3, new diaphragm wall.

8%), while at optimum moisture content the strength at $-15°C$ was 1.4 times that at $-5°C$.

In view of the low natural moisture content, slow irrigation was applied to the area being stabilized during the primary freeze period to raise the frozen moisture content to a level that would result in the high strength needed to safeguard the structural loads to be supported. Adits were then excavated at regular spacing, and concreted; when this concrete had cured, the intermediate ground could be excavated in its turn, which, when the whole had been concreted, produced a contiguous roof construction.

At one location the metro tunnel had to pass beneath a railway bridge which was supported on piles. The flanking walls of the new tunnel could be constructed under bentonite, but they were required to pass between and very close to the piled footings without causing any disturbance to them—see Figure 7.9(b). This was achieved by forming twin icewalls, one either side of the intended bentonite wall, to act as retaining walls which would prevent movement of the piled foundations.

(vii) In São Paulo, Brazil (Dumont-Villares, 1956), settlement occurred very rapidly as a 26-storey building was nearing completion in 1942, and urgent measures became necessary to arrest the movement, eliminate tilt and restore the building to its original elevation.

São Paulo is located on a basin of Tertiary sediments, successively partially

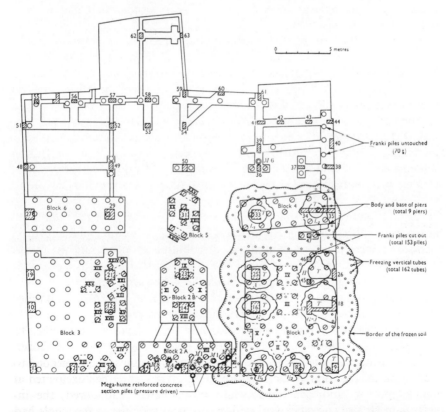

Figure 7.10 Plan showing area frozen for stabilizing, and the new piers (T). From Dumont-Villares (1953) with permission.

saturated clays, sands and silty sands which vary in thickness, strength and compressibility, saturated clayey sands of low to medium density, and decomposed then solid gneiss or granite at a depth of some 90 m. Considerable variations occur within short distances both horizontally and vertically, calling for careful investigation at all sites.

In accordance with recognized practice Franki piles were installed with their bulbs founded within the stiff clay layer identified over much of the site. Nothing untoward was observed during installation or testing of the piles, and construction of the building then proceeded rapidly without mishap until its full height was reached.

The significance and scale of the settlement was realized some five months after completion of the main structural work, when setting out of the lift guides was started. At that time the total settlement was about 60 mm, and tilt was 1:500 towards the front right-hand corner, the whole building moving monolithically. Investigation borings established that the settlements taking place resulted from the presence of a soft silty clay wedge which had not been detected before construction.

The primary task of arresting the tilting movement was achieved by ground freezing under the affected corner. A total of 162 freeze-tubes was placed in holes drilled though the heavily reinforced concrete floor slab and the underlying strata to a depth of 14 m. During placement of the freeze-tubes the rate of settlement increased alarmingly to a peak of 6 mm per day before commencement of refrigeration on 9 February 1942. The last freeze-tube was installed and commissioned on 25 May. During this $3\frac{1}{2}$-month period of increasing refrigerative effort the rate of settlement lessened, until on 19 June settlement ceased and the building became stable. Continuing refrigeration resulted in a small uplift recovery of 10 mm at the point of previous maximum settlement.

Preparations were then made to eliminate the tilt and restore the building as nearly as possible to its original elevation by jacking. A number of freeze-tubes were disconnected to ensure uniform distribution of effort, and to release capacity for additional freeze-tubes while two further columns were built. Several of the original Franki piles within the frozen area were by now under tension and had to be cut, while several columns near the frozen boundary were receiving increased loading. This dictated the provision of additional piles, and the 'Mega Hume' segmental reinforced type was used for this purpose.

Cast-in-situ mass concrete piles in belled pits were installed through the frozen ground into the deep sand to act as the permanent 5 kg/cm^2 (0.5 MPa) load support when the ground was allowed to thaw. Conventional inverted jacking methods, with steel wedges, were used to level the building on these piles and to take up changes during the thaw period which lasted some 18 months.

7.8 Summary

Ground freezing has played an increasing role in the civil engineering field generally, and underpinning problems specifically, in recent years, and may be expected to contribute there as well as in mining engineering in the future.

The advent of large-scale commercial development of liquid nitrogen as an inert refrigerant is a significant factor in the increasing popularity of freezing for small and emergency excavation problems. Speedy execution, coupled with minimal plant and power requirements at site, are undoubted advantages. The elimination of noise is environmentally attractive. Nevertheless, mechanical refrigeration is more attractive for large-scale applications and for those where the frozen state has to be retained for a long time.

References

1. Altounyan, P.F.R., Bell, M.J., Farmer, I.W. and Happer, C.J. (1982) Temperature, stress and strain measurements during and after construction of concrete linings in frozen sandstone. *Proc. ISGF '82*, Hanover, N.H., 343–348.
2. Andersland, O.B. and Anderson, D.M. (1978) *Geotechnical Engineering for Cold Regions*. McGraw-Hill, New York.
3. Anon. (1979) Soil is frozen to save Tippy Tavern. *Eng. News Record*, 10 May, 12.
4. Arvidson, W.D. and Morgernstern, N.R. (1977) Water flow induced by soil freezing. *Can. Geotech. J.* 14, 237–245.
5. Collins, S.P. and Deacon, W.G. (1972) Shaft sinking by ground freezing for the Ely Oyse–Essex scheme. *Proc. ICE*, May, 129–256.
6. Dumont-Villares, A. (1956) The underpinning of the 26-storey 'Companhia Paulista de Seguros' building, São Paulo, Brazil. *Géotechnique*, 1–14.
7. Gardner, A.R., Jones, R.H. and Harris, J.S. (1982) Strength and creep testing of frozen soils. *Proc. ISGF '82*, Hanover, N.H., 53–60.
8. Gardner, A.R., Jones, R.H. and Harris, J.S. (1984) A new creep equation for frozen soils and ice. *Cold Regions Sci. & Technol.* 9, 271–275.
9. Gregory, O. and Maishman, D. (1973) Motorway construction meets an unusual problem in old shaft treatment. *Proc. IMinE* (Manchester branch), February.
10. Harris, J.S. and Woodhead, F.A. (1978) Ground freezing for large-diameter foundation piers. *Consulting Engineer*, January.
11. Jumikis, A.R. (1966) *Thermal Soil Mechanics*. Chapter 11. Rutgers University Press, New Brunswick.
12. Lovell, C.W. (1957) Temperature effects on phase composition and strength of a partially frozen soil. *Highway Research Board Bull. 168*, Washington DC.
13. Maishman, D. (1975) Ground freezing (at Blackpool). In Bell, F.G. (ed.), *Methods of Treatment of Unstable Ground, Proc. Symp. Sheffield 1973*, Newnes-Butterworth, Sevenoaks, 159–171.
14. Sanger, F.J. and Kaplar, C.W. (1963) Plastic deformation of frozen soils. *Proc. Int. Conf. on Permafrost*, Purdue, 1963.
15. Sanger, F.J. and Sayles, F.H. (1978) Thermal and rheological computations for artificially frozen ground construction. In *1st Int. Symp. on Ground Freezing*, Bochum, 1978, 311–338. Reprinted in *Eng. Geol.* 13, 1–4.
16. Shuster, J.A. (1972) Controlled freezing for temporary ground support. *Proc. 1st Int. Conf. on Rapid Excavation and Tunnelling*, 1972, 863–894.
17. Vialov, S.S. (1966) Methods of determining creep, long term strength and compressibility characteristics of frozen soils. *Tech. trans. from Russian no. 1364*, Natl. Research Council of Canada.

8 Underpinning by chemical grouting

G.S. LITTLEJOHN

8.1 Historical introduction

The use of chemicals in grouting evolved logically from cement grouting practice where direct injection of neat cement into fine fissures or small pores was only partially successful. At Thorne in Yorkshire, for example, two shafts started in 1909 came to a standstill at a depth of 150 metres due to heavy water ingress through porous sandstone which contained fine fissures. With a background of proven experience from Hatfield colliery in 1911, the Belgian engineer François employed silicatization at Thorne in 1913, and this commercial success established the process in engineering practice. The technique involved the injection of sodium silicate and aluminium sulphate solution, after which neat cement grout was injected with comparable ease. François concluded that the chemical gel acted simply as a lubricant, which perhaps explains why he did not develop the system for the treatment of alluvium, in spite of the fact that the use of sodium silicate as a grout had been known since 1886 through a patent by Jesiorsky.[1] In reality the chemical gel filled the fine fissures and pores, thereby sealing the walls of the major fractures. Without such a seal and under high injection pressures the water would have been driven from the cement grout into the porous structure of the rock, leaving the grout to stiffen prematurely. Following the early commercial successes in shaft sinking with silicatization, the method was employed in many other countries, particularly South Africa.[2]

As a natural consequence of these successes mining engineers soon turned their attention to the grouting of finer-grained sandstones and sands as a cheaper and quicker alternative to the Poetsch freezing process then in use. The filtering effect of cement in fine-grained materials had been well known for some time through the work of Portier (1905),[3] the inventor of the cementation process for shaft sinking, so the need for a low-viscosity fluid to penetrate the pores and thereafter solidify by chemical reaction was understood. Although Lemaire and Dumont had patented a single-shot process based on dilute silicate and acid solution in 1909,[4] it was not until 1922 that Durnerin,[5] apparently unaware of the chemical grout patents, observed that in the field the reaction would require the use of two reagents, suggested those which would give a gelatinous precipitate of either silica gel or hydrated iron oxide, and then demolished his own proposals on practical grounds. Within three years the Dutch engineer Joosten had solved the practical problems by an ingenious method for the treatment of sands where small volumes of concentrated sodium silicate were injected in stages through a perforated pipe as the pipe was driven to the required depth. Subsequently, as the pipe was drawn back in the same stages a strong brine solution was injected (Figure 8.1). The brine displaced and reacted almost instantaneously with the silicate to form a soft gel in the pores, with the adsorbed film a hard dehydrated gel binding the sand grains together at their point of contact to form a sand mass with crushing strengths of 3 to $5 \, N \, mm^{-2}$.[6] The high cost of injecting two fluids and the close centres of holes (600 mm in sands) due to high initial viscosities led to a low viscosity system by Guttman who diluted the sodium silicate with sodium carbonate solution, but the main search was for a single-fluid grout of low viscosity which would set after a suitable time. In this respect the majority of commercial successes were based on sodium silicate, popular reagents including lime water, sodium bicarbonate and sodium aluminate. Whilst all gave a soft gel which greatly reduced permeability of the ground there was no appreciable gain in strength. Nevertheless such solutions were used on a large scale, e.g. 4530 tonnes of silicate injected by Rodio at Bou-Hanifia[7] in Algeria under the advice of Terzaghi. This project started in 1933, and it was here that Ischy used his invention, the tube à manchette, which permitted grouts of different properties to be injected in any order and at any interval of time from the same borehole (Figure 8.2).

Starting in 1934 Mayer,[8] at the Laboratoire du Bâtiment et des Travaux Publics, developed successfully a single fluid silicate grout with controlled gelling using hydrochloric acid and copper sulphate, and a cheaper version incorporating stabilized clay whose technical feasibility was confirmed at the Barrage du Sautet on the River Drac. The first large commercial success was in 1936 during the construction of the dam at Genissiat on the River Rhône.[9]

By this time the complex structures of alluvial deposits and methods of measuring permeability were becoming better understood following Terzaghi's early work on soil mechanics published in 1925, and in 1938 a simplified theory of injection into granular material was published by Maag[10] relating factors such as injection pressure, flow rate, density and viscosity of grout, ground porosity and permeability based on the assumption of spherical flow through homogeneous and isotropic material.

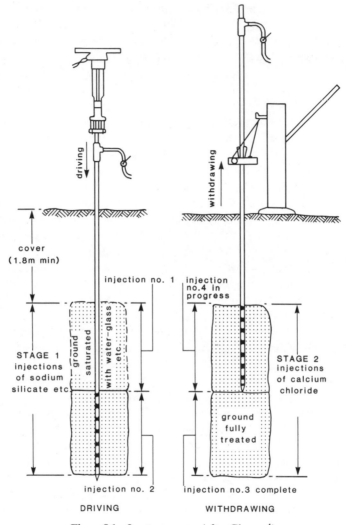

Figure 8.1   Joosten process (after Glossop[1]).

Whilst the 1939–45 war naturally hindered practical developments, the activity on patents covering new chemical formulations increased dramatically.[11] During the 1940s phenol–formaldehyde and resorcinol–formaldehyde systems evolved (phenoplasts), and by 1953 de Mello, Hauser and Lambe had filed a patent covering acrylate of polyvalent metal (AM-9). This American formulation, although now replaced by a non-toxic version, was unique as a waterproofing grout due to its very low viscosity (1.2 cP), excellent gel time control ranging from a minute to several hours, and its ability to treat fine silts.

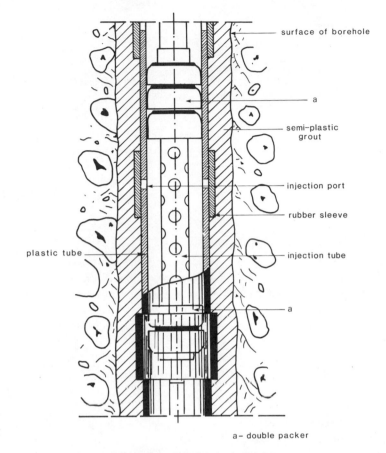

surface of borehole

a

semi-plastic
grout

injection port

rubber sleeve

plastic tube

injection tube

a

a – double packer

Figure 8.2 Ischy's tube à manchette.

On the practical front the early 1950s saw the establishment of chemical grouting as a recognized geotechnical process with particular regard to dam cut-offs and tunnel support, the most popular chemicals being silica-based, e.g. aureole grouting at Acif-el-Hammamam, Algeria (Figure 8.3). In this regard Soletanche created a hard silicate gel using an organic ester (ethylacetate)[12] in 1957, capable of producing grouted sand strengths of 2–3 N mm^{-2}. Over the same period the process of gelification of ligno-sulphonate using dichromate (chrome-lignins) received attention in England, Sweden and Russia.[12] These grouts provided good gel time control (5–120 min) and grouted sand strengths of 1–2 N mm^{-2}, but with a potential dermatitis risk to personnel.

In 1963 the state of the art in grouting was reviewed at the ICE Conference in London[13] and Table 8.1 illustrates the major commercial chemical grout systems considered practicable at that time.

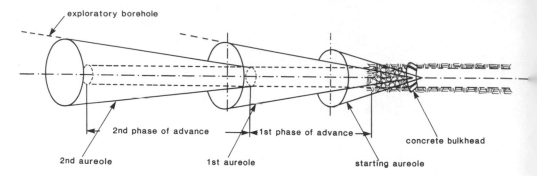

Figure 8.3   Pregrouting by aureoles.

Over the past two decades a great variety of chemical systems has been introduced into the grouting market covering a wide range of materials, properties and costs, but the basic objective has been to improve or replace existing grouts. Of particular note are the water reactive materials which gel or polymerize upon contact with water, such as TACSS introduced in Japan in 1967, with initial viscosity ranging ranging from 22 to 300 cP. Another polyurethane is CR250,[15] marketed by 3M in 1979 primarily as a sealant for leaking joints in sewers, in view of its remarkable elastic properties. Bearing in mind these recent innovations and the potential for wetting and drying in sewer sealing the durability of polyurethane grouts is a subject for study. In 1980 two low-toxic systems were introduced as replacements to AM-9. AC-400 grout[16] is an acrylate monomer with the same catalyst system as AM-9, giving a viscosity of 2 cP and grouted coarse sand strength of 0.2–0.3 N mm^{-2} (10% concentration). Injectite-80 is a polyacrylamide grout[17] which removes the toxicity problem at the expense of viscosity (50 cP) for a 10% concentration, but for short gel time mixes (20 s), as used in sewer sealing, grout strengths of nearly 1 N mm^{-2} are attained in 1 h. Current developments include inorganic reagents for sodium silicate in strengthening applications. There is also a general emphasis towards non-toxic systems which reflects the growing sensitivity to environmental hazards, both in the short-term handling of materials, and the long-term leaching of chemicals from the gel.

In this introduction on the historical development of chemical grouts up to the present time the writer has drawn liberally from the paper by Glossop (1961).[1] For the reader interested in further detail, reference can be made to the Progress Report of the ASCE Task Committee on Chemical Grouting (1957),[11] the ICE Symposium on Grouts and Drilling Muds in Engineering Practice (1963),[13] the ASCE Conference on Grouting in Geotechnical Engineering (1982)[18] and the 8th European Conference on

Table 8.1 Classification of grouts (after Skipp and Renner[14]).

Proprietary name (if used)	Basic composition	Type of action	Strength of gel or cement (lb in^{-2})*	Strength of treated soil (lb in^{-2})*	Reference
Joosten I	Sodium silicate, calcium chloride (2F)†	a, b, d‡	—	Up to 1000	H.J. Joosten R. Glossop
Joosten II	Sodium silicate, alkali dilution, calcium chloride (2F)	a, b, d		600	H.J. Joosten
Joosten III	Sodium silicate, heavy metal salt, ammoniacal colloid (1F)	a, b, d		120	H.J. Joosten
Guttman	Similar to Joosten II, sodium carbonate as alkali	a, b, d		200–700	I. Guttman R. Glossop
Rodio	Sodium silicate, lime water (1F)	a, b, d		100	K. Keil
Langer	Sodium silicate, heavy metal salt, coagulant	a, b, d		—	C.F. Kolbrunner
Polivka	Sodium silicate, sodium bicarbonate (1F)	a, b, d		70–100	J.J. Polivka
	Silicate–ethyl acetate (1F)	a, b, d	20–100	Up to 300	
	Resorcinol–formaldehyde (1F)	a, b, d	↑	Up to 300	
	Urea–formaldehyde (1F)	a, b, d	20–200	Up to 500	
AM-9	Acrylamide (1F)	a, b, d	—	Up to 300	R.L. Shiffman C.R. Wilson
	Calcium acrylate (1F)	a, b, d		—	J.J. Polivka
	Chrome–lignin (1F)	a, b, d		—	
	Polyester (1F)	a, b, c or b, c		—	P.H. Cardwell
Polythixon	Polyurethanes (1F)	a, b, c	20–200	Up to 500	P.H. Cardwell

*Literature gives little data on type and density of sands.
†1F = single-fluid; 2F = two-fluid.
‡a = void filler; b = adhesive; c = single-phase cement; d = two-phase cement.

J*

Soil Mechanics and Foundation Engineering 'Improvement of Ground' (1983).[19]

8.2 Ground investigation

Prior to any detailed design planning of a chemical grout treatment involving decisions on geometry of injection holes and choice of grouts, a ground investigation should be carried out.

The overall objective of the ground investigation is to provide a detailed geotechnical classification of the different ground types encountered together with their locations and thicknesses.

Where chemical grouting is envisaged, permeability and porosity data for each type of ground should be obtained along with hydraulic gradients and chemical properties of the ground water. The ground water details may influence choice of chemical formulation and extent of treatment, whilst the porosity dictates grout consumption. The coefficient of permeability (k) is the most useful single index of the groutability of soil or rock. For chemical grouts that are free of particles k influences the rate of injection, whilst for particulate grouts, permeability may set practical lower limits for grout injection by permeation, e.g.:

$5 \times 10^{-4}\,\mathrm{m\,s^{-1}}$ for cement grout
$1 \times 10^{-5}\,\mathrm{m\,s^{-1}}$ for clay chemical grout
$1 \times 10^{-6}\,\mathrm{m\,s^{-1}}$ for chemical grout.

Equally important, the measured ratio of ground permeability before and after treatment reflects the effectiveness of the grouting operation. In-situ short cell tests are preferred for permeability assessment of different soil horizons compared with a large scale drawdown measurement unless the latter is augmented by representative grading curves. For ground strengthening applications additional tests are required, e.g. shear strengths from tests on undisturbed samples or in-situ penetrometer or dilatometer values.

Broadly speaking, the data above are invariably lacking in quality and quantity, yet the information is vital when designing a chemical treatment and judging its effectiveness. A ground investigation is satisfactory only when it provides sufficient information to answer the following questions.

1. Can the ground be grouted?
2. For ground treatment what types and amounts of grout are required?
3. Following treatment what strength increase can be anticipated?

8.3 Principles of injection

Whilst ground is invariably irregular in nature, a theoretical appreciation of the injection process based on idealized isotropic conditions in the case of porous ground, nevertheless acts as a useful aid for grout selection and choice of appropriate technique during the assessment of the ground investigation results.

8.3.1 Permeation of porous ground

In permeation grouting chemical grout is injected into the fine pores of soils or rocks at pressures insufficient to disturb the ground structure. Under pressure the grout advances steadily, displacing air and water outwards, the direction of flow being determined by ground permeability, i.e. grout flows most readily into the zones offering least resistance.

In uniform isotropic soils spherical flow is observed and assuming Darcy's law and a Newtonian fluid, Raffle and Greenwood (1961)[20] show that the flow rate Q at a radius of penetration R is related to the hydraulic driving head H as follows:

$$H = \frac{Q}{4\pi k}\left[\mu\left(\frac{1}{r} + \frac{1}{R}\right) + \frac{1}{R}\right]$$

(8.1)

where k = ground permeability
μ = grout viscosity in centipoises
r = radius of spherical injection source (for a cylindrical injection source of length L and diameter D, $r = \frac{1}{2}\sqrt{LD}$ approx).

The time for the grout to penetrate to radius R is given by

$$t = \frac{nr^2}{kH}\left[\frac{\mu}{3}\left(\frac{R^3}{r^3} - 1\right) - \frac{\mu-1}{2}\left(\frac{R^2}{r^2} - 1\right)\right].$$

(8.2)

If the second component inside the main bracket is ignored, the relationship simplifies to the equation proposed by Maag in 1938.

The results of equation 8.2 are embodied in Figure 8.4 which illustrates how the radius of grout penetration increases with time for grout viscosities of 1 cP, 10 cP and 100 cP, respectively. Thus direct estimates can be made of the rate of progress of injection.

If a grout such as a clay-chemical has a shear strength (non-Newtonian fluid) then under constant injection pressure the opposing drag forces on the wetted surfaces of the ground structure gradually increase until the injection pressure is resisted, with no extra available to maintain viscous flow. According to Raffle and Greenwood the pressure gradient (i) required to overcome the Bingham yield strength may be expressed as

$$i = 4\tau_s/d$$

(8.3)

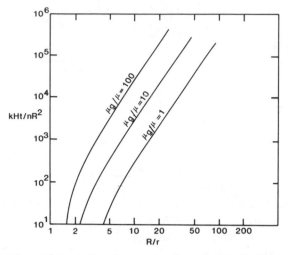

Figure 8.4 Dependence of penetration time on viscosity ratio (after Raffle and Greenwood[20])

k = soil permeability
H = hydraulic head
t = time
n = porosity of soil
r = radius of source
R = radius of grout at time t
μ = viscosity of water
μ_g = viscosity of grout.

where τ_s = Bingham yield stress
  and d = effective diameter of the average pore.

To maintain an advancing flow an additional pressure gradient is required.

With reference to equation 8.3 the average pore diameter can be estimated from the Kozeny equation.

$$d = 2\sqrt{\frac{8\mu k}{\delta_w gn}} \tag{8.4}$$

where δ_w = density of water
  and g = acceleration due to gravity.

Combining equations 8.3 and 8.4, Table 8.2 indicates typical average pore diameters for different permeabilities assuming a porosity of 25%. For the specific case of silts, experiments by Garcia-Bengochea et al. (1978)[21] indicate that the predominant pore size is approximately equal to the effective size (D_{10}) of the soil.

Table 8.2 Relationship between typical average pore diameter and permeability.

k $(\mathrm{m\,s^{-1}})$	d (mm)
1×10^{-2}	0.36
1×10^{-3}	0.114
1×10^{-4}	0.036
1×10^{-5}	0.0114
1×10^{-6}	0.0036

N.B. In ground where the pore or fissure is less than $3\,\mu\mathrm{m}$ chemical grouting is generally impracticable and uneconomic.

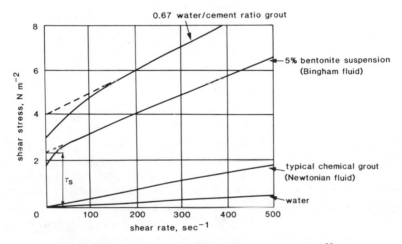

Figure 8.5 Flow properties of typical grouts (after Bell[22]).

For a ground permeability of 1×10^{-5} m s^{-1} and given a 5% bentonite solution (Figure 8.5), with a yield of value of $2\,\mathrm{N\,m^{-2}}$ then an injection head of 7 bars $(700\,\mathrm{kN\,m^{-2}})$ is required for each metre of grout penetration just to overcome the inherent yield strength. For convenience Table 8.3 shows approximate hydraulic gradients to maintain flow in Bingham-type fluids.

Where injection pressures must be limited to avoid ground disturbance and heave then there is a limiting radius of penetration R_L given by

$$R_L = \frac{\delta_w g H d}{4\tau_s} + r. \tag{8.5}$$

Table 8.3 Hydraulic gradient to maintain flow in non-Newtonian grouts (after Scott[23]).

Soil permeability (m s^{-1})	Yield value (N m^{-2})	Hydraulic gradient
10^{-2}	1	1.2
	10	12
	100	120
	1000	1200
10^{-3}	1	4
	10	40
	100	400
	1000	—
10^{-4}	1	12
	10	120
	100	1200
	1000	—
10^{-5}	1	40
	10	400
	100	4000
	1000	—

Using such expressions design curves may be drawn to create optimum injection hole patterns. For chemical grouting of alluvium, typical final spacings range from 0.5 to 1.5 m on a triangular or rectangular grid.

Whilst chemicals are marketed as pure solutions, they invariably contain particles up to 20 μm say, which may block off fine pores in the ground. Based on empirical rules similar to filter criteria, D_{15} (soil) should be greater than $25D_{85}$ (grout) for successful permeation. In this regard it is noteworthy that silt impurities in commercial bentonite may have particles up to 50 μm. Where particles may affect the efficiency of treatment of fine-grained rocks and soils, a more refined chemical is required, or alternatively the cruder chemical should be clarified by centrifuge.

Bearing in mind that ground is heterogeneous then for permeation of soils grout may penetrate initially the more open structures at the expense of the lower permeability zones. As a result in practice, predetermined quantities related to porosity are normally injected in phases as the hole spacing is gradually reduced, the objective of the subsequent injections being to progressively treat the finer materials and thereby tighten up the ground. In planning a sequence of injections it is normal to commence grouting through holes spaced at intervals 2 to 3 times the final spacing. By this method of 'split spacing' (Figure 8.6) the treatment is less dependent ultimately on the theoretical design and more reliant on the observed effectiveness of the successive phases of treatment.

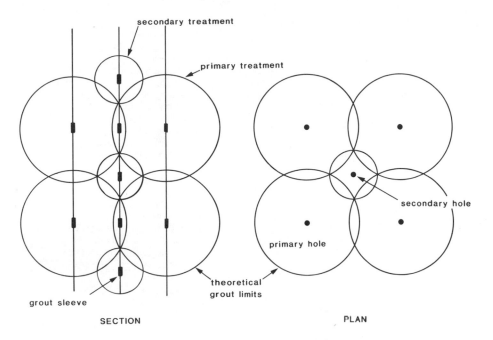

Figure 8.6 Pattern of primary and secondary injections (split-spacing).

8.4 Grout systems

8.4.1 Grout selection

While most of the recent developments in chemical grouting technology have been in the field of single-fluid low-viscosity systems capable of penetrating fine-grained materials, soil and rock formation vary significantly in terms of permeability and porosity, the former being particularly sensitive to small changes in void size. The selection of the most suitable chemical grouts is therefore largely a matter of judgement on the part of the experienced engineer, and he should also be aware of the range of grout suspensions available, since considerable economies can result from the use of these cheaper grouts in advance of the more costly and penetrative chemicals.

Table 8.4 contains common grout compositions which are currently in use, and in judging how best to meet a performance specification, the following aspects should be taken into account.

1. Extent and quality of ground investigation with particular reference to permeability and porosity.
2. Optimum injection method and hole pattern.
3. Availability of grout materials.

Table 8.4 Grouts used in alluvial grouting (after Skipp[24]).

Suspensoids	Two-shot solutions	Single-shot solutions
Cement	Sodium silicate–	Chrome–lignin, Sumisol*,
Cement–sand	calcium chloride	T.D.M.
Cement–clay	Hydrochloric acid–	Sodium silicate–sodium
Cement–bentonite	urea formaldehyde	bicarbonate
Cement–bentonite, P.F.A.	monomer	Sodium silicate–sodium
Waste mine slurries		aluminate
Bentonite–gel (with sodium		Sodium silicate–ethyl acetate†
silicate and acid phosphate)		Sodium silicate–mixed esters
		(Durcisseur*)
		Sodium silicate–formamide (base)
		(Siroc*)
		Sodium silicate–oxalate salt
		(Cemex)†
		Resorcinol–formaldehyde (acid
		or alkali catalysis)†
		Polyphenolic–formaldehyde,
		alkali catalyst (MQA4*, MQ5*,
		Terranier†)
		Acrylamide, AM9*, Progil
		R.1295*

*Proprietary grouts on sale.
†Patent protected.

4. Viscosity—time development of grout including sensitivity to temperature, dilution and mix proportioning errors.
5. Stability of grout in-situ.
6. Degree of saturation of ground during service including risk and effect of grout desiccation.
7. Chemical composition of groundwater.
8. Permanence of grout in-situ.
9. Toxicity of grout and chemical components and working environment.
10. Aggressivity of grout and chemical components towards plant and equipment.
11. Residual permeability or strength of grouted ground.
12. Degree of site supervision required including sophistication of systems.
13. Overall cost including materials, mixing and injection.

In practice the in-situ permeability of the ground dictates initially the technical options available in terms of grout selection (Table 8.5, Figure 8.7) but thereafter overall cost dominates final choice of system (Table 8.6).

Table 8.5 Grouting limits of common mixes (after Caron[25]).

Type of soils	Coarse sands and gravels	Medium to fine sands	Silty or clayey sands, silts
Soil characteristics:			
Grain diameter	$D_{10} > 0.5$ mm	$0.02 < D_{10} < 0.5$ mm	$D_{10} < 0.02$ mm
Specific surface	$S < 100$ cm^{-1}	100 cm$^{-1} < S < 1000$ cm^{-1}	$S > 1000$ cm^{-1}
Permeability	$k > 10^{-3}$ m s^{-1}	$10^{-3} > k > 10^{-5}$ m s^{-1}	$k < 10^{-5}$ m s^{-1}
Type of mix	Bingham suspensions	Colloid solutions (gels)	Pure solutions (resins)
Consolidation grouting	Cement $(k > 10^{-2}$ m s$^{-1})$ Aerated mix	Hard silica gels: double-shot: Joosten (for $k > 10^{-4}$ m s^{-1}) single-shot: Carongel Glyoxol Siroc	Aminoplastic Phenoplastic
Impermeability grouting	Aerated mix Bentonite gel Clay gel Clay/cement	Bentonite gel Lignochromate Light carongel Soft silica gel Vulcanizable oils Others (Terranier)	Acrylamide Aminoplastic Phenoplastic

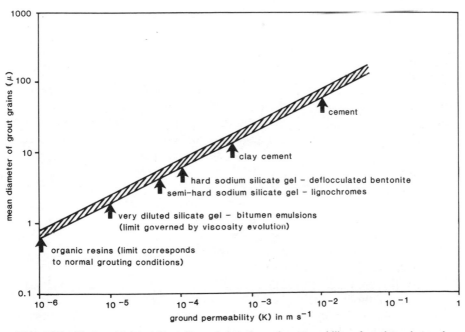

Figure 8.7 Limits of injectability of grouts based on the permeability of sands and gravels (after Cambefort[26]).

Table 8.6 Relative material costs of grout formulations.

Formulation	Relative cost of materials
Cement–bentonite	
w/c = 3, 5% bentonite by wt. of water	1.0
w/c = 2, 3% bentonite by wt. of water	1.3
w/c = 1, 1% bentonite by wt. of water	2.3
Cement	
(w/c = 0.5)	3.4
Silicate–bentonite	
20% bentonite, 7% silicate (by wt. of water)	1.3
Silicate–chloride (Joosten)	4.0
Silicate–ester	
37% silicate, 4.4% ester (by volume)	5.0
47% silicate, 5.6% ester (by volume)	6.5
Silicate–aluminate	
46% silicate, 1.4% aluminate (by weight)	5.0
Phenol–formaldehyde	
13% (by volume)	10.5
19% (by volume)	15.3
Acrylate	
10% (by weight)	18.5
Resorcinol–formaldehyde	
21% (by volume)	23.0
28% (by volume)	31.0
Polyacrylamide	
5% (by volume)	20.0
10% (by volume)	40.0

8.4.2. Viscosity

Bearing in mind the important distinction between suspensions (particulate structures—Bingham fluids) and solutions (Newtonian fluids—see Figure 8.5), then subject to specified limiting injection pressures related to depth of overburden, chemical grout viscosity–time development curves (Figure 8.8) in conjunction with flow equations, determine hole patterns and the time of injection (Figure 8.9).

The viscosity of chemical grouts varies with the concentration of the reactive chemicals (Figure 8.10), and as some of these grouts contain minute particles in suspension it is perhaps more correct to use the term apparent viscosity in such cases. Temperature increases can reduce initial viscosities but the reductions are marginal and quickly compensated by the accelerated gelling process.

Generally speaking, chemical grouts with viscosities less than 2 cP can permeate without trouble ground with a permeability as low as $1 \times 10^{-4}\,\mathrm{m\,s^{-1}}$. For higher viscosities of say 20 cP it may be necessary to restrict the grout application to more permeable ground or reduce hole spacing for the same gel time.

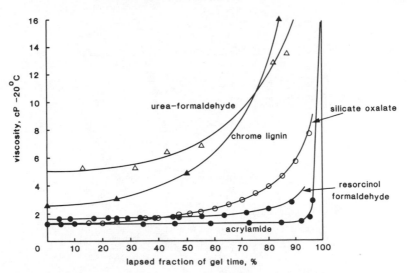

Figure 8.8 Growth of viscosity in period before gelation (modified after James[27]).

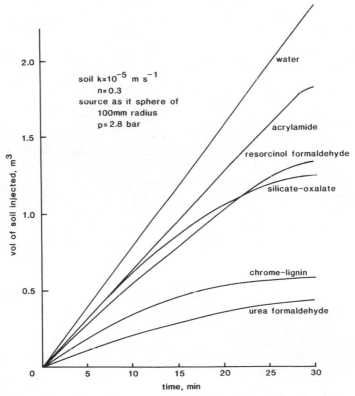

Figure 8.9 Relative volumes of soil filled when injection continued until gelation (modified after James[27]).

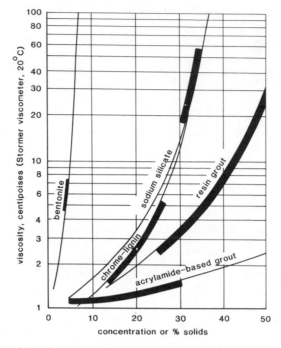

Figure 8.10   Viscosities of various grouts. Heavy lines indicate the solution concentrations normally used in the field (after Karol[4]).

8.4.3 Setting time

Setting or gel time is commonly regarded as the time between initial mixing or addition of the catalyst and the formation of a gel. Between initial mixing and attainment of the hardened state a number of inter-mediate times may be distinguished on an arbitrary basis.

1. Limiting injection time, at which the apparent viscosity has increased to the extent that injection becomes uneconomically slow.
2. Zero displacement time, when the grout has attained sufficient strength to resist displacement under the imposed hydraulic gradients in the formation.
3. Setting time, defined by some empirical test, e.g. no flow from upturned flask or 100 cP for low viscosity system (2 cP). This time may be used as a quality control for grout mixed on site and on occasions dictates the limiting injection time e.g., 75% of setting time.
4. Fully cured time at which final properties have been developed and the chemical reaction has ceased.

The setting time of most chemical grouts can be varied from minutes to hours, but is temperature-sensitive e.g., gel time halved for temperature increase of 10°C. Traditional control is by concentration of solids although catalysts are also used. For greater concentrations the set is reduced but the effects of dilution in flowing groundwater may extend the set again. Under normal circumstances setting times of 45–90 minutes are employed to give adequate time for mixing, pumping and placement. Where setting times are less than 30 minutes or ambient temperatures are high (>30°C) proportioning pump systems are preferred which delay the mixing of chemical components until the injection point.

In design planning choice of setting time is primarily influenced by grout volume to be injected, ground permeability, groundwater conditions and temperature.

8.4.4 Stability

Many single-fluid chemical grouts are subject to syneresis, i.e. the expulsion of water from the gel. If this property is present to a significant extent new seepage channels can be created even if the voids within a formation are filled initially. In silicate-based grouts exhibiting syneresis, water exudes from the gel within a few hours of setting and the process stabilizes generally after 3 to 4 weeks. Syneresis can however be controlled readily in the mix formulation by increasing the concentration of the silicate and the coefficient of neutralization.

In practice the degree of syneresis for a given grouted material is a function of the ratio of volume to surface area within the grouted structure, since bonding of the gel and solid surface resists internal shrinkage stresses and thereby reduces grout volume change. As a consequence, grouts which may be unsuitable for coarse gravels may be entirely appropriate for fine sands (Figure 8.11). Where grouts exhibiting high syneresis in-situ have been employed the consequence for the split spacing technique is greater grout consumptions in the subsequent injection phases, e.g. secondary and tertiary stages.

8.4.5 Strength of grouted formation

Chemical grouting of a cohesionless soil has the effect of increasing cohesion whilst the angle of internal friction remains sensibly the same (Figure 8.12). The magnitude of the cohesion depends upon the grout type injected, and several researchers over a period of time (Schiffman and Wilson, 1958;[28] Skipp and Renner, 1963;[14] Warner, 1972;[29] Farmer, 1975;[30] Krizek et al., 1982[31]) have published the results of triaxial testing of soils impregnated with various grout systems. In general, strength increases with increasing density and decreasing effective grain size (D_{10}). Well-graded soils have higher strengths than uniform soils of the same effective grain size.

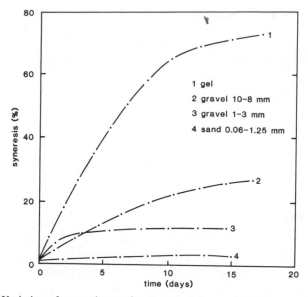

Figure 8.11   Variation of syneresis as a function of grain size; 60% silicate–ethyl acetate gel (after Caron[25]).

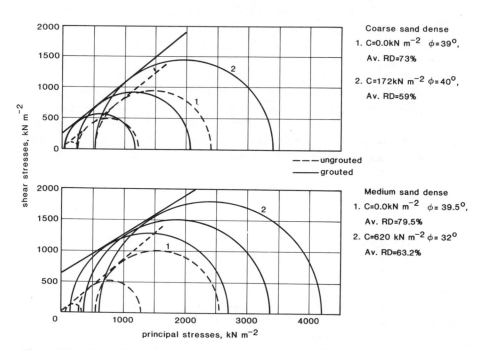

Figure 8.12   Drained triaxial test results for silicate-grouted coarse and medium sands (after Skipp and Renner[14]).

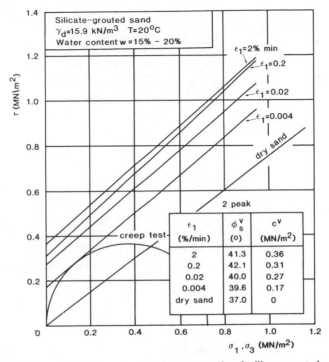

Figure 8.13 Influence of strain rate on shear strength of silicate-grouted sand (after Stetzler[33]).

Most published strength results are taken from unconfined compression tests but there is a lack of standardization on sample size or strain rate. Since the gels are visco-elastic their properties are strain dependent and increase in strain rate increases strength,[32] so that quoted laboratory strengths may be exaggerated when subsequently the treated ground is subjected to a slow rate of loading as in some underpinning applications. Figure 8.13 illustrates the significance of strain rate on the shear strength of silicate grouted sand. Much of the literature also reports dry strengths, where water in the grout is lost through desiccation and the grout matrix shrinks. In such circumstances the intergranular bond may increase and again the stronger results which are recorded may be totally misleading. Since the vast majority of chemical treatments take place in saturated or damp conditions, strength testing should simulate the environment concerned in order to produce relevant data.

In this regard alternating wet and dry cycles in service can be particularly detrimental.[29] In-situ tests or tests on undisturbed samples from full-scale grouting programmes are rare, but a comprehensive field assessment of silicate grouted sands has recently been published by Davidson and Perez[34] covering a variety of engineering properties before and after grouting including in-situ, density, horizontal stress, elastic modulus, shear strength, creep and permeability.

In strong rocks the ultimate set strength of grout is not usually a design consideration since rock is normally self-supporting in applications such as open excavations or tunnels, provided water ingress is controlled.

8.4.6 Creep of grouted formation

Chemically grouted soils are subject to creep, the magnitude depending to some extent upon the ratio of applied stress to inherent strength.[29] According to Karol,[4] limited data suggest that for unconfined tests negligible creep will occur for ratios less than 25%. For confined tests at K_0 'at rest' lateral pressure the ratio may be increased to 50%. These ratios give some guidance on appropriate load safety factors in design, but much more research is required generally on stress–strain–time behaviour to ensure that predictions are based on reproducible test results from representative samples.[35]

8.4.7 Resistance of grout to extrusion

Once injected into pores or fissures a grout must have sufficient strength to resist displacement by hydraulic gradient. If τ_f is the shear strength of the set gel the limiting hydraulic gradient (i) to initiate extrusion can be estimated by reference to equations 8.3 and 8.4.

$$i = \frac{4\tau_f}{d\delta_w g}.$$
(8.7)

In the case of a grouted cut-off the hydraulic gradient (i) is calculated as the maximum differential head divided by the width of the curtain. From Table 8.3 it is clear that the demand for high shear strength is greatest in ground of high permeability. Traditionally, grouted cut-offs in alluvium are designed conservatively for a hydraulic gradient of 3 to 5.

Once the grouted cut-off has been designed to resist extrusion, in certain applications involving very high hydraulic gradients e.g. grout sealing around deep mine shafts, the choice of grout must also take account of creep properties.

8.4.8 Permanence

If a grout treatment is required to be permanent, the set grout must not deteriorate with time. It should be resistant to chemical attack and dissolution by groundwater, particularly under an hydraulic gradient.

Chemical grouts based upon an aqueous solution may redissolve on long-term contact with groundwater and the process of dissolution governs the permanence of the grout treatment.

Defining chemical grout permanence as the period of time after which a grout treatment fails to meet its intended function, Hewlett and Hutchinson (1983)[36] suggest a 1–2 order increase in residual permeability for water stopping applications, and a loss of 50% gel forming solids in strengthening work, which for the common formulations is equivalent to a reduction in gel strength of up to 40%.

Slow percolation of groundwater through a gel (assuming typical gel permeabilities of $10^{-10}\,\mathrm{m\,s^{-1}}$, or less) causes the leaching water to become progressively more saturated with dissolved gel solids, and this in turn reduces further gel dissolution. However, as the grout dissolves, the permeability and hydraulic gradient increase, both of which will cause the process to accelerate. In general, where water percolates through the grout, e.g. mine shaft lining, the dissolution or disintegration of the gel will be long-term, even at high pressure gradients.

On the other hand where stratified ground is partially treated with grout, e.g. untreated silts interbedded with grouted sands, water flow through the silt can wash the gel surface of the grouted sand. In this case the saturation solubility of dissolving material may not be met and gel removal may be sustained resulting in reduced grout treatment properties.

According to Hewlett and Hutchinson, material residing within the gel network can move through the gel either due to the passage of water resulting from an hydraulic gradient and/or as a result of concentration gradients of dissolved material causing diffusion. The rate at which the gel structure actually dissolves (S) and the rate at which the dissolved material diffuses through the gel structure to the outside (D) can be measured in the laboratory, and if the mechanism of dissolution is diffusion-controlled, the grout retracts from its outer face over a period of time leaving behind untreated ground (Figure 8.14a). Tests to date indicate that weak silicate/oxalate and silicate/bicarbonate gels suffer face retraction, whilst in the case of chrome lignin, phenoplast, aminoplast and acrylamide gels the rate of diffusion exceeds the rate of dissolution, i.e., the mechanism is dissolution-controlled, and the gel structure gradually weakens but retains its overall dimensional structure (Figure 8.14b). In underpinning work the grout treatment is invariably temporary and permanence is not a major concern. As a consequence, cheaper and more dilute systems are often employed in practice.

Overall, the soundest defence is good grouting practice to ensure maximum void filling which in turn precludes access of aggressive water to the grout. Choice of gels which do not suffer shrinkage nor collapse by syneresis helps to reduce decay and in the field, completion of each grouting phase with gradually increasing injection pressures is beneficial.

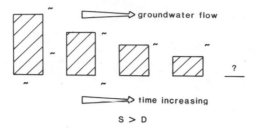

S > D

(a) Face retraction

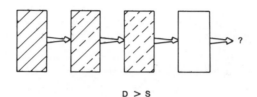

D > S

(b) Volume unchanged

Figure 8.14   Types of grout dissolution (after Hewlett and Hutchinson[36]).

8.4.9 Health and safety aspects

Although there are few accounts of harm or damage, instances of skin reactions have occasionally been reported, always in association with poor hygiene and ineffective clothing. From Japan there have been reports of environmental pollution caused by the use of acrylic and acrylamide grouts.

When presenting the virtues of a product or material, the chemical supplier should at the same time describe as far as possible any hazards likely to arise from its use and the conditions when it will not function properly.

Chemical constituents should be labelled for toxicological, explosive (flashpoint), flammable (boiling point), corrosive, cytoxic (interferes with cell division) and environmental hazards. In this regard the materials used for ground treatment have recently been identified by CIRIA,[37,38] and a guide to the potential hazards to people and the environment is provided.

Generally speaking, toxic hazards from the use of grouts are negligible after gelation since practical hydraulic gradients are incapable of removing significant quantities of grout material from such impervious materials. The greatest toxic hazard is to the workforce and due to spillage of ummixed chemicals and cleaning plant following injection.

8.5 Grouting operations

Once the purpose of grouting, choice of grout and hole pattern have been defined, open grout holes are drilled and prepared for treatment or alternatively the grouting pipes are drilled or jetted to the appropriate depth.

Grout is normally introduced into the ground in one of four ways, choice being dictated by ground conditions and the degree of control required for grout placement into different horizons:

(1) into an open hole in self-supporting ground through pipes caulked at the surface;

(2) through an injection pipe held in place in the hole or casing by a packer (Figure 8.15);

(3) from a pipe driven into the ground and withdrawn as injection proceeds (Figure 8.1);

(4) through a pipe left in place in the ground, as with a tube à manchette (Figure 8.2).

Chemical grouting rates are not large and injection hole diameters generally lie in the range 20 to 100 mm, with hole spacings of 0.5 to 2.5 metres. Where holes are divided into stages for localized treatment of horizons, lengths normally vary from 5 metres in deep rock to 0.25 metres in tube à manchette grouting of highly stratified alluvium.

In terms of grout batching, mixing and pumping, installations can vary from high-speed colloidal mixers[39] which can be used effectively for both powder compositions and single-fluid chemical grouts, in conjunction with in-line grout pumps, to mixing/pump stations holding stock solutions and incorporating automatic dosing systems, based on either volume dosing pumps or flow rate control valves. All these systems are based on in-line pumping of the grout but, as already described, in high ambient temperatures or where short gel times are employed, in-line proportioning

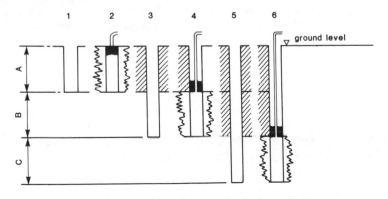

Figure 8.15 Stage and packer grouting in descending stages.

pumps are recommended where the constituent chemical solutions of two-component systems are pumped separately but in the correct proportions to a mixing head at the injection point.

Grout monitoring of flow and pressure ranges from simple visual observations of pressure gauges and pump stroke counters and manual recording, to sophisticated fully automatic continuous recording systems. During grouting operations it is important to maintain on a daily basis the following records for each stage of injection.

Date
Hole number
Depth of injection
Period of injection
Grout type and consumption
Injection pressure at inlet
Remarks e.g., uplift and surface leakage.*

When these records are systematically plotted on sections as the work proceeds, the charts provide an instant picture of progress and tightening-up as the injection sequence progresses (primary→secondary→tertiary). For each major injection phase, pre- and post-treatment water tests should be carried out where reduced permeability is the design objective. For strength improvement, penetrometer tests are most commonly employed (Figure 8.16) and a two-fold increase reflects good grout treatment. Crosshole shear wave velocity measurements have been reported by Davidson and Perez[34] to be effective in determining grout penetration in soil. A back-analysis of grout consumption against ground porosity is also useful for comparison with the design assumptions.

8.6 Applications

To illustrate that chemical grouting is now a well-established geotechnical process for the strengthening of ground in relation to underpinning and improving the loadbearing characteristics of foundations, case records are described which have been drawn from civil engineering practice over the past 25 years.

8.6.1 Ground treatment at Wuppertal, West Germany[40]

Deep excavations were required through 7 metres of water-bearing alluvium immediately adjacent to existing 4- and 8-storey buildings. The alluvium comprised a continuous grading from cobbles to fine sands, with

---

*Surface leakages indicate that further grouting will be ineffective and injection should cease until the grout in-situ has set.

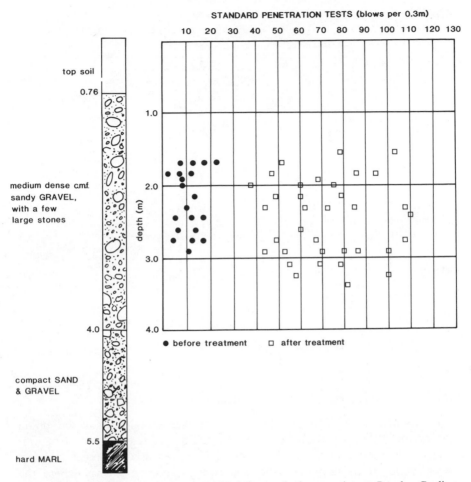

Figure 8.16 Standard penetrometer results before and after grouting at Rugeley Cooling Tower, England.

a permeability in the region of $10^{-4}\,\mathrm{m\,s^{-1}}$, and overlying a hard meta-morphic schist.

To protect the properties against loss of ground during excavation, a grouted wall solution (Figure 8.17) was accepted. Initially, clay–cement grout was injected through pipes C to fill the larger voids and limit the spread of the more expensive chemical grout on the excavation side. Thereafter, silicate–acetate grout was injected through pipes A and B. Contact grouting by clay–cement was also undertaken immediately under the foundation to ensure the prior filling of any major voids at this location.

K

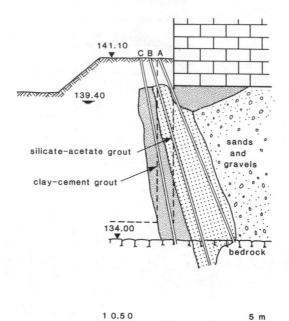

Figure 8.17 Ground treatment at Wuppertal, West Germany.[40]

8.6.2 *Increase of formation strength, Minneapolis, Minnesota*[4]

On this project, a 50-metre brick chimney was founded on wood piling which had deteriorated above the water table, and reduced the structural support to the foundation slab. Figure 8.18 shows how chemical grouting was employed to strengthen the underlying sands to a level where the structural load from the foundation could be transferred to the sound portion of the piles below the water table. A silicate-based grout was used for the main strengthening and injected within an outer curtain of calcium chloride which acted as a quick-setting hardener and thereby reduced wastage of sodium silicate.

8.6.3 *Ground strengthening at East Greenwich sewer, London*[41]

In advance of driving a new tunnel in water-bearing sands and gravels under a length of main road with many services overhead and an old brick sewer alongside (Figure 8.19), grouting from the surface was carried out using the tube à manchette method. Initially, bentonite–cement was injected followed by silicate–acetate. Of particular interest is the use of a diluted silicate–acetate in the zone of excavation for the new sewer, to reduce the mechanical strength of the treated ground and thereby ease the

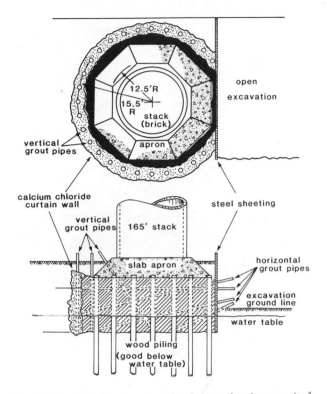

Figure 8.18 Strengthening of sand to increase bearing capacity.[4]

miners' task. As a result of the grouting the required air pressure was reduced which in turn avoided the risk of ground loss or disruption via loss of air or water ingress.

8.6.4 Reduction in pile settlement at Jeddah, Saudi Arabia[42]

Large-diameter piles (960–1200 mm) founded at a depth of 11 metres were designed in end bearing for working loads up to 5800 kN and a specified limiting settlement of 80 mm at 1.5 times working load, but preliminary pile tests (Nos. 190 and 214—see Figure 8.20) indicated excessive settlement caused primarily by ground disturbance beneath the pile during construction. To treat the variable low-permeability silty sand ($k = 1 \times 10^{-5}$ to $5 \times 10^{-7} \text{ m s}^{-1}$), a tube à manchette was installed through the base of each pile (Figure 8.21) after which resorcinol–formaldehyde chemical grout was injected in a controlled sequence to form an enlarged base of strengthened soil.

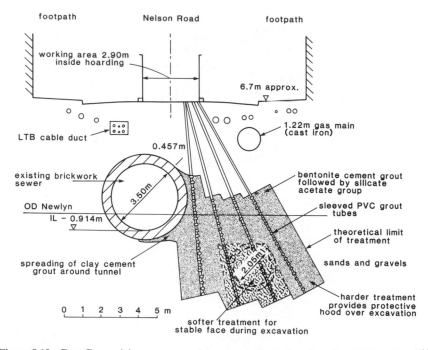

Figure 8.19 East Greenwich sewer: ground treatment. Typical section along Nelson Road.[41]

During production grouting 349 piles were injected using 338 5000 litres of resorcinol–formaldehyde grout. Subsequent loading tests of piles (Figure 8.20), although limited in number, were taken at random (Piles Nos. 18, 114 and 166) and confirmed that high-capacity shallow piles could be constructed economically with grout consolidation compared with much longer friction piles.

8.6.5 *Underpinning of multistorey blocks, Paris*[43]

At the rue de Monttessuy in Paris, a 3.5 m deep excavation required for a new electric substation was planned with multistorey blocks on three sides. Grouting was employed firstly to create an impermeable curtain round the site extending down to impermeable marls (Figure 8.22) and secondly to strengthen the soil beneath the adjacent foundations thereby underpinning the buildings and reducing risk of settlement during excavation.

Voids which existed beneath the old basement floors were filled with clay–cement, followed by a strong silicate–acetate injection into the sand and gravel immediately adjacent to the excavation. A weaker silicate–aluminate grout was employed in the lower horizon of alluvium to form

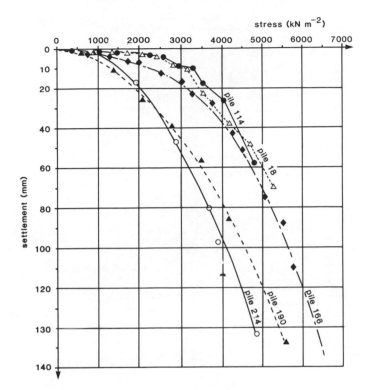

Figure 8.20 Pile test results showing applied stress *v.* head settlement.[42]

the cut-off. Subsequent excavation proceeded without difficulty and the silicate–acetate treatment was so hard that side trimming by pneumatic pick was necessary.

Other successful examples of underpinning include Great Cumberland Place,[44] Rugeley cooling tower (UK), Maryland National Bank (USA),[45] Austrian National Bank (Vienna),[46] and Timisoara Opera (Rumania).[47]

8.7 Conclusions

In fine-grained ground formations chemical grouting is an established engineering expedient for ground impermeabilization and strengthening. In such circumstances, grouting can be indispensable in tunnels and deep excavations as a temporary support and for underpinning buildings and foundations as a permanent ground strengthening.

Nevertheless, after 60 years grouting remains an art where field experience counts. Local variations in the ground cannot be predetermined and a flexible attitude should be maintained at the expense of rigorous

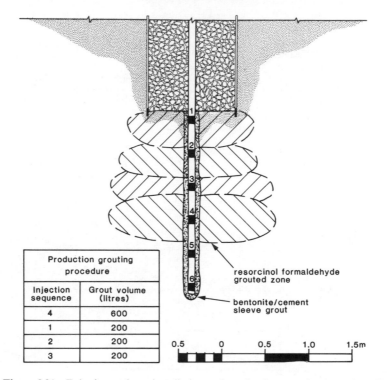

Production grouting procedure	
Injection sequence	Grout volume (litres)
4	600
1	200
2	200
3	200

resorcinol formaldehyde grouted zone

bentonite/cement sleeve grout

0.5   0   0.5   1.0   1.5m

Figure 8.21   Tube à manchette installation and production grouting procedure.[42]

specification of techniques, so that variations can be implemented where appropriate, to improve the engineering result.

Over the past two decades in particular with the introduction of more sophisticated single-fluid grouts and development of injection techniques, there has been a steady reduction in grout material quantity injected per unit volume of ground and a reduction in the number and intensity of grout holes considered necessary. Both these reductions are indicative of a growing confidence in the efficiency and effectiveness of grouting which augurs well for the future.*

---

*However, there is still no relaxation in the quest by Scottish engineers for a single-fluid grout with the viscosity of water and strength of concrete, where water is the most expensive constituent.

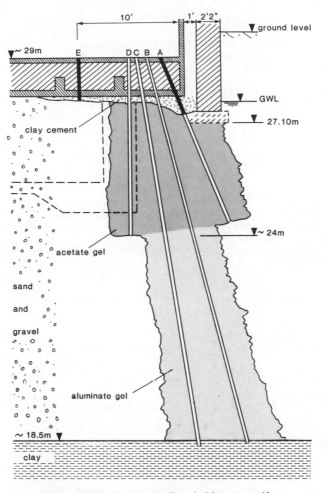

Figure 8.22 Grouting at Rue de Monttessuy.[43]

References

1. Glossop, R. (1961) The invention and development of injection processes. Part II: 1850–1960. *Geotechnique* 11 (4) 255–279.
2. Atherton, F.G. and Garrett, W.S. (1959) The history of cementation in shaft sinking. *Symposium on Shaft Sinking and Tunnelling*, Institution of Mining Engineers, London.
3. Portier (1905) Cimentation des terrains aquifères en vue du creusement des puits. *Congres. Int. Mines*, Liège. Sect. des Mines, Tome 1.
4. Karol, R.H. (1983) *Chemical Grouting*. Marcel Dekker, New York.
5. Durnerin, M. (1922) Le Problème du Foncage des puits sur le Prolonguement du Bassin Houiller de la Sarre en Lorraine. *Congres Scient. Assoc. Ingens. sortie de l'Ecole de Liège.*
6. Joosten, H.J. (1954) *The Joosten process for chemical soil solidification and sealing and its development from 1925 to date*. N.V. Amsterdamsche Ballast Maatschappij.
7. Drouhin, M. (1938) La lutte contre les érosions souterraines au barrage de Bou-Hanifia, etc. *Trans. 2nd Congr. Large Dams*, Washington, Vol. 4, 29–49.

274   UNDERPINNING

8. Mayer, A. (1958) Cement and clay grouting of foundations. French grouting practice. *Proc. ASCE*, Paper 1550 (February).
9. Cambefort, H. (1955) Parafouilles spéciaux en terrains perméables. *Cinquième Congr. Grands Barrages,* Paris, Vol. 1, 883–96.
10. Maag, E. (1938) Ueber die Verfestigung und Dichtung das Baugrundes (Injektionen). *Erdbaukers der ETH.*
11. ASCE (1957) Chemical Grouting Report. *Proc. ASCE* 83 (SM4), 1–106.
12. Caron, C. (1963) The development of grouts for the injection of fine sands. *Symposium on Grouts and Drilling Muds in Engineering Practice.* Butterworths, London, 136–141.
13. ICE (1963) *Grouts and Drilling Muds in Engineering Practice.* Butterworths, London.
14. Skipp, B.O. and Renner, L. (1963) The improvement of the mechanical properties of sands. *Symposium on Grouts and Drilling Muds in Engineering Practice.* Butterworths, London, 29–35.
15. 3M Company (1981) *3M Sealing Gel System Field Manual.* 3M Company, St. Paul, Minnesota.
16. Clarke, W.J. (1982) Performance characteristics of acrylate polymer grout. *Proc. ASCE Conf. on Grouting in Geotechnical Engineering,* New Orleans, 418–432.
17. Berry, R.M. (1982) Injectite—80 Polyacrylamide Grout. *Proc. ASCE Conf. on Grouting in Geotechnical Engineering,* New Orleans, 394–402.
18. ASCE (1982) *Proceedings of Conference on Grouting in Geotechnical Engineering.* ASCE, 345 East 47th Street, New York.
19. ISSMFE (1983) *Improvement of Ground. Proc. 8th European Conf. on Soil Mech. & Found. Engng.,* Helsinki, Vols. 1 and 2.
20. Raffle, J.F. and Greenwood, D.A. (1961) The relationship between the rheological characteristics of grouts and their capacity to permeate soils. *Proc. 5th Int. Conf. Soil Mech. & Found. Engng.,* Vol. 2, 789–793.
21. Garcia-Bengochea, I., Lovell, C.W. and Altschaeffli, A.G. (1978) Pore distribution and permeability of silty clays. *Proc. ASCE,* 105 (GT7).
22. Bell, L.A. (1978) *Alluvial Grouting.* M.Sc. Dissertation, University of Durham.
23. Scott, R.A. (1975) Fundamental conditions governing the penetration of grouts. In *Methods of Treatment of Unstable Ground* (ed. F.G. Bell), Newnes-Butterworths, London.
24. Skipp, B.O. (1975) Clay grouting and alluvial grouting. In *Methods of Treatment of Unstable Ground* (ed. F.G. Bell), Newnes-Butterworths, London, 141–158.
25. Caron, C. (1965) Etude physico-chimique des gels de silice. *Annals de l'Institut du Bâtiment et des Travaux Public,* 207–208 (March–April).
26. Cambefort, H. (1977) The principles and applications of grouting. *Q.J.E.G.* 10 (2), 57–95.
27. James, A.N. (1963) Discussion to Session 3—*Grouting Symposium on Grouts and Drilling Muds in Engineering Practice.* Butterworths, London, 168–169.
28. Schiffman, R.L. and Wilson, C.R. (1958) The mechanical behaviour of chemically treated granular soils. *Proc. ASTM,* 58, 1218–1244.
29. Warner, J. (1972) Strength properties of chemically solidified soils. *Proc. ASCE* 98, (SM2), 1163–1185.
30. Farmer, I.W. (1975) Undrained strengths of chemically grouted cohesionless soils. *Proc. 2nd Int. Cong. Int. Ass. Eng. Geol.,* Sao Paulo, Vol. 1, 1–6.
31. Krizek, R.J., Benltayf, M.A. and Dimitrios, K. (1982) Effective stress–strain strength behaviour of silicate-grouted sand. *Proc. ASCE Conf. on Grouting in Geotechnical Engineering,* New Orleans, 482–497.
32. Clough, W., Kuck, W. and Kassali, G. (1979) Silicate-stabilized sands. *Proc. ASCE,* 105 (GT1), 65–82.
33. Stetzler, B.U. (1982) Mechanical behaviour of silicate-grouted soils. *Proc. ASCE Conf. on Grouting in Geotechnical Engineering,* New Orleans, 498–514.
34. Davidson, R.R. and Perez, J-Y. (1982) Properties of chemically grouted sand at locks and dam No. 26. *Proc. ASCE Conf. on Grouting in Geotechnical Engineering,* New Orleans, 433–449.
35. Borden, R.H., Krizek, R.J. and Baker, W.H. (1982) Creep behaviour of silicate grouted sand. *Proc. ASCE Conf. on Grouting in Geotechnical Engineering,* New Orleans, 450–469.
36. Hewlett, P.C. and Hutchinson, M.T. (1983) Quantifying chemical grout performance and potential toxicity. *Proc. 8th European Conf. on Soil. Mech. & Found. Engng.* Vol. 1, 361–366.

37. CIRIA (1981) A Guide to the safe use of chemicals in construction. *Special Publication 16*, Construction Industry Research and Information Association, London.
38. CIRIA (1982) Health and safety aspects of ground treatment materials. *Report 95*. Construction Industry Research and Information Association, London.
39. Littlejohn, G.S. (1983) Plant and equipment for cement based grouts. *SAICE Grouting Course*, Geotechnical Division, University of Witwatersrand, Johannesburg.
40. Leonard, M.W. and Moller, K. (1963) Grouting for support, with particular reference to the use of some chemical grouts. *Symposium on Grouts and Drilling Muds in Engineering Practice,* Butterworths, London, 156–163.
41. Dempsey, J.A. and Moller, K. (1970). In *Grouting in Ground Engineering (Proc. Conf. Ground Engineering)*, ICE, London, 3–10.
42. Littlejohn, G.S., Ingle, J. and Dadasbilge, K. (1983) Improvement in base resistance of large diameter piles founded in silty sand. *Proc. 8th European Conf. on Soil Mech & Found. Engng.* Vol. 1, 153–156.
43. Ischy, E. and Glossop, R. (1962) An introduction to alluvial grouting. *Proc. I.C.E.* 21, 449–474.
44. Neelands, R.J. and James, A.N. (1963) Formulation and selection of chemical grouts with typical examples of their use. *Symposium on Grouts and Drilling Muds in Engineering Practice.* Butterworths, London, 150–155.
45. Zeigler, E.J. and Wirth, J.L. (1982) Soil stabilisation by grouting on Baltimore Subway. *Proc. ASCE Conf. on Grouting in Geotechnical Engineering,* New Orleans, 576–590.
46. Stadler, G. and Comte, C.H. (1983) Specific grouting projects in the pre-Alpine region. *Proc. 8th European Conf. on Soil & Mech. Found. Engng.* Vol. 1, 163–166.
47. Bally, R.J. and Klein, R. (1983) Some research works and applications of grouting of fine grained soils in Romania. *Proc. 8th European Conf. on Soil Mech. & Found. Engng.,* Vol. 1, 127–130.

9 Soil improvement by jet grouting

A. PERELLI CIPPO and R. TORNAGHI

9.1 Introduction

The improvement of soils as regards the reduction of permeability and the increase of strength can be achieved by various injection techniques which may be summarized as follows.

(a) *Permeation* grouting in which the grout fills the voids without any essential change of the original soil volume and structure.
(b) *Displacement* (compaction) grouting in which a stiff mix acts as a radial hydraulic jack, creating bulbs or lenses and thus compressing the surrounding soil.
(c) *Encapsulation* grouting in which the ground is fragmented by hydraulic fracturing; the grout coats and compresses but does not permeate the individual fragments.
(d) *Jet grouting* in which the soil is mixed in place with a stabilizing mixture, under very high nozzle pressures (20 to 50 MPa in general); by an alternative procedure soft fine-grained soils can be partly removed by air–water jetting and then replaced by the grout.

Permeation grouting is feasible by a wide variety of mixtures ranging from particulate suspensions to colloidal and pure chemical solutions; but more and more problems arise with decreasing soil permeability, both from the technical and economic points of view.

In terms of coefficient k the normal limits are orders of $10^{-3}\,\mathrm{cm\,s^{-1}}$ for silicate based mixtures and $10^{-4}\,\mathrm{cm\,s^{-1}}$ for the most expensive grouts based on resins.

Displacement grouting and deliberate hydrofracturing (also termed 'squeeze' grouting) are procedures used in particular cases, mostly as temporary or remedial measures for underpinning, correction of differential settlements of structures or recompression of ground loosened by tunnelling.

The great interest of the most recent techniques based on jet grouting is

276

due to the peculiar possibility of treating any type of soil (from gravel to clay) even by means of simple cement grouts. Hence we may obtain an effective soil improvement bypassing the problems of penetrability raised by pure permeation criteria and overcoming the inconveniences and limits of other modes of injection such as displacement and hydrofracturing. In fact jet grouting techniques offer a valuable alternative to conventional grouting, and moreover to slurry trenching, freezing and other soil stabilization methods.

This paper deals with fundamental principles, equipment, design criteria, quality control and performance, with reference to the Rodinjet procedure developed by Rodio Co. and to some typical applications in Italy.

9.2 Jet grouting techniques

The general basis for jet grouting is a special high-speed jet acting under a nozzle pressure which may range, according to the type of equipment, up to 70 MPa. The soil may be mixed in place with a suitable grout or alternatively removed (to a certain extent depending on grain size and consistency) by air–water jetting and simultaneously replaced by grout jetting.

In the Rodinjet equipment, according to the former procedure, the injection tool (monitor) is fitted with one or two pairs of nozzles diametrically opposed and a few centimetres apart along the vertical axis. The sequence of operations to obtain mixed-in place columns is outlined in Figure 9.1.

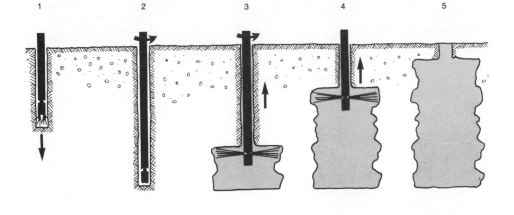

1. Beginning of drilling   3. Beginning of lateral jetting   5. Completion

2. End of drilling   4. Revolving and drawing up

Figure 9.1 Sequence of jet-grouting operations.

After the required depth has been reached (end of drilling) the grout jetting is started while revolving and drawing up the monitor. The grout acts simultaneously as a fracturing medium and stabilizing agent, forming columns with sizes and mechanical properties dependent on the combined influence of the following main factors:

1. Type of soil and composition of the grout.
2. Grout discharge and pressure, related to the number and size of nozzles.
3. Rotational speed of the monitor and lifting rate.

The diameter of single columns, normally ranging between 0.4 and 0.8 m, may be increased up to 2 m or more by the alternative procedure involving air–water jetting through a nozzle placed just above the grout injection nozzle.

9.3 Drilling and grouting equipment

The mode of drilling is selected according to the soil conditions, general features of the site and design specifications as regards length and inclination of holes. Rotary drilling is preferred in medium–fine grained soils, requiring fairly small rigs. The use of a rotation unit with an hydraulic chuck running on a feed beam 4–5 m long allows the use of a single rod up to a depth of 16–17 m. In coarse-grained soils including boulders, rotopercussion may be more suitable in terms of drilling speed; however this procedure requires heavier rigs with feed beams as long as single rods (Figure 9.2).

Figure 9.3 shows a rig specially designed by Rodio Co. (SR-500) for sub-horizontal rotopercussion drilling. A system of hydraulic jacks allows rotation of the feed beam (20 m long) over 180° with an inclination up to 15°. Therefore all the holes necessary for the treatment of a tunnel section ahead of the excavation face can be drilled with a single rod up to a length of 15 m and without any displacement of the jig.

The jet grouting is made by means of a special heavy-duty pump capable of delivering cement grouts up to a pressure of 70 MPa (Figure 9.4).

The grout is prepared in automatic plants designed to obtain accurate batching and mixing of the components and to produce adequate quantities for continuous treatment; each rig may require 5 to 8 m^3 of grout per hour.

A typical mixing plant is shown in Figure 9.5.

9.4 Design criteria

9.4.1 Preliminary site investigation and testing

The preliminary study of any geotechnical problem demands a thorough

Figure 9.2   Roto-percussion drilling rig for vertical holes (Rodio SK-20).

site investigation to enable the most convenient solution to be reached. If a stabilizing treatment is necessary, an accurate design may require supplementary testing that is specifically related to the solution proposed. In comparison with conventional grouting requirements, the factors that affect the feasibility and the selection of jet grouting parameters can be assessed by a less complex experimental program, which may be summarized as follows.

(1) Detailed soil profiles and general hydrogeological information.
(2) Simple in-situ tests such as cone penetration or SPT, to estimate soil consistency or relative density.

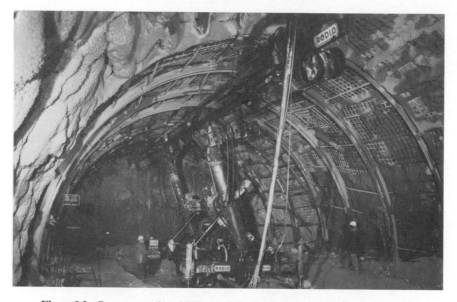

Figure 9.3   Roto-percussion drilling rig for sub-horizontal holes (Rodio SR-500).

Figure 9.4   Heavy-duty pump for Rodinjet treatments.

Figure 9.5 Grout mixing plant.

(3) Simple laboratory tests on representative soil samples, to evaluate grain size distribution of cohesionless materials and water content, bulk density, Atterberg limits of cohesive formations.

(4) Laboratory tests on trial grout and soil–grout mixtures, to be defined according to the importance and specific requirements of the work.

(5) In-situ jet grouting tests to check the operational parameters and to a larger extent, if necessary, to provide more detailed information for the final design.

9.4.2 Geometry of treatment

The great flexibility of the Rodinjet method allows various problems to be solved by suitable geometrical patterns, such as the following.

(1) Continuous strip treatment by one or more rows of vertical overlapping elements, to form cut-off walls for ground water control or earth-retaining structures; such barriers may have a circular or elliptical form, for instance when required to protect deep shaft excavation.

(2) Block treatment by vertical staggered columns to increase bearing capacity of foundations or to improve mechanical properties of soils in tunnelling problems; if conditions permit the treatment is done from the surface around the periphery of a planned tunnel or extended to the entire area to be excavated.

(3) Sub-horizontal treatment ahead of the excavation face in deep tunnelling, when operations from the surface are impossible or not convenient.

A typical and well-documented example of continuous strip treatment is the jet grouted cut-off executed around the existing Outlet Station of the ENEL thermal power plant at Porto Tolle in northeastern Italy, in order to prevent further seepage and internal erosion through loose medium–fine silty sand.

The Rodinjet method seemed to be the most adequate solution in obtaining a continuous impervious cut-off, considering the specific demands in terms of full safety, programme (the activity of the power plant was interrupted) and accessibility of equipment. It must be underlined that the selected procedure had no practical alternative on the outlet channel side owing to the presence of 3.5 m of water (Figure 9.6).

Figure 9.6 Porto Tolle Power Plant: Execution of jet-grouting cut-off at outlet channel.

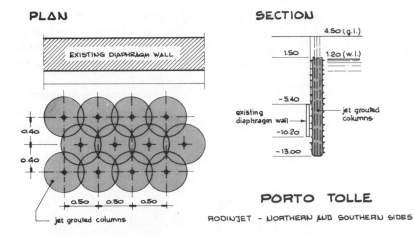

PLAN

EXISTING DIAPHRAGM WALL

0.40

0.40

0.50 0.50 0.50

jet grouted columns

SECTION

4.50 (g.l.)

1.50   1.20 (w.l.)

-5.40

existing
diaphragm wall

-10.20

-13.00

jet grouted
columns

PORTO TOLLE

RODINJET - NORTHERN AND SOUTHERN SIDES

Figure 9.7   Scheme of Rodinjet treatment to form an impervious cut-off.

The cut-off was formed by three rows of staggered overlapping columns 17.5 m deep and penetrating about 3 m in a soft silty clayey formation underlying loose silty sand with random presence of organic matter (Figure 9.7).

Continuous barriers with both hydraulic and earth-retaining functions have been obtained to allow the execution of several shaft foundations for long viaducts along the Udine–Tarvisio motorway and a nearby railway. Some shafts, having axes of 12 and 8 m, had to be excavated down to 22 m depth under a water head of 15 m or more in detrital soil with a widely variable grain size distribution (including boulders) and permeability from low to very high. The cut-offs were formed by two rows of Rodinjet columns 26 m long, just around the areas to be excavated.

A single row or jet-grouted columns was sufficient to allow the excavation of a circular service shaft 22 m deep 4 m below water table in the central area of Milan for the Underground Railway System. The columns were 24.5 m long at 0.5 m spacing, in sandy-gravelly alluvial soil (Figure 9.8).

Block treatments by means of staggered columns have been carried out to improve the bearing capacity of alluvial soil, allowing direct shallow foundations for about 50 piers of viaducts along Flaminia State Highway near Foligno (Central Italy). In this case the columns were not overlapping (Figure 9.9) and the most convenient spacing was selected after site trials, in order to obtain an overall suitable improvement by increasing the relative density of untreated soil between jet grouted columns. The solution of shallow foundations on improved soil was preferred to piling as it was more economic and safer in case of seismic events.

An example of a sub-horizontal conic pattern is shown in Figure 9.10.

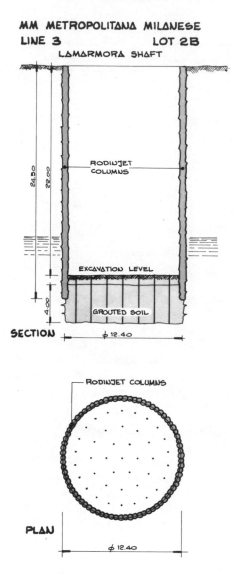

Figure 9.8   Scheme of Rodinjet treatment to protect deep shaft excavation.

This type of treatment is being used ahead of the excavation face of a railway tunnel 12 m in diameter through detrital soil at Moggio Udinese in Northern Italy, by means of the special equipment shown in Figure 9.3. Successive series of about 40 overlapping columns 13 m long are formed by holes drilled with an initial spacing of 0.45 m, allowing excavation stages on 10 m sections in alternation with treatment stages. The work has progressed successfully at an average rate of 10 metres in 4 days of jet grouting and 3 days for subsequent excavation.

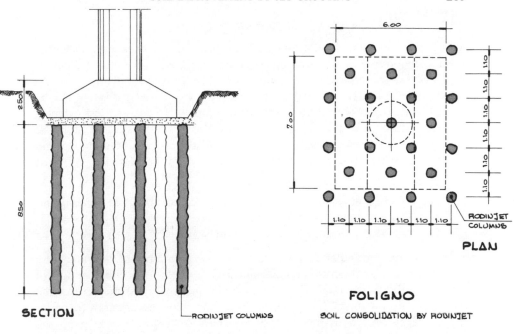

Figure 9.9 Layout of Rodinjet treatment to improve soil-bearing capacity for shallow foundations.

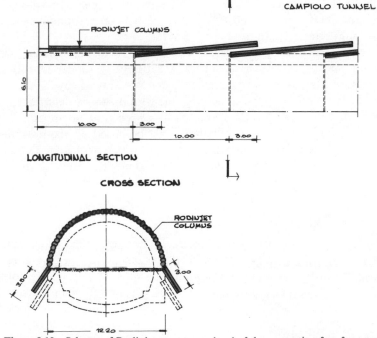

Figure 9.10 Scheme of Rodinjet treatment ahead of the excavation face for tunnelling.

9.4.3 Selection of the grout

The grout mix constituents and composition can be varied to meet the specific requirements for strength and permeability, with quite different and less restrictive criteria in comparison with conventional injection. As regards the initial rheological properties, viscosity and rigidity should be fairly low in any case to allow a uniform treatment to the greatest extent.

Where strength is the main design criterion a simple cement slurry is employed, with a cement/water ratio (c/w) mostly ranging between 0.5 and 1.0 to be selected according to various factors besides the required strength, such as:

(1) The type of soil as regards grain size and permeability in general and water content in cohesive formations.
(2) The estimated amount of grout per unit volume of treated soil.

In permeable granular formations a considerable amount of water may be drained out both from the soil and grout, while in a cohesive soil of low permeability the final water content may nearly equal the sum of the two original contents. This is the main reason why the strength (depending primarily on c/w) is lower for a day than for a sand treated with the same amount of the same grout.

Based on a uniform soil-grout mixture with no water loss, Figure 9.11 shows the influence of the individual water content on the volume of the grout and on the quantity of cement that are required (per unit volume of soft clay) to obtain an overall c/w ratio of 0.3, corresponding to an estimated long-term strength of about 0.5 MPa.

Both the volume of grout and quantity of cement increase with decreasing concentration of the grout for a constant water content of the clay. Therefore the amount of cement may be limited by a suitable selection of composition and volume of grout within ranges determined by experience to obtain an effective treatment as cheaply as possible. In stratified soils the jet-grouting parameters must be based on the prevailing type of soil or on the most favourable conditions likely to be encountered. The addition of bentonite and reduction in the cement content of the mix may be made if reduction of soil permeability is the major concern.

9.4.4 Selection of jet-grouting parameters

The influence of nozzle diameter, pressure, type and quantity of grout, monitor rotation and withdrawal speed have been widely investigated in various soils and hydrological conditions.

According to previous experience on job-sites and in field trials, the orders of magnitude of the main parameters are:

pressure: 20 to 50 MPa

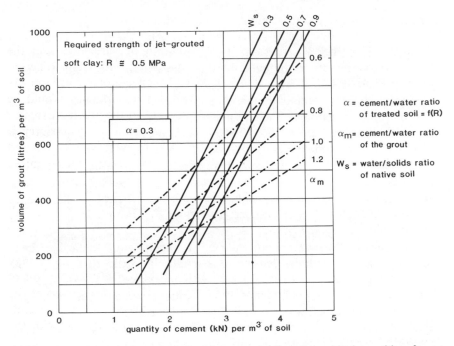

Figure 9.11 Influence of water contents of grout and soil on the required quantities of grout and cement.

nozzle diameter: 1.8 to 3 mm
rod rotation speed: 10 to 20 revolutions per minute
rod drawing-up speed: 20 to 70 cm min^{-1}, by steps of a few cm
grout discharge 1 to 3 litres s^{-1}
volume of delivered grout: 150 to 350 litres m^{-1}.

A suitable selection of these parameters (besides grout composition, previously dealt with) requires practical experience and may demand site trials.

The radius of influence obtained by the normal Rodinjet procedure ranges mostly between 0.2 and 0.4 m, tending to increase in soft or loose soils and with increasing pressure and delivered amount of grout.

9.4.5 Characteristics of treated soils

The results of any treatment, in terms of uniformity and mechanical properties, depend on a number of interconnected factors concerning the soil and the jet-grouting parameters. A good opportunity to look into these relations has been offered by the above-mentioned site at Porto Tolle (Figure 9.7). After completion of the work nearly one hundred samples were recovered from eight boreholes drilled inside the jet-grouted cut-off, mostly by rotary core barrels. An extensive laboratory investigation has been carried out by systematic unconfined compression tests and determinations of bulk density; the results are plotted versus depth in Figure 9.12.

Disregarding the data of borehole S6 (affected by too-early sampling after the end of treatment) the compressive strength of grouted silty sand ranges mostly between 2 and 10 MPa with peaks over 20 MPa. The arithmetic and harmonic mean values are 5.7 and 3.4 MPa respectively for this formation. Beyond 14 m depth there is a transition zone from sand to clay, where strength decreases remarkably with increasing clay content. The harmonic mean, still fairly high between 14 and 16 m (2.1 MPa) drops to about 0.5 MPa in the lowest section (16 to 17.5 m) involving a purely cohesive silty–clayey soil.

A thorough statistical interpretation of experimental data has been made by correlating bulk density to strength in order to estimate the actual composition of treated soils with reference to that resulting theoretically from original compositions and proportions of grout and soil. The contents of water, cement and dry soil particles have been calculated assuming a general relation between overall cement/water ratio (c/w) and strength as suggested from wide testing experience.

Table 9.1 shows a statistical comparison between theoretical and experimental compositions of the two main types of soil, treated with the

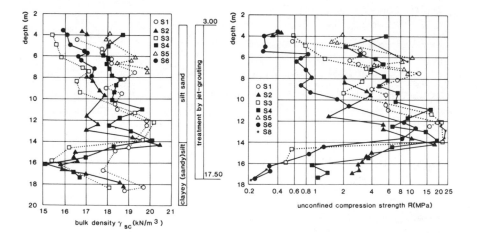

Figure 9.12 Plots of bulk density and strength v. depth (samples of jet-grouting soil at Porto Tolle).

Table 9.1

Components (kN m^{-3})	Grout	Silty sand			Silty clay		
		Natural	Treated		Natural	Treated	
			Theor.	Exper.		Theor.	Exper.
s	—	14.00	6.55	7.75	12.85	6.00	7.27
w	8.56	4.80	6.85	5.59	5.15	7.01	6.59
c	4.28	—	2.30	4.62	—	2.30	2.16
$s+w+c$	12.84	18.80	15.70	17.96	18.00	15.31	16.02
c/w	0.5	—	0.336	0.825	—	0.328	0.328

s=dry soil, w=water, c=cement.

same grout ($c/w=0.5$) in a theoretical proportion of $1.15\,\mathrm{m^3}$ of grout per $\mathrm{m^3}$ of native soil. The loss of water in the fairly permeable silty sand in effect doubles the cement content and increases even more the over-all c/w ratio. On the other hand, the treatment of silty clay has involved a small decrease of cement content and practically no change in c/w, according to the theoretical grout–soil proportions. The differing results obtained on the two types of soil, in terms of strength, can be justified by analysing all the factors influencing the final composition of treated materials and mainly the c/w ratio.

9.5 Controls during the work

In general the volume of grout delivered by jetting is larger than the volume of voids present in the natural soil. This is due to the primary need of utilizing the grout as a fracturing medium. It follows that, during jet-grouting treatment, the amount of injected fluid in excess gives rise, in practice, to soil displacements and outflows of both grout constituents and soil particles from the holes. Depending on the importance of the job, the following controls are carried out:

(a) Precise levelling to check vertical movements on surface or existing structures.
(b) Inclinometer measures to assess horizontal displacement at various distances from the treated area.
(c) Quantitative and qualitative evaluations of the outflown materials.

The latter are essential for estimating the amount of cement refused and consequently to check the actual composition of the treated ground, jointly with laboratory tests carried out subsequently on samples of jet-grouted soil, as mentioned above. The analysis of surplus materials serves the purpose both of verifying the design criteria and supplying all data required to modify, if necessary, the jet-grouting parameters.

9.6 Performance records

All works executed so far by the Rodinjet technique have attained good results fulfilling the design requirements. Below is a brief review of performance records with reference to some sites mentioned earlier.

One month after completion of the jet-grouted cut-off at Porto Tolle the outlet station basin could be dried out without any further inconvenience (Figure 9.13). After this and under a 6 m water head of the

Figure 9.13 Porto Tolle Power Plant: Outlet station basin dried out after completion of the jet-grouted cut-off.

outlet channel, seepage flow into the basin was less than $1 \, \mathrm{ls}^{-1}$ and remained constant with time. The effectiveness of the cut-off was also confirmed by piezometric measures underneath the basin bottom and on the outside, made during the dewatering and afterwards.

The excavation of the service shaft in central Milan (Figure 9.8) shows a perfect continuity of the overlapping jet-grouted columns (Figure 9.14). The excavation was carried out by steps with the aid of ribs at 1 m intervals. No movements have been recorded in adjacent buildings, controlled by precision levelling. The design, based on finite element analysis, required an elastic modulus of the order of 2500 MPa to the treated alluvial soil and hence an important static function that has been fully satisfied by actual performance. Laboratory tests on samples recovered radially from jet-grouted columns are planned and will be useful to check both mechanical properties of treated soil and design assumptions.

The sub-horizontal treatment at Moggio Udinese, according to the scheme shown in Figure 9.10, is progressing very successfully. The tunnel excavation is carried out by a shovel crane and a down-the-hole hammer to break up boulders. The treatment appears uniform and continuous; large rock fragments, in spite of vibration produced by hammering, are well encompassed in the treated mass (Figure 9.15). By the Rodinjet procedure a bearing arch of soil 60 to 70 cm thick has been created

Figure 9.14 Milan Underground Railway System: Jet-grouted columns to allow excavation of a deep service shaft.

Figure 9.15 Moggio Udinese Railway Tunnel: View of the sub-horizontal jet-grouting treatment ahead of the excavation face.

presenting good mechanical properties. The ribs, usually installed at 0.5 to 1.0 m spacings, in this case could be placed at 2–2.5 m intervals and seemed to be practically unloaded. This shows that the jet-grouted soil may support by itself the earth pressures acting on the created arch structure.

References

Aschieri, F., Jamiolkowski, M. and Tornaghi, R. (1983) Case history of a cut-off wall executed by jet-grouting. *Proc. 8th European Conf. Soil Mechanics and Foundation Engineering,* Helsinki, Vol, 1, 121–126.

Index